Significant Changes

TO THE *NEC*® 2017

 IN COLLABORATION WITH

This book conveys the information related to each change as of August 1, 2016, but does not reflect potential action taken by the NFPA editors or the NFPA Standards Council. Changes covered in this textbook that are known to be impacted are identified with the text similar to the following:

Subsequent NFPA Standards Council Action Pending

This text appears in the Code Language segment of any such change that could possibly be affected by such actions incorporated into the Code AFTER the printing of this textbook.

Contents

Chapter 1

Articles 90, 100, and 110 2
Introduction, Definitions, and Requirements for Electrical Installations

Contents

Chapter 2

Contents

Chapter 2 (continued)

Contents

Chapter 3

Contents

Chapter 4

Articles 400–480 116
Equipment for General Use

Contents

Chapter 4 (continued)

Chapter 5

Contents

Chapter 5 (continued)

Contents

Chapter 6

Contents

Chapter 6 (continued)

Chapter 7

Special Conditions

Contents

Chapter 7 (continued)

Chapter 8

Introduction

The *National Electrical Code*® (*NEC*®) is the most widely used electrical installation standard in the United States and North America. In fact, the *NEC* is being adopted more globally as electrical codes and standards evolve internationally. It is a living document and is in a continuous state of evolution. As new technologies, equipment, wiring methods, and industry needs evolve, the *NEC* must stay current to effectively address essential installation and safety requirements. An established three-year revision cycle effectively facilitates a dynamic and timely development process. The *NEC* is integral to the electrical business and used daily by electrical contractors, electricians, maintainers, inspectors, engineers, designers, and others.

The *NEC* development process begins with submission of public inputs (PIs). The National Fire Protection Association (NFPA) recently implemented a new revision process for all codes and standards that they publish. In previous revision cycles, the public submitted proposals, which are known in the new process as public inputs or PIs. There were 4,012 PIs submitted this cycle, which resulted in 1,235 first revisions (FRs). The deadline for PIs to change the 2014 *NEC* was November 7, 2014. In January 2015, the technical committees (commonly referred to as Code Making Panels or CMPs) met to act on all PIs to begin revising existing and developing new requirements. After the CMPs meet and act on all PIs and final balloting is complete, the results are made publicly available on the internet in a document titled *National Electrical Code First Draft*. NFPA no longer publishes a paper copy of the results in a book form. The public then has an opportunity to modify or reverse the actions initially taken by the technical committees by submitting public comments on any FR or PI. Public comments (PCs) for this revision cycle were accepted up until September 25, 2015. There were 1,513 PCs submitted this cycle resulting in 559 second revisions (SRs). In November 2015, the CMPs met to act on all PCs submitted. After the CMP meetings and final balloting is complete on the PCs, the results are made available to the public on the internet in a document titled *National Electrical Code Second Draft*. Throughout this entire process, the *NEC* Correlating Committee reviews the work in the First Draft and Second Draft stages to ensure that there are no conflicting actions between the work of the CMPs, and that all revisions conform to the *NEC Style Manual* and NFPA Regulations Governing Committee Projects. Once the Second Draft is made available, there is a final opportunity for the public to submit a "notice of intent to make a motion" (NITMAM) directed at any revision accepted during this process as well as any public comment submitted. Actions on these motions are made during the Technical Session at the NFPA annual meeting. The NFPA Standards Council reviews these NITMAMs and all that are in order become "certified amending motions" (CAMs). At the NFPA annual meeting, the work of the CMPs can be modified by such motions, if accepted by the body present at the Technical Meeting. The NFPA annual meeting for the 2017 *NEC* was held in Las Vegas in June 2016. Appeals can be submitted to the NFPA Standards Council from any individual or any organization. The NFPA Standards Council met in Boston in August 2016 to hear appeals. After appeals had been heard and acted upon by the Standards Council, they issued the 2017 *NEC*.

This open consensus revision process provides all users of the *NEC* with an opportunity to mold the next edition through individual and organizational participation. As readers learn about these significant changes for the 2017 *NEC*, they should be sure to note their ideas for an improved *Code* and submit them as PIs for the next edition of the *NEC*.

About This Book

This text is written to inform electrical contractors, electricians, maintenance personnel, inspectors, engineers, and system designers of the most significant revisions and new requirements in the 2017 *National Electrical Code* (*NEC*). The coverage of each change provides readers with an authoritative review by providing insight and detailed information about the reasons for the changes and how these changes impact the industry, daily work, and business operations. The information in this book is a must for active electrical contracting businesses that need to stay current on the installation requirements they manage every day. This textbook is used most effectively in conjunction with the actual 2017 *NEC* textbook.

Features

RELOCATE   **NEW**   **DELETION**

REORGANIZE   *REVISION*

Icons graphically show the Type of Change

310.15(B)(

Article 310 Conductors for General W
Part II Installation

REVISION

Single-Phase Dwelling Services and Feeders

Code Language

310.15(B) Tables

(7) Single-Phase Dwelling Services and Feeders.

For one-family dwellings and the individual dwelling units of two-family and multifamily dwellings, single-phase feeder conductors consisting of 2 ungrounded conductors and the neutral conductor from a 208Y/120 volt system shall be permitted to be sized in accordance with 310.15(B)(7)(1) through (3).

(No change (1) through (4))

Where correction or adjustment factors are required by 310.15(B)(2) or (3), they shall be permitted to be applied to the ampacity associated with the temperature rating of the conductor.

(See NEC for actual text)

The **Code Language** is "ripped" from the 2017 *National Electrical Code*.

Photos and **Graphics** visually illustrate each change.

Change Summary

- 310.15(B)(7) is no longer limited to 120/240-volt systems, single-phase 120/208-volt systems are now included.
- Single-phase feeders from a 208Y/120-volt system are permitted to use 310.15(B)(7)(1) through (3).
- Correction or adjustment factors in 310.15(B)(2) or (3) are permitted to be applied to the ampacity associated with the temperature rating of the conductor.

FR: 1503
SR: 1505

94   Chapter 3 • Articles 300–396

Significance of the Change

Second level subdivision 310.15(B)(7) permits the installation of reduced ampacity service and feeder conductors under specified conditions in dwelling units. Service/feeder conductors supplying the entire load associated with a one-family dwelling, or the service/feeder conductors supplying the entire load associated with an individual dwelling unit in a two-family or multifamily dwelling, are permitted to have an ampacity not less than 83 percent of the service or feeder rating. This permissive requirement is no longer limited to single-phase 120/240-volt systems. This revision will permit a reduction in conductor size where single-phase 208Y/120-volt services and feeders are installed. Correlation is now achieved with the *Canadian Electrical Code*, which allows reduced conductor sizes for single dwellings, apartments and similar buildings for both 120/240- and 208Y/120-volt service/feeder conductors. The load diversity in residential applications is similar whether the residence is fed with 120/240- or 208Y/120-volts.

A new last sentence is added to clarify that temperature and correction factors in 310.15(B)(2) and 310.15(B)(3)(a), should be applied to the conductor temperature rating and not the ampacity in the temperature column associated with the equipment termination values. Informational note No. 1 is revised for clarity referencing standard ampacity ratings from 240.6(A).

The **First Revisions** sequence numbers and **Second Revisions** sequence numbers are provided to allow the user to the ability to do additional research on a particular change.

Features

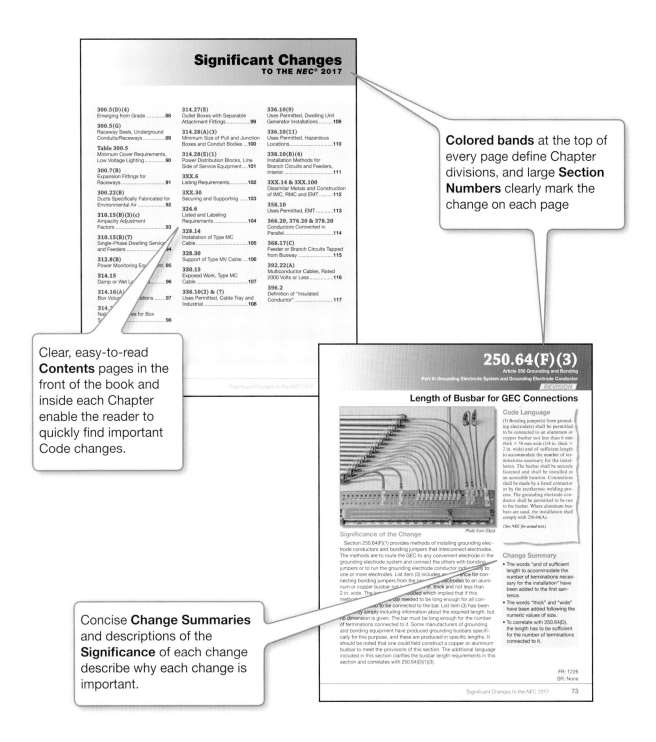

Significant Changes
TO THE *NEC* 2017

Significant Changes to the NEC 2017

Colored bands at the top of every page define Chapter divisions, and large **Section Numbers** clearly mark the change on each page

Clear, easy-to-read **Contents** pages in the front of the book and inside each Chapter enable the reader to quickly find important Code changes.

250.64(F)(3)
Article 250 Grounding and Bonding
Part III Grounding Electrode System and Grounding Electrode Conductor
REVISION

Length of Busbar for GEC Connections

Photo from iStock

Code Language

(3) Bonding jumper(s) from grounding electrode(s) shall be permitted to be connected to an aluminum or copper busbar not less than 6 mm thick × 50 mm wide (1/4 in. thick × 2 in. wide) and of sufficient length to accommodate the number of terminations necessary for the installation. The busbar shall be securely fastened and shall be installed in an accessible location. Connections shall be made by a listed connector or by the exothermic welding process. The grounding electrode conductor shall be permitted to be run to the busbar. Where aluminum busbars are used, the installation shall comply with 250.64(A).

(See NEC for actual text)

Significance of the Change

Section 250.64(F)(1) provides methods of installing grounding electrode conductors and bonding jumpers that interconnect electrodes. The methods are to route the GEC to any convenient electrode in the grounding electrode system and connect the others with bonding jumpers or to run the grounding electrode conductor individually to one or more electrodes. List item (3) includes a... ...ce for connecting bonding jumpers from the ... ...ectrodes to an aluminum or copper busbar not ... ... th thick and not less than 2 in. wide. The ... ...dded which implied that if this method ... ...to be connected to the bar. List item (3) has been ... ...ly simply including information about the required length, but no dimension is given. The bar must be long enough for the number of terminations connected to it. Some manufacturers of grounding and bonding equipment have produced grounding busbars specifically for this purpose, and these are produced in specific lengths. It should be noted that one could field construct a copper or aluminum busbar to meet the provisions of this section. The additional language included in this section clarifies the busbar length requirements in this section and correlates with 250.64(D)(1)(3).

Change Summary

- The words "and of sufficient length to accommodate the number of terminations necessary for the installation" have been added to the first sentence.
- The words "thick" and "wide" have been added following the numeric values of size.
- To correlate with 250.64(D), the length has to be sufficient for the number of terminations connected to it.

FR: 1226
SR: None

Significant Changes to the NEC 2017   **73**

Concise **Change Summaries** and descriptions of the **Significance** of each change describe why each change is important.

Acknowledgments

3M Company Electrical Markets Division
The Aluminum Association
Bill Brooks
Steve Campolo
Jim Conrad
Donny Cook
Copper Development Association Inc.
Tim Crnko
Tom Domitrovitch
Eaton
Eaton, Bussmann Division
Eaton, Crouse-Hinds Division
Electric Vehicle Infrastructure Training Program
Fluke Corporation
Graybar
Greenlee, a Textron Company
Rachel Guenther
Jay Halferty
Crystal Hunter

IDEAL Industries, Inc.
Stan Kauffman
David Kendall
Klein Tools, Inc.
Legrand, North America
Lutron Electronics, Inc.
Milwaukee Tool Corporation
Dan Neeser
Mark Ode
PDE Total Energy Solutions
Schneider Electric
Southwire Company
Steel Tube Institute
Greg Stienman
Thomas & Betts, a Member of the ABB Group
Rod West
Tim Windey
Underwriters Laboratories, LLC

Contributing Writers

Michael J. Johnston is NECA's executive director of standards and safety. Prior to working with NECA, he worked for the International Association of Electrical Inspectors as the director of education, codes, and standards. He also worked as an electrical inspector and electrical inspection field supervisor for the City of Phoenix, AZ, and achieved all IAEI and ICC electrical inspector certifications. Johnston achieved a bachelor of science in business management from the University of Phoenix. He served on *NEC* Code-Making Panel 5 in the 2002, 2005, 2008 cycles and has chaired the Code-Making Panel 5 representing NECA during the 2011 *NEC* cycle. He currently chairs the *NEC* Correlating Committee and serves on the NFPA *NEC* Smart Grid Task Force. He is also currently a member of *NEC* Code-Making Panel 1. Among his responsibilities for managing the codes, standards, and safety functions for NECA, Johnston is secretary of the NECA Codes and Standards Committee. He has been a consistent contributor to the NJATC curriculum, authoring titles such as the *Health Care Systems, Hazardous Locations, Applied Grounding and Bonding,* and *Significant Changes to the NEC*. Johnston is a member of the IBEW and has experience as an electrical journeyman wireman, foreman, and project superintendent. He has achieved journeyman and master electrician licenses in multiple states. Johnston is an active member of IAEI, ICC, NFPA, ASSE, SES, the NFPA Electrical Section, Education Section, the UL Electrical Council, and National Safety Council.

Jim Dollard is a journeyman wireman in IBEW Local 98 in Philadelphia, PA, where he currently holds the position of safety coordinator. He is a master OSHA 500 instructor and works toward safe working conditions on all jobs. As a current member of the following NFPA committees, Dollard plays a significant role in the development of electrical codes and standards: The *National Electrical Code* Correlating Committee, Code Making Panels 10 and 13, *NFPA 70E the Standard for Electrical Safety in the Workplace,* and *NFPA 90A Standard for the Installation of Air-Conditioning and Ventilating Systems.*

Dollard is also a member of the Underwriters Laboratories Electrical Council. He is the author of the NJATC *Codeology* textbook, the 2008 NJATC *NEC Significant Changes*, co-author of the 2011 NJATC *NEC Significant Changes*, and the 2015 NJATC/NECA *NFPA 70E Significant Changes*. His excellent presentation skills, knowledge of the electrical industry, extensive background in the electrical construction field, and involvement in electrical safety and codes/standards allow Dollard to make the most complex requirements easy to understand and apply.

Listed/Labeled

In this cycle, there were dozens of actions by CMPs to revise requirements for "listed" products to be both "listed and labeled." Both terms are defined in Article 100 and are under the purview of Standards Council, which means that the *NEC* committees cannot revise the terms. The *NEC* Correlating Committee held those revisions to allow a task group to determine the best path forward. The efforts were targeted at making sure everything that is listed is identified with a "label." Stay tuned for action here in the 2020 edition of the *NEC*.

Reconditioned Equipment

In previous editions of the *NEC*, the term *equipment* could have been applied to new, reconditioned, refurbished or remanufactured equipment. Section 110.3(A) is revised to recognize refurbished equipment. This revision provides the needed clarification that examination of equipment for suitability can be applied to reconditioned, refurbished or remanufactured equipment, in addition to new equipment labeling on the equipment.

110.16 Arc Flash Hazard Warnings at Service Equipment

New subdivision 110.16(B) is titled "Service Equipment" and requires additional information to be provided on a field or factory-applied label. This section continues to require that equipment be generally marked to warn qualified persons of arc flash hazards, but now requires more specific detail about the service equipment installation. This will typically result in labeling in accordance with NFPA 70E.

600 Volt Threshold to 1000 Volts

CMPs 1 and 8 completed their revisions of 600-volt thresholds to a 1000-volt threshold, which was started in the 2014 *NEC* revision cycle. Additionally, work space clearances in 110.26(A) now use a 1000-volt threshold for correlation.

GFCI Requirements

First level subdivision 210.8(C) now requires all crawl space lighting not exceeding 120-volts to be GFCI protected.

The parent text of 210.8(B) for GFCI protection for personnel in other than dwelling units is expanded beyond the previous requirement of only 125-volt, 15/20 amp receptacles. The revised text now includes all single phase receptacles rated 150 volts to ground or less at 50 amperes or less and all three phase receptacles rated 150 volts to ground or less at 100 amperes or less.

Safety by Design

A new section 240.67 now requires a means to reduce "arc energy" where fuses are applied at 1200 amps or higher. Arc energy reduction now applies to both fuses and circuit breakers with a threshold of 1200 amps and higher. This new requirement for fuses mirrors the existing requirement for circuit breakers in 240.87 in many ways. This new requirement will become effective January 1, 2020.

New list items (5) and (6) in 240.87(B) now recognize an instantaneous trip setting that is less than the available arcing current and an instantaneous override that is less than the available arcing current.

Second level subdivision 408.3(A)(2) now requires panelboards used as service equipment be installed with barriers to prevent inadvertent contact with the line side energized parts. Barriers will likely be provided as a "field installed kit" to be applied where panelboards are used as service equipment.

Rooftop Correction Factors

The ampacity reduction requirements for conductors on rooftops are deleted and correction factors only apply where a raceway or cable is installed closer to the roof that is ⁷/₈ inch. Where less than ⁷/₈ inch above the roof to the bottom of the raceway or cable adding a temperature adder of 60°F will apply.

Grounded Conductors at Switches

New section 404.22 now supplements 404.2(C) (which requires grounded conductors to be installed) with a requirement effective on January 1, 2020, for installation of electronic lighting control switches (with exceptions) that do not permit current on the equipment grounding conductor during normal operation.

Rapid Shutdown of PV Systems

Section 690.12 is significantly revised and separated into parent text and four first level subdivisions. An "array boundary" is established with requirements for circuits "outside" and "inside" the array boundary. Three rapid shut-down methods are provided for circuits inside the array boundary with an effective date of January 1, 2019.

Maintenance

First level subdivisions 700.3(C) and 701.3(C) are revised to require maintenance on all emergency and legally required system equipment. Electrical equipment in these systems must be maintained in accordance with manufacturer's instructions and *NFPA 70B*. This will have a significant impact on Health Care and other institutional facilities.

Article 425 – Fixed Commercial and Industrial and Industrial Process Heating Equipment

This new article covers fixed industrial process heating employing electric resistance or electrode heating technology. For the purpose of this new article, heating equipment includes boilers, electrode boilers, duct heaters, strip heaters, immersion heaters, process air heaters, or other approved fixed electric equipment used for industrial process heating. *NEC* Code-Panel 17 will have technical responsibility for this new article.

Article 691 – Large Scale Photovoltaic (PV) Electric Power Production Facility

This new article will cover the installation of large-scale photovoltaics (PV) electric power production facilities operated for the sole purpose of providing electric supply to the utility transmission or distribution system with an output power rating of no less than 5,000 kW. Electric supply stations are locations containing the generating stations and substations, including their associated generator, storage battery, transformer, and switchgear areas. Facilities covered by this article have specific design and safety features unique to large-scale PV facilities. *NEC* Code-Panel 4 will have technical responsibility for this new article.

Article 706 – Energy Storage Systems (ESS)

This new article covers all permanently installed energy storage systems (ESS), which may be stand-alone or interactive with other electric power production sources. An energy storage system is defined in this new article as a device or more than one device assembled together capable of storing energy for use at a future time. ESS(s) include but are not limited to electrochemical storage devices (e.g. batteries), flow batteries, capacitors, and kinetic energy devices (e.g. flywheels and compressed air). These systems can have ac or dc output for utilization and can include inverters and converters to change stored energy into electrical energy. *NEC* Code-Panel 13 will have technical responsibility for this new article.

Article 710 – Stand Alone Systems

This new article includes requirements for electric power production sources operating in the stand-alone mode. An important provision in this new article conveys that even though the system may not be connected to a serving utility, the system must be adequate to meet the requirements of the *NEC* as if it were supplied by a feeder or service. All equipment installed for these systems must be listed or labeled. *NEC* Code Panel 13 will have technical responsibility for this new article.

Article 712 – Direct Current Micro-grids

This new article covers direct current micro-grids which are defined within the article as power distribution systems consisting of one or more interconnected dc power sources, dc-dc converters, dc loads, and ac loads powered by dc-ac inverters. A dc micro-grid is typically not directly connected to an ac primary source of electricity, but some dc micro-grids interconnect via one or more dc-ac bidirectional converters or dc – ac inverters. *NEC* Code-Panel 13 will have technical responsibility for this new article.

Chapter 1

Articles 90, 100, and 110

Introduction, Definitions, and Requirements for Electrical Installations

Significant Changes
TO THE NEC® 2017

Scope Includes Installation and Removal

Code Language

(A) Covered. This *Code* covers the installation, and removal of electrical conductors, equipment, and raceways; signaling and communications conductors, equipment, and raceways; and optical fiber cables and raceways for the following:

(1) Public and private premises, including buildings, structures, mobile homes, recreational vehicles, and floating buildings.

(remainder unchanged)

(See NEC for actual text)

Change Summary

- The words "and removal" have been added in the first sentence of 90.2(A).
- This revision expands the scope of the *NEC* beyond just installation requirements to include requirements addressing removal of equipment.
- Current *NEC* rules require removal of equipment such as those for removal of temporary power wiring and those for removing abandoned communications cables.

Significance of the Change

Adding the words "and removal" to 90.2(A) expands the scope to align with existing *Code* rules that call for removal of electrical wiring or other equipment. Although the *NEC* is generally understood as the installation *Code* for electrical wiring and equipment, it does contain some removal rules related to safe electrical installations and building safety. A good example of an *NEC* removal requirement can be found in 590.3(D), which requires temporary wiring to be removed upon completion of the construction or purpose for which the temporary wiring was installed. This is an important safety requirement. Previous to this requirement there were instances of energized temporary wiring that remained within hollow spaces of buildings after the construction project was complete. Other important *NEC* removal requirements are found within the communications articles of the *Code*, such as in 800.25. These rules require the accessible portions of abandoned cables be removed unless identified for future use. The goal is to reduce the smoke load within the building. This requirement is typically enforced during remodels and retrofit projects. Removal of conductors or cables is also required in many other *NEC* sections including 640.3(C), 725.25, 760.25, 770.25, 820.25, 830.25, and 840.

FR: 1

SR: None

Energy Storage that is Not Covered

Courtesy of PDE Total Energy Solutions

Significance of the Change

This revision adds "energy storage" to the list of *NEC* scope exclusions, which enhances clarity of the *Code* as it relates to installations that are excluded from the scope. This revision provides a clear exemption for energy storage installations that are not covered by *NEC* rules, but could be covered by other Codes such as the *National Electrical Safety Code (NESC)*. Previously these exclusions in 90.2(B) did not specifically mention energy storage. This meant that an energy storage system could have been interpreted as being subject to the requirements of *NEC* and inspection by the local AHJ. The revision provides the clarification about what is covered and not covered. The service point provides the demarcation point to assist users with applying the appropriate safety rules whether covered by the *NEC* or not. These revisions resulted from work by the DC task group assigned by the *NEC* Correlating Committee to incorporate energy storage rules throughout the *NEC*. A new Article 706 titled "Energy Storage Systems" has been added in Chapter 7.

Code Language

90.2(B) Not Covered.
(1) Unchanged...
(2) Unchanged...
(3) Installations of railways for generation, transformation, transmission, energy storage, or distribution of power...communications purposes.
(4) Unchanged...
(5) (a) Unchanged...
(5) (b) Are on property.....transformation, transmission, energy storage, or distribution of electric energy, or
(d) Are located...These written agreements shall be limited to installations for the purpose of communications, metering, generation, control, transformation, transmission, energy storage, or distribution...

(See NEC for actual text)

Change Summary

- The words *energy storage* have been incorporated in three locations within 90.2(B).
- The revision makes it clear that energy storage equipment and installations on the supply side of the service point are not covered by the rules in the *NEC*.
- Energy storage is already included in the coverage of the *NEC* as 90.2(A) applies to all equipment.

FR: 2
SR: None

Code Arrangement Clarified

Code Language

90.3 *Code* **Arrangement.** This *Code* is divided into the introduction and nine chapters, as shown in Figure 90.3. Chapters 1, 2, 3, and 4 apply generally. Chapters 5, 6, and 7 apply to special occupancies, special equipment, or other special conditions and may supplement or modify the requirements in Chapters 1 through 7.

Chapter 8 covers communications systems and is not subject to the requirements of Chapters 1 through 7 except where the requirements are specifically referenced in Chapter 8. Chapter 9 consists of tables that are applicable as referenced.

(See NEC for actual text)

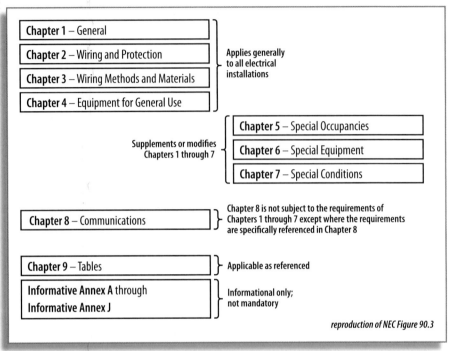

reproduction of NEC Figure 90.3

Change Summary

- Section 90.3 and associated Figure 90.3 have been revised.
- The revision clarifies that Chapters 5, 6, and 7 may modify or supplement requirements in Chapters 1 through 7.
- The revision also clarifies that Chapter 8 is not subject to the requirements in Chapters 1 through 7 except where specifically referenced therein.

Significance of the Change

Section 90.3 has historically provided an arrangement and use roadmap for the *NEC*. It is the basis for many *NEC* training programs. Chapters 1 through 4 have general application while Chapters 5, 6, and 7 could modify or supplement the rules in 1 through 4. Chapter 8 is independent of the other chapters unless specifically referenced from within Chapter 8. The revision to this section clarifies that Chapters 5, 6, and 7 may modify or supplement requirements in Chapters 1 through 7 as compared to only Chapters 1 through 4 as provided in previous editions. In addition, Chapter 8 is not subject to the rules in Chapters 1 through 7 unless they are specifically referenced from rules in Chapter 8. Essentially this permits requirements within Chapters 5, 6, and 7 to modify more than Chapters 1 through 4, but rules could be modified between such chapters as specifically referenced from within such rules. As an example, a requirement for hazardous (classified) locations may modify not only Chapters 1 through 4, but may have to be applied for a Class 2 wiring system covered in Article 725. The rules in Chapters 5 and 7 can now refer to one another and 90.3 recognizes it as revised. Figure 90.3 has also been revised to reflect the changes in the text.

FR: 3
SR: None

Examination of Equipment For Safety

Courtesy of PDE Total Energy Systems

Code Language

90.7 Examination of Equipment For Safety. For specific…(as in 2014 *NEC* with new last sentence added)

Suitability shall be determined by application of requirements that are compatible with this *Code*.

Informational Note No. 3: Informative Annex A contains a list of product safety standards that are compatible with this *Code*.

(See NEC for actual text)

Significance of the Change

Code-Making Panel 1 reconsidered the concepts introduced by Public Inputs 4655 and 4774 and acted favorably to revise Section 90.7 accordingly. Information provided in the substantiation with Public Comment 573 emphasized the relevance of conforming to product safety standards that align with *NEC* rules. Equipment standards are developed in coordination with installation codes to ensure safety and compatibility. Product standards that do not specifically anticipate compliance or coordination with the *NEC* present installation problems such as specifying metric conductor sizes, noncompliance issues with *Code* specific construction requirements, and some safety concerns, such as overcurrent protection schemes that are incompatible with the *NEC* rules. Product standards that are developed to align with the *NEC* identify this intention in the scope of each respective product standard, and unless additional evaluation is performed, only these products can be assured to meet *NEC* requirements. The revision clarifies that suitability of equipment is related to application of requirements in standards that are consistent with rules in the *NEC,* which improves usability for installers, and increases enforceability by authorities having jurisdiction.

Change Summary

- A new last sentence has been added to the second paragraph of Section 90.7.
- The words "that are compatible with this *Code*" have been added to Informational Note No. 3.
- The revision clarifies that suitability of equipment is related to application of requirements in standards that are consistent with *NEC* rules.

FR: None

SR: 1

Definition of Accessible, Readily (Readily Accessible)

Code Language

Accessible, Readily (Readily Accessible). Capable of being reached quickly for operation, renewal, or inspections without requiring those to whom ready access is requisite to take actions such as to use tools (other than keys), to climb over or under, to remove obstacles, or to resort to portable ladders, and so forth. (CMP-1)

Informational Note: Use of keys is a common practice under controlled or supervised conditions and a common alternative to the ready access requirements under such supervised conditions as provided elsewhere in the *NEC*.

(See NEC for actual text)

Change Summary

- The definition of the term *Readily Accessible* has been revised.
- The definition maintains most of its existing text and now includes the words "other than keys."
- A new informational note has been added to address the common practice and use of keys in gaining accessibility under controlled conditions.

Significance of the Change

Several public comments were submitted related to the First Revision created by Code-Making Panel 1 during the first draft stage of the 2017 *NEC* development process. The Panel carefully considered the subsequent relevant points made in Public Comments 1731, 1039, 199, and 300 and maintains that the existing definition of *Accessible, Readily* as provided in the 2014 *NEC* is appropriate with only minor revisions. The new words "other than keys" have been incorporated in the definition addressing the concerns about use of keys expressed in Public Comments 1731 and 199. Code-Making Panel 1 also resolved to maintain the text "to whom ready access is prerequisite," addressing specific concerns identified in Public Comments 1039, 1731, and 300. The Panel affirms that the definition as revised provides consistent and appropriate application of various *NEC* requirements that use the term. The new informational note provides users with clarification about how to treat supervised or controlled conditions that exist in the *NEC* that sometimes modify a general requirement for ready access by specific conditions that recognize controlled access is often gained by use of keys.

FR: 8
SR: 6
SCR: 35

Definition of Building

Code Language

Building. A structure that stands alone or that is separated from adjoining structures by firewalls. (CMP-1)

(See NEC for actual text)

Significance of the Change

The definition of the term *building* has been revised to improve clarity and simplify applicability. This revision incorporates the concepts introduced by Public Inputs 2894 and 2109. The reference to "fire doors" is deleted since leaving the term in the *Code* is misleading as not all openings in fire walls are doors. Building codes address openings permitted in firewalls that are not limited to just fire doors and they must be closed with rated windows, dampers, doors, or sealed with approved fire-rated materials such as caulking or fire-rated wraps or pads. Even though the definition of building refers to it as a structure, not all structures are buildings. The two terms are not always interchangeable. For example, a house is a building that incorporates a structure, typically the structural frame. A billboard sign along the highway is also a structure, but would not qualify as a building. The primary purpose of this revision is to remove the limitation using of fire-rated doors only to achieve a fire rating, and thus accomplish the "separation" necessary to align with, and achieve compliance with the rules that use the term *building*. It should also be noted that the term *building* is used in other NFPA Codes and Standards and beyond.

Change Summary

- The words "with all openings therein protected by approved fire doors" and "cut off" have been removed from this definition.
- The word "separated" replaces the words "cut off."
- The term *firewall* already implies that any openings such as windows and doors would be required to be fire rated.

FR: 9
SR: None

Definition of Communications Equipment

Code Language

Communications Equipment. The electronic equipment that performs the telecommunications operations for the transmission of audio, video, and data, and includes power equipment (e.g., dc converters, inverters, and batteries), technical support equipment (e.g., computers), and conductors dedicated solely to the operation of the equipment. (CMP-16)

Informational Note: As the telecommunications network transitions to a more data-centric network, computers, routers, servers, and their powering equipment, are becoming essential to the transmission of audio, video, and data and are finding increasing application in communications equipment installations.

(See NEC for actual text)

Change Summary

- A new informational note has been added to the definition of the term *Communications Equipment*.
- Previously the definition could have been interpreted that the communications equipment was limited only to those items mentioned in the definition.
- The new informational note clarifies that additional equipment such as routers and servers also fall under this definition.

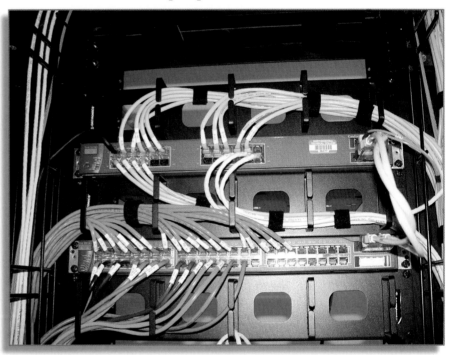

Significance of the Change

Action by CMP-16 results in a new informational note following the definition of the term *Communications Equipment*. Telecommunications equipment used for the transmission of audio, video and data is evolving. As a result, computers and data processing equipment (e.g., routers and servers) are used to control, monitor and process telecommunications functions and are becoming an essential part of that equipment. The new informational note informs the *Code* users that such equipment will likely be encountered in newer/updated telecommunications networks and facilities. Servers, computers, and routers along with their powering equipment are already being used in the telecom industry and are an integral part of communications networks and infrastructure. A good example includes email servers and routers and modem/router combinations that are either direct wired or installed as wireless communications equipment. Informational notes are not enforceable as *Code* requirements but certainly add value by improving clarity of definitions and of requirements that use such defined terms.

FR: 4505
SR: 4506

Definition of Cord Connector for Hazardous Locations

Courtesy of Eaton Corp.

Code Language

Cord Connector [as applied to Hazardous (Classified) Locations]. A fitting intended to terminate a cord to a box or similar device and reduce the strain at points of termination and may include an explosionproof, a dust-ignitionproof, or a flameproof seal. (CMP-14)

(See NEC for actual text)

Significance of the Change

NEC CMP-14 is responsible for definitions of words and terms used within requirements for hazardous (classified) locations. This includes definitions located in Article 100 and in .2 of the applicable Chapter 5 Article in the *NEC*. Section 2.2.2.1 of the *NEC Style Manual* requires that terms appearing in more than two articles be defined in Article 100. The inclusion of specifically designated cords as wiring methods in Articles 501, 502, 503, 505, and 506 requires an appropriate cord connector (fitting). The current term for this device, as used in the hazardous locations industry and within the product standards, is *cord connector*, which should not be confused with the same term also used by the wiring device industry, indicating a female electrical connector. The differentiation has been addressed by denoting [as applied to hazardous (classified) locations]. The term is currently used multiple times in the Chapter 5 articles dealing with hazardous (classified) locations. While there is currently no definition for the term *cord connector* as it is used within *NEC* chapters 1 through 4, a clear differentiation is established by the description provided in this new definition. Connectors used for cords in hazardous locations must be suitable for that location.

Change Summary

- A new definition of "Cord Connector [as applied to hazardous (classified) locations]" has been added to Article 100.
- This term was previously undefined, yet appears in multiple general *NEC* articles including those covering hazardous (classified) locations.
- There is currently no definition for the term *cord connector(s)* appearing in *NEC* Chapters 1 through 4.

FR: 3997
SR: 3913

DELETION / **REVISION**

Definition of Dusttight

Code Language

Dusttight. Enclosures constructed so that dust will not enter under specified test conditions. (CMP-14)

Informational Note No. 1: Enclosure Types 3, 3S, 3SX, 4, 4X, 5, 6, 6P, 12, 12K, and 13, per ANSI/NEMA 250-2014, Enclosures for Electrical Equipment, are considered dusttight and suitable for use in unclassified locations and in Class II, Division 2; Class III; and Zone 22 hazardous (classified) locations.

Informational Note No. 2: For further information, see ANSI/ISA-12.12.01-2013, Nonincendive Electrical Equipment for Use in Class I and II, Division 2, and Class III, Divisions 1 and 2 Hazardous (Classified) Locations.

(See NEC for actual text)

Change Summary

- The definitions of *Dusttight* and associated Informational Notes previously located in Sections 500.2 and 506.2 have been deleted.
- The existing definition of *Dusttight* in Article 100 has been revised to incorporate the concepts contained in the deleted *dusttight* definitions formerly in 500.2 and 506.2.
- The revision attains compliance with Section 2.2.2.1 of the *NEC Style Manual.*

Courtesy of Eaton Corp.

Significance of the Change

Compliance with the *NEC Style Manual* is essential. Many of the defined terms that apply to hazardous (classified) locations appeared in more than one article. The term *dusttight* is one such term. This term previously was defined in Article 100, Section 500.2, and Section 506.2 and the definitions were each slightly different. This not only was in violation of Section 2.2.2.1 of the *NEC Style Manual*, but it created confusion for users. Action by CMP-14 resolves the Style Manual conflict and improves usability. The two definitions formerly located in 500.2 and 506.2 have been deleted. The existing definition of *dusttight* in Article 100 was revised to correlate with how the term is used generally in the *NEC* as well as how it is used within Articles 500 and 506. Informational Note No. 1 provides clarification about the NEMA enclosure types that are considered dusttight. Informational Note No. 2 refers users to ANSI/ISA-12.12.01-2013 for information about installing and use of nonincendive electrical equipment in Class I and II, Division 2, and Class II, Divisions 1 and 2 locations. All definitions will include a (CMP-x) designation indicating which CMP is responsible for that definition.

FRs: 3909, 3910, 3911
SR: None

Definition of Field Evaluation Body (FEB) and Field Labeled

No. FE 00123456

This product has been evaluated in accordance with the procedures and limitations specified in the issued report

EVALUATED

UL LLC © 2014

Contact UL 1.877.854.3577 #2
field@ul.com

Courtesy of Underwriters Laboratories, Inc.

Code Language

Field Evaluation Body (FEB). An organization or part of an organization that performs field evaluations of electrical or other equipment. [NFPA 790, 2012] (CMP-1)

Field Labeled (as applied to evaluated products). Equipment or materials to which has been attached a label, symbol, or other identifying mark of an FEB indicating the equipment or materials were evaluated and found to comply with requirements as described in an accompanying field evaluation report. (CMP-1)

(See NEC for actual text)

Significance of the Change

The term *Approved* is defined as "Acceptable to the authority having jurisdiction." Section 110.2 requires conductors and equipment covered by the *NEC* be approved by the authority having jurisdiction (AHJ). In carrying out the approving responsibility as provided in 90.4, the AHJ typically uses product certification as a basis for approvals. If unique or one-of-a-kind equipment is encountered, it usually has not been certified or listed by a qualified electrical testing laboratory. Field evaluation and field labeling processes and services are available from many qualified electrical testing laboratories. NFPA 790 *Standard for Competency of Third-Party Field Evaluation Bodies* is a fairly new NFPA standard that is intended to standardize and level the playing field so to speak for qualified electrical testing laboratories offering field evaluation services. These defined terms are an essential part of NFPA 790. Action by CMP-4 results in inclusion of the terms *Field Evaluation Body (FEB)* and *Field Labeled* into Article 100 to meet the *NEC Style Manual* because the terms appear in multiple articles. These definitions are necessary to provide consistency and clarity within the field evaluation process requirements where they appear in the *NEC*. CMP-1 has technical responsibilities for these two new defined terms.

Change Summary

- Definitions of the terms *Field Evaluation Body (FEB)* and *Field Labeled* have been incorporated into Article 100.

- The *NEC Style Manual* indicates that terms appearing in more than two articles qualify for definitions in Article 100.

- These definitions have been developed from concepts derived from terms in NFPA 790 *Standard for Competency of Third-Party Field Evaluation Bodies*.

FR: 1041
SR: 918

Multiple Definitions from 500.2

Code Language

Multiple Definitions have been relocated from Section 500.2 to Article 100. The following represents an example of how each will appear in Article 100.

Combustible Dust [as applied to Hazardous (Classified) Locations]. Dust particles that are 500 microns or smaller (material passing a U.S. No. 35 Standard Sieve as defined…(See NEC text) (CMP-14)

(See NEC for actual text)

Change Summary

- Multiple definitions previously located in 500.2 have been relocated to Article 100.
- Section 2.2.2.1 of the *NEC Style Manual* requires that if a term appears in more than two articles it shall be included in Article 100.
- The words [as applied to Hazardous (Classified) Locations] have been added in brackets following each relocated defined term, but before the definition.

FRs: 3929, 3904, 3906, 3907, 3912, 3915, 3916, 3913, 3909, 3918
SR: None

Significance of the Change

Compliance with the *NEC Style Manual* is essential. Many of the defined terms that apply to hazardous (classified) locations appeared in more than just Article 100. To resolve the Style Manual conflict and improve usability, the following 500.2 definitions are now located in Article 100:

Combustible Dust [as applied to Hazardous (Classified) Locations], Combustible Gas Detection System [as applied to Hazardous (Classified) Locations], Control Drawing ([as applied to Hazardous (Classified) Locations], Dust-Ignitionproof [as applied to Hazardous (Classified) Locations], Hermetically Sealed [as applied to Hazardous (Classified) Locations], Purged and Pressurized [as applied to Hazardous (Classified) Locations], Unclassified Locations [as applied to Hazardous (Classified) Locations]…(See *NEC* text)

No technical revisions were made to these definitions. Adding the words [as applied to Hazardous (Classified) Locations] following each relocated term provides a differentiation from the same term that may apply to general wiring methods or equipment, and thus not located within Chapter 5.

Multiple Definitions from Chapter 5

Significance of the Change

Compliance with the *NEC Style Manual* is essential. To resolve the Style Manual conflicts and improve usability, The 504.2, 505.2, and 506.2 definitions (in part) are relocated to Article 100:

Associated Apparatus (as applied to Hazardous (Classified) Locations), Intrinsically Safe Apparatus (as applied to Hazardous (Classified) Locations), Intrinsically Safe System (as applied to Hazardous (Classified) Locations), Simple Apparatus (as applied to Hazardous (Classified) Locations), Combustible Gas Detection System (as applied to Hazardous (Classified) Locations), Associated Nonincendive Field Wiring Apparatus (as applied to Hazardous (Classified) Locations), Nonincendive Equipment…(for balance of relocations see Article 100)

No technical revisions were made to these definitions. Adding the words "(as applied to Hazardous (Classified) Locations)" to each definition provides a differentiation from the same term that may apply to general wiring methods or equipment, and thus not located within Chapter 5. All definitions will include a (CMP-x) designation indicating which CMP is responsible for that definition.

Code Language

Multiple Definitions have been relocated from Sections 504.2, 505.2 and 506.2 to Article 100. The following represents a couple of examples of how each will appear in Article 100.

Intrinsically Safe Apparatus [as applied to Hazardous (Classified) Locations]. Apparatus in which all the circuits are intrinsically safe. (CMP-14)

Associated Nonincendive Field Wiring Apparatus [as applied to Hazardous (Classified) Locations]. Apparatus in which the circuits are not necessarily nonincendive themselves but… (CMP-14)

(See NEC for actual text)

Change Summary

- Multiple definitions previously located in 504.2, 505.2, and 506.2 have been relocated to Article 100.
- Section 2.2.2.1 of the *NEC Style Manual* requires that if a term appears in more than two articles it shall be included in Article 100.
- The words [as applied to Hazardous (Classified) Locations] have been added in brackets following each relocated defined term, but before the definition.

FRs: 3919, 3920, 3921, 3917, 3923, 3903, 3905, 3908, 3924, 3914, 3925
SR: None

Definition of Process Seal

Code Language

Process Seal [as applied to Hazardous (Classified) Locations]. A seal between electrical systems and flammable or combustible process fluids where a failure could allow the migration of process fluids into the premises wiring system. (CMP-14)

(See NEC for actual text)

Change Summary

- The term *Process Seal* is defined in ANSI/ISA 12.27.01-2011.
- A new definition of the term *Process Seal* has been added to Article 100.
- This term was previously undefined, yet was used in multiple *NEC* articles covering hazardous (classified) locations.

Significance of the Change

NEC CMP-14 is responsible for definitions of words and terms used within requirements for hazardous (classified) locations. This includes definitions located in Article 100 and in .2 of the applicable Chapter 5 Article in the *NEC*. Section 2.2.2.1 of the *NEC Style Manual* requires that terms appearing in more than two articles be defined in Article 100. Process seals are typically required between an electrical instrument and the pipeline or vessel to which it is attached. The function of process seals is to keep the explosive liquid, gas, or vapor from migrating from the containment vessel, pipeline, tank, and so forth into the electrical instrument or equipment and ultimately into the wiring system. Process seals are typically an inherent part of this type of equipment. The seal is accomplished by use of diaphragms, "O" rings, or other means of creating a seal or dam creating the isolation. Action by CMP-14 results in the new definition because the term appears multiple times within the *NEC* articles that apply to hazardous locations. This new definition will help users understand the purpose of process sealing and how they differ from conventional conduit and equipment sealing fittings and methods for wiring in hazardous locations.

FR: 3999
SR: None

Definition of Structure

Code Language

Structure. That which is built or constructed, other than equipment. (CMP-1)

(See NEC for actual text)

Significance of the Change

This revision resulted from work of a special task group assigned by the *NEC* Correlating Committee. The scope of this work was to address inconsistencies associated with interpretations that electrical equipment constitutes a structure. The problem surfaced during the 2014 *NEC* development cycle as CMP-19 dealt with a proposal to require grounding electrodes at power outlet pedestals for mobile home parks, whether supplied as a service or by a feeder. Confusion resulted from the language proposed that would have indirectly imposed a requirement for installing a grounding electrode at power outlets supplied by feeders. The wording was along the lines of "For the purpose of this section, a power outlet shall be considered a structure." This is not "Good Code." The proposed revision was not accepted as a result. There are documented instances of jurisdictions interpreting electrical equipment as *structures* which in turn could impose other *NEC* requirements unnecessarily. A mobile home power outlet that is supplied by a feeder is not a service, and there is no requirement for a grounding electrode. Any installed electrode is an optional auxiliary electrode in this case. As revised, the term *structure* is better differentiated from what constitutes electrical equipment, promoting more consistent *NEC* application.

Change Summary

- The definition of the term *structure* has been revised by adding the words "other than equipment."
- The revision provides a clear differentiation between what constitutes electrical equipment as compared to structures.
- The revision will promote more consistent application of *NEC* requirements related to structures, such as when grounding electrodes are optional or required.

FR: 13
SR: None

REVISION / **RELOCATE**

Definition of Substation

Code Language

Substation. An assemblage of equipment (e.g., switches, interrupting devices, circuit breakers, buses, and transformers) through which electric energy is passed for the purpose of distribution, switching, or modifying its characteristics. (CMP-9)

(See NEC for actual text)

Courtesy of Schneider Electric

Change Summary

- The title for Part II of Article 100 has been changed from "Over 600 Volts, Nominal" to "Over 1000 Volts, Nominal."

- The previous definition of *Substation* has been relocated from Part I to Part II.

- The definition has been revised to clarify its physical characteristics and how it is usually intended to perform.

Significance of the Change

In the 2014 development cycle, an assigned high-voltage task group submitted revisions to raise the 600 volt threshold to 1000 volts, Code wide. While most *NEC* panels accepted the revisions, CMP-8 and CMP-1 did not, due to additional work needed for the transition. Action by CMP-1 in this 2017 *NEC* development cycle results in the completion of raising the voltage threshold in the chapter 1 articles from 600 to 1000. The changes related to the substation definition are to revise and add clarity to it, in addition to relocating it from Article 100, Part I, to Part II. The reason is that most substations handle voltages exceeding those covered in Part I (1000 volts). Also, there is no restriction from applying the relocated definition to substations that do not include medium voltage components. The revised definition provides enhanced clarification about incorporated components present in substations and information about power sources for substations as well as performing transformation functions. The additional clarity was needed because the previous definition was too vague and could have been applied to various types of equipment such as an industrial control panel. As revised, the physical and performance characteristics are more clearly described.

FRs: 6, 2429, 2430
SR: 2413

Equipment Examination and Use Suitability

Code Language

(A) Examination. In judging equipment, considerations such as the following shall be evaluated:

(1) Suitability for installation and use in conformity with the provisions of this Code

Informational Note No. 1: Equipment may be new, reconditioned, refurbished, or remanufactured.

Informational Note No. 2: Suitability of equipment use may be identified by…(remainder unchanged)

(See NEC for actual text)

Significance of the Change

Section 110.3(A) addresses examination and judgment of equipment relative to its suitability for use. There is a list of factors that should be included in the determination of equipment suitability and compliance with the *NEC*. Some of the factors include electrical insulation, mechanical strength, arcing effects, and wire-bending space. As provided in previous editions of the *NEC*, the term *equipment* could have been applied to new, reconditioned, refurbished or remanufactured equipment. However with new installations installed, the *Code* is generally applied to new equipment. This revision provides the needed clarification that examination of equipment for suitability can be applied to reconditioned, refurbished or remanufactured equipment, in addition to new equipment. Evidence of suitability is often provided in the instructions and identification, including labeling on the equipment. New requirements for identification and marking of reconditioned, refurbished or remanufactured equipment have been incorporated in a new list item 2 to 110.21(A). This revision should assist installers, owners, inspectors, and others by having clear language in the *NEC* that indicates the term *equipment* applies to more than just new equipment, unless stated differently within any specific requirement.

Change Summary

- A new informational note No. 1 has been added to 110.3(A)(1).
- Previous Informational Note No. 1 has been renumbered as Informational Note No. 2.
- The new informational note clarifies that the term *equipment* used in this section applies to new, reconditioned, refurbished or remanufactured equipment.

FR: 31
SR: 2

Product Use, Listing, and Certification

Code Language

110.3 Examination, Identification, Installation, and Use, and Listing (Product Certification) of Equipment.

(C) Listing. Product testing, evaluation, listing (product certification) shall be performed by recognized qualified electrical testing laboratories and shall be in accordance with applicable product standards recognized as achieving equivalent and effective safety…(See *NEC* text).

Informational Note: The Occupational Safety and Health Administration…(See *NEC* text)

(See NEC for actual text)

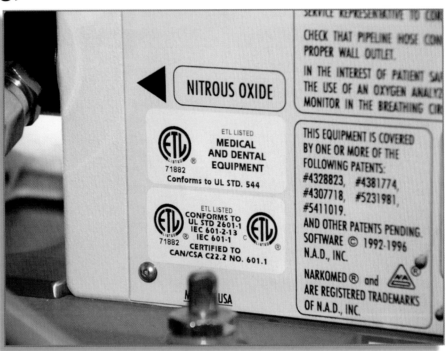

Change Summary

- The title of 110.3 has been revised to include listing (product certification)
- A new Subdivision (C) and associated informational note have been added to Section 110.3.
- The revision clarifies that listing (product certification) be performed by recognized qualified electrical testing laboratories and the new informational note indicates that OSHA provides a list of such qualified laboratories.

Significance of the Change

Code-Making Panel 1 responded favorably to reconsidering the original concepts introduced by Public Input 2839. This new subdivision (C) provides a requirement that listing (product certification) be performed by qualified electrical testing laboratories to achieve effective safety anticipated by the *NEC* and applicable product standards. As indicated in the substantiation with Public Comment 938, in exercising their approving authority in 90.4, the AHJ depends on listing and product certification as the most common basis for approvals of installations in accordance with the *National Electrical Code*. The additional subdivision (C) titled "Listing" provides clarification about requirements for listing product certification and that it must be accomplished by qualified electrical testing laboratories; and that the product testing and certification process is in accordance with applicable and appropriate product standards. The new informational note provides users and authorities having jurisdiction with information about a list of nationally recognized testing laboratories that meet or exceed OSHA criteria. Product listing (certification) is the most common basis for AHJ approvals and the product listing must meet or exceed the minimum product safety requirements developed by recognized standards development organizations.

FR: None
SR: 2

Copper or Aluminum Conductors

Courtesy of PDE Total Energy Solutions

Code Language

110.5 Conductors. Conductors normally used to carry current shall be of copper or aluminum unless otherwise provided in this *Code*. Where the conductor material is not specified, the sizes given in this *Code* shall apply to copper conductors. Where other materials are used, the size shall be changed accordingly.

Informational Note: For copper-clad aluminum conductors, see 310.15.

(See NEC for actual text)

Significance of the Change

This section has been revised to generally reference both aluminum and copper conductors. The *NEC* Code-Making Panels have done an excellent job throughout the *Code* of specifying instances where a particular metal is required or prohibited in a particular installation. This long-standing requirement has been revised to align with evolution and industry practices of requiring and prohibiting specific conductor materials for installations covered in the *Code*. A restriction of conductors other than copper is no longer appropriate as previously provided in the blanket statement in 110.5. As revised, 110.5 clarifies that the rules apply to both aluminum and copper conductors. The *NEC* specifically addresses instances where other metals are allowed or are restricted for reasons such as current-carrying capacity or concerns about corrosion or deterioration affects. For example, Section 517.13(B)(1) requires branch circuit wiring for patient care spaces to be provided with an insulated copper equipment-grounding conductor. Section 505.18 requires copper conductors for the increased safety protection technique "e" because of the requirements for the copper conductor at terminations. The informational note to this section remains because Article 310 still addresses copper-clad aluminum conductors. Although copper-clad conductors are no longer generally manufactured, they are still present within many premises wiring systems.

Change Summary

- The word *aluminum* has been removed from the informational note and added to the first sentence of this section.
- Rules in the *Code* applying to conductors generally apply to both copper and aluminum, unless specified otherwise for reasons such as ampacity, corrosion, and so forth.
- Information exists in Article 310 relative to copper-clad aluminum conductors.

FR: 39
SR: None

110.9

Article 110 Requirements for Electrical Installations

Part I General

Interrupting Rating

Code Language

110.9 Interrupting Rating. Equipment intended to interrupt current at fault levels shall have an interrupting rating at nominal circuit voltage at least equal to the current that is available at the line terminals of the equipment. Equipment intended to interrupt current at other than fault levels shall have an interrupting rating at nominal circuit voltage at least equal to the current that must be interrupted.

(See NEC for actual text)

Change Summary

- The words "sufficient for" have been replaced with the words "at least equal to" in both sentences of this section.
- The revision removes a vague and subjective term to attain conformity with the *NEC Style Manual*.
- The revision clarifies the minimum interrupting ratings necessary for equipment that is intended to interrupt fault current.

Significance of the Change

Section 110.9 is an important requirement intended to mandate minimum interrupting ratings. This revision removes the vague and subjective term "sufficient for" to attain conformity with Section 3.2.1 of the *NEC Style Manual*. The use of the words "sufficient for" in 110.9 does not literally imply that the interrupting rating must be equal to the current that must be interrupted. The new words "at least equal to the current" provide clear text for application and the enforcement of this requirement. As revised, the interrupting ratings for equipment intended to interrupt current due to a short circuit or ground fault event. It is interesting to note that equipment could also be installed in a series rated combination, and could have a rating less than the amount of available fault current at that point on the system, as provided in 110.22. The key in that section is that those OCPDs are listed series rated combinations or engineered series rated combinations. There is an opportunity for an exception to be incorporated after 110.9 that refers to 110.22, which permits ratings less than the available fault current. These series combinations that are listed and/or engineered to provide equal and effective protection intended by 110.9.

FR: 37
SR: None

22   Chapter 1 • Articles 90, 100, and 110

Tightening Torque at Terminations

Code Language

110.14 Electrical Connections. Because of different characteristics of dissimilar metals...(section text remains unchanged other than to delete the informational note)

110.14(D) Installation. Where a tightening torque is indicated as a numeric value on equipment or in installation instructions provided by the manufacturer, a calibrated torque tool shall be used to achieve the indicated torque value, unless the equipment manufacturer has provided installation instructions for an alternative method of achieving the required torque.

(See NEC for actual text)

Significance of the Change

Electrical connections are critical in electrical systems and are typically the weakest link. Proper terminations can mean the difference between long lasting service and failure. Many types of electrical equipment such as switchboards, panelboards, and motor control centers are equipped with labels that address tightening torque for terminals. Use of a proper torque tool is essential to verify that terminations are properly made and the equipment will function properly throughout its life cycle. To get it right, it is important not to under tighten or over tighten terminations. Using a torque-measuring tool was already a *Code* requirement because of manufacturer's installation instructions and markings on equipment. Section 110.3(B) requires equipment to be installed and used in accordance with any instructions included in the listing. Because of this, actual text addressing torque measuring was never included in the *NEC*. Information provided in Public Input 1323 indicated testing has shown that installers use the wrong torque values in up to 75% of installations unless a torque-measuring tool is used. CMP-1 has taken a different direction this cycle and acted favorable to include tightening torque requirements within the *NEC*, rather than just in accordance with installation instructions that are mandatory because of 110.3(B).

Change Summary

- A new subdivision (D) titled "Installation" has been added following 110.14(C).

- This new subdivision incorporates mandatory tightening torque requirements for electrical terminations in accordance with manufacturer's instructions, or allows for alternate methods as provided in the instructions.

- The informational note to 110.14 has been deleted because it is no longer necessary.

FRs: 40, 41
SR: None

Arc-Flash Hazard Warning Label at Service

Code Language

(B) Service Equipment. In other than dwelling units, addition to the requirements in (A), a permanent label shall be field or factory applied to service equipment rated 1200 amperes or more. The label shall meet the requirements of 110.21(B) and contain the following information:

(1) Nominal system voltage

(2) Available fault current...(See *NEC* text)

(3) The clearing time...(See *NEC* text)

(4) The date the label was applied

Exception: Service equipment labeling shall not be required if an arc flash label is applied in accordance with industry practice.

(See NEC for actual text)

⚠ **WARNING**

Arc Flash & Shock Hazard
Appropriate PPE Required

Date Label was Applied_____
Nominal System Voltage_____
Available Fault Current_____
Service Overcurrent Device Clearing Time_____

Arc Flash Boundary_____
At least one of the following:_____
(1) Incident Energy _____ at working distance of _____ or
    Arc Flash PPE Category_____
(2) Minimum arc rating of clothing_____
(3) Specific level of PPE _____

Yellow Highlights indicate arc-flash warning label requirements in the NEC

Change Summary

- A new (B) titled "Service Equipment" and informational note have been added to 110.16.
- The provisions in 110.16 now required more *installation-related* detail and information for determining *electrical workplace safety related* criteria for information such as arc-flash energy levels and required PPE.
- New informational note No. 3 references *NFPA 70E* for specific criteria related to arc-flash labels and determining appropriate PPE.

FR: 55
SR: 11

Significance of the Change

Section 110.16 has been expanded and separated into two subdivisions and a new exception. New subdivision (B) is titled "Service Equipment" and requires additional information to be provided on a field or factory-applied label. This section continues to require that equipment be generally marked to warn qualified persons of arc-flash hazards, but now requires more specific detail about the service equipment installation. The marking required in (B) applies only to service equipment and must include the nominal system voltage, the available fault current at the service overcurrent devices, the clearing time of the service overcurrent device(s) and the date the label was applied. Because the available fault current is required for determining the minimum short-circuit current rating of the equipment, the additional information required in list (2) is fairly routine to acquire. Both the service OCPD clearing times and the available fault current are characteristics related to the service equipment installation and *NEC* compliance. This information is also used to establish specific values required for *NFPA 70E* arc flash warning labels. The new informational note references *NFPA 70E* which contains specific provisions related to establishing the arc-flash boundaries, incident energy at working distance(s), minimum arc rating of clothing required, site-specific PPE required for justified energized work.

Marking Requirements for Reconditioned Equipment

MANUFACTURER NAME:
BRUNER BREAKER

EQUIPMENT RECONDITIONED ON: *2/12/2016*

≡BRUNER
≡BREAKER
16021 UNION AVE
LONGVIEW, WA
97230

Code Language

(A) Equipment Markings.

(1) General. The manufacturer's name, trademark...(See *NEC* text)

(2) Reconditioned Equipment. Reconditioned equipment shall be marked with the name, trademark, or other descriptive marking by which the organization responsible for reconditioning the electrical equipment can be identified, along with the date....(See *NEC* text)

Exception: In industrial occupancies, where conditions of maintenance and supervision ensure that only qualified persons service the equipment, the markings indicated in 110.21(A)(2) shall not be required.

Informational Note: Industry standards are available...(See *NEC* text)

(See NEC for actual text)

Significance of the Change

Section 110.21(A) has been expanded to cover marking of reconditioned equipment. The revisions to this section clarify that reconditioned or remanufactured equipment is included in the equipment that must comply with *NEC* rules. Section 110.3(A) now includes an informational note that relates to equipment examination and criteria that can be used to determine suitability for electrical installations. The new informational note clarifies that the term *equipment* applies to not only new, but applies to reconditioned, refurbished, or remanufactured equipment. New list item (2) has been added to include specific marking requirements that apply to reconditioned equipment. The key elements that must be included in the markings are identifying the equipment as "reconditioned," the name of the organization, trademark, or other descriptive marking of the responsible organization, and the reconditioning date. This revision clarifies that approval of reconditioned equipment must not be based solely on the original listing of the equipment. Organizations performing reconditioning must conform to applicable industry product standards. An exception relaxes the requirement for industrial occupancies under controlled conditions and the new informational note conveys that industry standards provide information applicable to reconditioned equipment. The new marking requirements provide inspectors with a more effective means for approving installations of reconditioned equipment.

Change Summary

- The title of subdivision (A) has been changed from "Manufacturer's Markings" to "Equipment Markings."

- Section 110.21(A) has been renumbered as list items (1) and a new list item (2) with a new exception and informational note.

- New list item (2) provides marking requirements for reconditioned equipment including the responsible organization, and date of reconditioning.

FR: 42
SR: 9
SCR: 22

Calculation Required and Made Available

Code Language

110.24(A) Field Marking. Service equipment at other than dwelling units shall be legibly marked in the field with the maximum available fault current. The field marking(s) shall include the date the fault current calculation was performed and shall be of sufficient durability to withstand the environment involved. The calculation shall be documented and made available to those authorized to design, install, inspect, maintain, or operate the system.

Informational Note: (See *NEC* text)

(See NEC for actual text)

Change Summary

- A new last sentence has been added to 110.24(A) addressing calculations.
- The additional requirements are to document the calculation and make it available to those authorized to design, install, inspect, maintain, or operate the system.
- The maximum level of available fault current can be obtained from published utility data or by use of calculation methods.

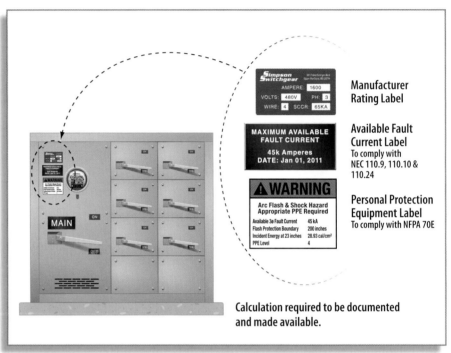

Manufacturer Rating Label

Available Fault Current Label
To comply with NEC 110.9, 110.10 & 110.24

Personal Protection Equipment Label
To comply with NFPA 70E

Calculation required to be documented and made available.

Significance of the Change

The marking requirements in 110.24 are fairly new to the *NEC* and have made a significant improvement in ensuring suitable short circuit current ratings of equipment in new installations as well as in older or legacy installations. Service equipment must be suitable for the maximum available fault current regardless if it is new or existing. There are no exceptions. The requirements in 110.24 raise the level of awareness of the necessary short-circuit current ratings for new services and existing. The maximum available fault current values are typically provided by the serving utility and are published in hard copy and on the Internet. In situations where the values of maximum available fault current are not available, a calculation is often performed to establish the maximum. This value must be known to ensure that service equipment is adequately rated for the AFC. The revision in this edition of the *NEC* addresses such calculations and requires that the calculation be documented and made available to those authorized to design, install, inspect, maintain, or operate the system. The new calculation requirement will assist installers, design teams, owners and inspectors in attaining more accurate information that demonstrates suitable service equipment short-circuit current ratings.

FR: 45
SR: 10

Voltage Thresholds Increased to 1000 Volts

Code Language

(A) Working Space. Working space for equipment operating at 1000 volts, nominal, or less to ground and likely to require examination, adjustment, servicing, or maintenance while energized shall comply with the dimensions of 110.26(A)(1), (A)(2), (A)(3), and (A)(4) or as required or permitted elsewhere in this *Code.*

Informational Note: NFPA 70E-2015, *Standard for Electrical Safety in the Workplace*, provides guidance, such as determining severity of potential exposure, planning safe work practices, arc flash labeling, and selecting personal protective equipment.

(See NEC for actual text)

Significance of the Change

The voltage threshold of 600 volts within Article 110 and Table 110.26(A)(1), have been increased to 1000 volts in addition to the title of Part II. A new row has been added to Table 110.26(A)(1) providing minimum working spaces for equipment with operating voltages between 601 – 1000 volts. The revision of this table incorporates the voltage ranges and clearance distances from Table 110.34(A). These revisions resulted from work of an assigned Correlating Committee Task Group to: (1) resolve issues with actions taken by Code-Making Panels 1 and 8 on proposals and comments in the 2014 *NEC* cycle relative to changing the voltage threshold in articles under their purview from 600 volts to 1000 volts, (2) address electrical substations, and (3) evaluate other higher voltage threshold requirements to be included relative to present trends. The SI units within Table 110.26(A)(1) have been revised to be consistent with other tables in Article 110 such as Table 110.34(A). CMP-1 also acted favorably to include an informational note referencing NFPA 70E *Standard for Electrical Safety in the Workplace,* as it provides guidance on items such as determining severity of potential exposure, planning safe work practices, arc-flash labeling, and selecting personal protective equipment (PPE).

Change Summary

- Part II of Article 110 has been retitled as "1000 Volts, Nominal, or Less."
- The value of 600 volts within Table 110.26(A)(1) has been increased to 1000 volts.
- A new informational note following subdivision (A) refers users to *NFPA 70E* for guidance on exposure to electrical hazards when working within spaces covered by 110.26.

FRs: 15, 18
SR: None

Working Space for Limited Access Equipment

Code Language

(4) Limited Access. Where equipment operating at 1000 volts, nominal, or less to ground and likely to require examination, adjustment, servicing, or maintenance while energized is required by installation instructions or function to be located... the following shall apply:

(a) Where equipment is installed above a lay-in ceiling...(See *NEC* text)

(b) The width of the working space shall be the width...(See *NEC* text)

(c) All enclosure doors or hinged panels shall be...(See *NEC* text)

(d) The space in front of the enclosure shall...(See *NEC* text)

(See NEC for actual text)

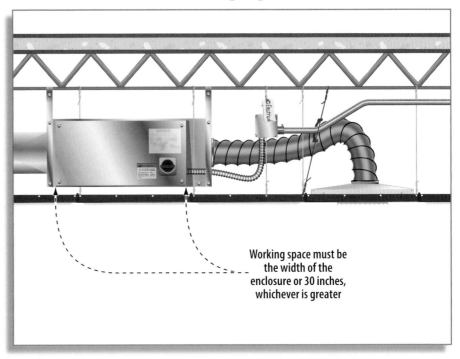

Working space must be the width of the enclosure or 30 inches, whichever is greater

Change Summary

- A new list item (4) titled "Limited Access" has been added to 110.26(A).
- Minimum working spaces for equipment located above lay-in ceilings is now included within the general working space requirements in 110.26(A).
- The space requirements now apply to all electrical equipment that is covered by 110.26(A) and Table 110.26(A)(1).

Significance of the Change

A new list item (4) has been added to address equipment in spaces with limited access. The requirement applies to equipment operating at 1000 volts, nominal, or less to ground and likely to require examination, adjustment, servicing, or maintenance while energized, and installed above lay-in ceilings. Access space could be a requirement specified by instructions or required by the function of the equipment. The minimum working space required for limited access equipment covered by this section includes specific conditions related to ceiling grids. Equipment qualifying for the limited access provisions must meet the following requirements: (1) above a lay-in ceiling, (2) width of the working space, (3) doors or hinged panels be capable of opening a minimum of 90 degrees, and (4) space in front of the enclosure. The maximum height of the working space must be the height necessary for equipment in the limited space. A horizontal ceiling structural member or access panel shall be permitted in this space. The 2014 edition of the *NEC* included a limited access working space rule in 424.66, but it applied only to duct heaters. Including limited access working space requirements in Article 110 makes it a general requirement for all equipment requiring working space and located with limited access.

FR: 15
SR: 12

Separation from High-Voltage Equipment

Code Language

(5) Separation from High-Voltage Equipment. Where switches, cut-outs, or other equipment operating at 1000 volts, nominal, or less are installed in a vault, room, or enclosure where there are exposed live parts or exposed wiring operating over 1000 volts, nominal, the high-voltage equipment shall be effectively separated from the space occupied by the low-voltage equipment by a suitable partition, fence, or screen.

(See NEC for actual text)

Significance of the Change

New list item (5) in 110.26(A) is titled "Separation from High-Voltage Equipment" and correlates with similar separation provisions for over 1000 volts in Part III, Section 110.31(A). This new requirement resulted from work of an assigned Correlating Committee High-Voltage Task Group to resolve issues with actions taken by Code-Making Panels 1 and 8 on proposals and comments in the 2014 *NEC* cycle relative to globally increasing voltage thresholds from 600 volts to 1000 volts within articles under their purview. The work of this group also addressed both indoor and outdoor electrical substations, and evaluated other higher-voltage threshold requirements to be included in Part II of the article. Recognizing separation between exposed high voltage parts and low voltage equipment is essential, this provision has been incorporated to provide specific requirements in Part II of Article 110 and applies to equipment of 1000 volts or less. High- and medium-voltage distribution systems are common in premises wiring, and often require transforming to lower voltages in either unit substations of transformers located in vaults or other enclosures. The separation required between the exposed high-voltage live parts and low-voltage equipment of 1000 volts or less is typically accomplished by installing suitable partitions, fences or screen walls.

Change Summary

- A new list item (5) titled "Separation from High Voltage Equipment" has been added to 110.26(A).

- In vaults, rooms, or other enclosures with exposed live parts, low voltage equipment must be separated from high voltage equipment.

- Separation must be accomplished with a suitable partition, fence, or screen.

FR: 15
SR: None

110.26(B)

Article 110 Requirements for Electrical Installations

Part II 1000 Volts, Nominal, or Less

REVISION

Sign for Working Space and Egress Area

Code Language

(B) Clear Spaces.

Working space required by this section shall not be used for storage. When normally enclosed live parts are exposed for inspection or servicing, the working space, if in a passageway or general open space, shall be suitably guarded. Permanent and conspicuous signs shall be provided. The sign shall meet the requirements in 110.21(B) and shall read as follows:

NOTICE
ELECTRICAL EQUIPMENT WORKING SPACE AND EGRESS AREA — NO OBSTRUCTION OR STORAGE ALLOWED

(See NEC for actual text)

Change Sum...

- Two new se...
  datory te...
  has b...
- Th...
- The...
  requir...
  developi...
  with ANSI...

[Diagonal overlay text: Example of a Created First Revision rejected by a Second Revision (SR 13). Included for instructor use and discussion purposes only. The change never occurred.]

...ge

...ly to Public Input 641 and expanded ...working spaces and egress areas not ...is a perpetual problem with keeping required ...paces and egress paths clear of obstructions ...ed as storage areas. The problem is that often after ...cupied, personnel unfamiliar with the requirements of ...electrical equipment rooms and areas handy for stor- ...s common in many facilities and is a bad practice that can ...safety concerns for Electrical Workers and personnel having ...rvice electrical equipment. The other problem is obstructing the ...y of egress away from the equipment in the event of a failure such as an arc-flash event that could occur during justified energized work. This first revision introduces a new requirement for a sign and specific text with an appropriate reference to 110.21(B). The specific location of the sign is not mentioned because each installation is unique and the optimal location must be selected to perform as intended. The reference to 110.21(B) will assist users by triggering the consistent methods of developing signage as provided in ANSI Z535.4.

FR: 17
SR: None

Lighting Control By Automatic Means

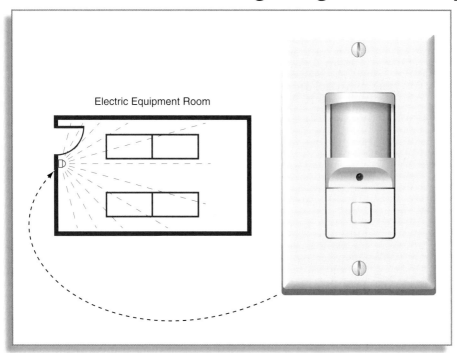

Electric Equipment Room

Code Language

(D) Illumination. Illumination shall be provided for all working spaces about service equipment, switchboards, switchgear, panelboards, or motor control centers installed indoors. Control by automatic means only shall not be permitted. Additional lighting outlets shall not be required where the work space is illuminated by an adjacent light source or as permitted by 210.70(A)(1), Exception No. 1, for switched receptacles.

(See NEC for actual text)

Significance of the Change

This revision improves clarity and usability that illumination in working spaces for the identified electrical equipment in indoor locations must have means of control other than just automatic, such as manual operation without relying on automatic controls. Occupancy sensor devices are an effective means of saving energy and provide a means for meeting requirements in energy codes. Safety concerns will always trump saving energy. This revision clarifies that lighting control in electrical equipment areas or rooms can be accomplished using automatic occupancy or motion-sensing devices, but they must be equipped with manual override capability. This ensures that when the device is placed in the manual "on" mode, the space remains illuminated as work within those locations is being performed. Qualified persons are still responsible for utilizing the manual feature. Information in the substantiation with Public Input 451 indicated that an Electrical Worker could enter the room to perform work, but be out of the sensing range of the device and possibly be left in the dark as the device does not sense movement. This situation presents serious safety concerns for workers that may be performing justified energized work within equipment and are suddenly left in complete darkness.

Change Summary

- The first sentence of this section has been revised by removing the words "and shall not be controlled by automatic means."

- A new second sentence has been added and addresses automatic control means more specifically.

- Automatic control only is not permitted, meaning automatic devices with manual overrides are suitable for these locations.

FR: 19
SR: None

Dedicated Space For Equipment Outdoors

Code Language

(2) Outdoor. Outdoor installations shall comply with 110.26(E)(2)(a) through (c).

(a) *Installation Requirements.* Outdoor electrical equipment shall be the following:

(1) Installed in identified enclosures

(2) Protected from accidental contact by unauthorized personnel, or by vehicular traffic

(3) Protected from accidental spillage or leakage from piping systems

(b) *Work Space.* The working clearance space shall include the zone described in 110.26(A). No architectural appurtenance or other equipment shall be located in this zone.

Exception: Structural overhangs or roof extensions shall be permitted in this zone.

(c) *Dedicated Equipment Space.* The space equal to...(as in 2014 *NEC*)

(See NEC for actual text)

Change Summary

- Section 110.26(E)(2) has been rewritten in a list format for clarity and usability.

- A new Exception to (b) has been added to address structural overhangs and roof extensions.

- The exception permits structural overhangs and roof extensions within this space that otherwise is dedicated for just electrical equipment.

Significance of the Change

Code-Making Panel 1 acted favorably to the concepts introduced by Public Inputs 1226 and 4628 and SR 14. This section has been rewritten into a list format for enhanced clarity and usability. The equipment must be identified for the location as provided in list item (1). The dedicated space required for equipment is essential for personnel safety and provides for practical access for wiring to be added to equipment in addition to performing other servicing operations. A new exception has been added and applies specifically to (b). The exception relaxes the requirement for completely dedicated space above equipment where unreasonable due to structural appurtencies such as roof overhangs. The Panel recognizes that it is not practical to maintain clear space in all cases due to building and structural varying designs of the building exterior(s). In outdoor locations, keeping this zone completely clear is the general rule, but where this is not practical because of the above reasons, relief is provided. It is also a recognized common practice to route wiring methods through non-structural overhangs or roof extensions to enter such located equipment. The new exception provides the necessary relief for installers and inspectors. There were no revisions to the existing requirements now provided in list item (c).

FR: 20
SR: 14

Guarding of Exposed Live Parts

Code Language

(A) Live Parts Guarded Against Accidental Contact. (text in part)

(4) By elevation above the floor or other working surface as follows:

a. A minimum of 2.5 m (8 ft) for 50 volts to 300 volts between ungrounded conductors

b. A minimum of 2.6 m (8 ft 6 in) for 301 volts to 600 volts between ungrounded conductors

c. A minimum of 2.62 m (8 ft 7 in.) for 601 volts to 1000 volts between ungrounded conductors

(See NEC for actual text)

Significance of the Change

These revisions resulted from work of an assigned Correlating Committee High-Voltage Task Group to resolve issues with actions taken by Code-Making Panel 1 on proposals and comments in the 2014 *NEC* cycle relative to globally increasing voltage thresholds from 600 to 1000 volts. Action on Second Revision 16 removes the proposed list item (3) that was added during the First Revision phase of the process. CMP-1 resolves that the new list item was not necessary and already covered in other *NEC* rules. As revised installations of 1000 volts, nominal, or less, are covered by this section. The vague term *suitable* has been removed from this section to meet requirements of the *NEC Style Manual*. The voltage ranges in (4)(a) through (c) have been clarified relative with regard to whether they are from phase-to-phase, or from phase-to-ground. This revision also adds to the text of 110.27(A)(4) covering insulated live parts at 601 to 1000 volts is based on a voltage adder of 10 mm (0.4 in) per kV. The phrase "600 volts nominal to ground" was removed improving clarity and correlates with similar changes to 110.33(A)(2). The voltage ranges in (4)(a) through (c) have been expanded to include 601 through 1000 and clarified relative to distinguish between phase-to-phase voltages or phase-to-ground voltages.

Change Summary

- Installations of 1000 volts, nominal, or less are now covered by this section.
- The vague and unenforceable word "suitable" has been removed in accordance with the *NEC Style Manual*.
- The voltage ranges in (4)(a) through (c) have been clarified relative with regard to whether they are from phase-to-phase, or from phase-to-ground.

FR: 48
SR: 16

Lighting Control By Automatic Means

Code Language

(D) Illumination. Illumination shall be provided for all working spaces about electrical equipment. Control by automatic means only shall not be permitted. The lighting outlets shall be arranged so that persons changing lamps or making repairs on the lighting system are not endangered by live parts or other equipment. The points of control shall be located so that persons are not likely to come in contact with any live part or moving part of the equipment while turning on the lights.

(See NEC for actual text)

Change Summary

- A new second sentence has been added and addresses automatic control means more specifically.
- Automatic control only is not permitted, meaning automatic devices with manual overrides are suitable for these locations.
- This section now directly correlates with the same illumination control requirements specified in 110.26(D).

FR: 301
SR: None

Significance of the Change

This revision improves clarity and usability that illumination in working spaces for the identified electrical equipment must have means of control other than just automatic, such as manual operation without relying on automatic controls. Occupancy sensor devices are an effective means of saving energy and provide a means for meeting requirements in energy codes. Safety concerns will always trump saving energy. As revised, this requirement aligns with 110.26(D) for illumination in working spaces about electrical equipment identified in indoor locations to permit other means of control such as manual operation without relying on automatic controls. This revision clarifies that lighting control in electrical equipment areas or rooms can be accomplished using automatic occupancy or motion-sensing devices, but they must be equipped with manual override capability. This ensures that when the device is placed in the manual mode "on" the space remains illuminated as work within those locations is being performed. Qualified persons working in these areas and requiring illumination are still responsible for utilizing the manual feature. Obviously sudden automatic shutdown of illumination about medium and high voltage equipment creates a hazard for those installing, maintaining, and operating electrical equipment, or performing justified energized work on the equipment.

Inspections, Operating Tests, and Reports

Code Language

110.41 Inspections and Tests.

(A) Pre-energization and Operating Tests. Where required elsewhere in this *Code*, the complete electrical system design, including settings for protective, switching, and control circuits, shall be prepared in advance and made available on request to the authority having jurisdiction and shall be tested when first installed on-site.

(B) Test Report. A test report covering the results of the tests required in 110.41(A) shall be available to the authority having jurisdiction prior to energization and made available to those authorized to install, operate, test, and maintain the system.

(See NEC for actual text)

Significance of the Change

A new requirement for pre-energization operational testing has been incorporated into Part III of Article 110. This new Section 110.41 correlates with inspection and testing requirements contained in other *NEC* rules such as those in Article 225. Including this requirement in Article 110 results in a general requirement for these systems whether indoors or outdoors. System acceptance testing, design settings for protective, switching, and control circuits as well as test results are just as important for indoor and outdoor locations. This requirement ensures that electrical installations greater than 1000 volts will perform to design specifications and that the records for verifying the proper settings and test data are available to the authority having jurisdiction, installers, operators, testers, and maintainers after the equipment is put into service. This provision is essentially the same as 225.56, except for additional text 110.41(B) "and made available to those authorized to install, operate, test, and maintain the system." Circuits and equipment of these types inside of buildings have equal priority for assurances the initial installation is as designed and the equipment will operate as intended. The requirement to have the test results available to the AHJ also serves as a basis for system and equipment approvals.

Change Summary

- A new section 110.41 titled "Inspections and Tests" has been added to Part III of Article 110.
- Pre-energization and operational testing of the complete system is required when equipment is first installed on site.
- Test results must be made available to those authorized to install, operate, test, and maintain the system.

FR: 36
SR: None

Chapter 2

Articles 210–250
Wiring and Protection

More Than One Nominal Voltage System

Code Language

210.5(C)(1) Branch Circuits Supplied from More Than One Nominal Voltage System...(*no changes*)

(a) *Means of Identification...(no changes)*

(b) *Posting of Identification Means...* (See *NEC* text) The label shall be of sufficient durability to withstand the environment involved and shall not be handwritten.

Exception: In existing installations where a voltage system(s) already exists and a different voltage system is being added, it shall be permissible to mark only the new system voltage. Existing unidentified systems shall not be required to be identified at each termination, connection, and splice point in compliance with 210.5(C)(1)(a) and (b). Labeling shall be required at each voltage system distribution equipment to identify that only one voltage system has been marked for a new system(s). The new system label(s) shall include the words "other unidentified systems exist on the premises."

(See NEC for actual text)

Change Summary

- Required labels must be of sufficient durability to withstand the environment involved and shall not be handwritten.

- A new exception is added to address existing installations where a voltage system(s) already exists and a different voltage system is being added. This exception requires marking of only the new system.

FR: 302

SR: 304

SCR: 68

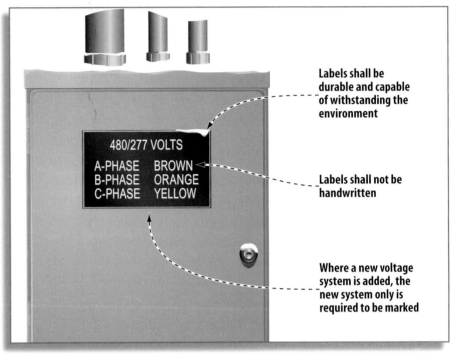

Labels shall be durable and capable of withstanding the environment

480/277 VOLTS
A-PHASE   BROWN
B-PHASE   ORANGE
C-PHASE   YELLOW

Labels shall not be handwritten

Where a new voltage system is added, the new system only is required to be marked

Significance of the Change

210.5(C)(1) requires that where a premises wiring system has branch circuits supplied from more than one nominal voltage system, each ungrounded conductor of a branch circuit must be identified by phase or line and system at all termination, connection, and splice points. This is typical where both 208/120 and 480/277 volt systems are present. 210.5(C)(1)(b) requires the identification means be posted. A new last sentence has been added in 210.5(C)(1)(b) to provide clarity and additional requirements for the posting of identification means. The label is now required to be of sufficient durability to withstand the environment involved. For example, a panelboard that is mounted in an outdoor location must have a suitable label applied. The revision also prohibits the label from being handwritten. A new exception is added to address existing installations where a voltage system(s) already exists and a different voltage system is being added. This exception requires marking of only the new system voltage at each termination, connection, and splice point. The exception does require that labeling be provided for the existing system. Where the exception is applied, all distribution equipment for each voltage system must be labeled and must inform the label reader that other unidentified systems exist.

Identification of DC Systems

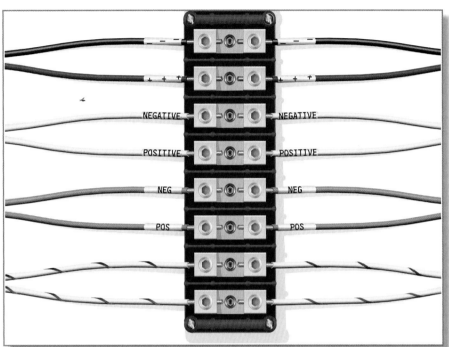

Code Language

210.5 Identification for Branch Circuits. (215.12(C)(2) for Feeders)

(C) Identification of Ungrounded Conductors.

(C)(2) Branch Circuits Supplied From DC Systems. Where a branch circuit is supplied from a dc system operating at more than 60 volts... (See *NEC* text) **(a)** *Positive*...(See *NEC* text) **(b)** *Negative Polarity Sizes 6 AWG or Smaller*... (See *NEC* text)

(4) An approved permanent marking means such as sleeving or shrink tubing that is suitable for the conductor size, at all termination, connection, and splice points, with imprinted plus signs (+) (minus signs (−) or the word POSITIVE or POS (NEGATIVE or NEG) durably marked on insulation of a color other than green, white, gray, or black/red.

(See NEC for actual text)

Significance of the Change

A new list item (4) is added to 210.5(C)(2)(a) for positive polarity and in 210.5(C)(2)(b) for negative polarity. This new list item requires marking in a similar manner to the markings in list item (3) of both 210.5(C)(2)(a) and (b). However, this new list item does not require the marking to be at 24-inch intervals. This new list item is added to facilitate the use of existing branch circuit conductors that may be reused in a DC system. In lieu of the marking at 24-inch intervals, this new requirement mandates a more robust, more durable marking such as sleeving or shrink tubing that is suitable for the conductor. The marking on the sleeving or shrink tubing can be done in three different ways (similar to list item (3)) in order to comply:

(1) The marking can be a plus (+) sign for positive or minus (−) sign for negative or

(2) The marking can be POSITIVE or NEGATIVE

(3) The marking can be POS or NEG

This marking may only be applied on insulation that is on insulation of a color other than green, white, or gray. Black insulation is not permitted to be identified as positive and red insulation is not permitted to be identified as negative.

Note that this new marking method is not limited to the reuse of existing branch circuits and may be applied in a new installation.

The same revision was made in 215.12(C)(2) for feeders.

Change Summary

- Identification requirements for ungrounded DC conductors are revised to more than 60 volts as part of a global effort to correlate requirements to recognize DC voltages that may float above 50 volts when charging.

- A new list item (4) permits identification of conductors sized 6 AWG or smaller with sleeving or shrink tubing.

- The same revision occurred in 215.12(C)(2) for feeders.

FR: 302
SRs: 305, 327

Ground-Fault Circuit-Interrupter Protection for Personnel

Code Language

210.8 Ground-Fault Circuit-Interrupter Protection for Personnel... (See *NEC* text)

Informational Note No. 2: See 422.5(A) for GFCI requirements for appliances.

For the purposes of this section, when determining distance from receptacles, the distance shall be measured as the shortest path the cord of an appliance connected to the receptacle would follow without piercing a floor, wall, ceiling, or fixed barrier, or passing through a door, doorway, or window.

(A) Dwelling Units. (7) Sinks... (See *NEC* text) 6 ft from the top inside edge of the bowl of the sink

(E) Crawl Space Lighting Outlets. GFCI protection shall be provided for lighting outlets not exceeding 120 volts installed in crawl spaces.

(See NEC for actual text)

Change Summary

- A new informational note has been added in 210.8 to direct *Code* users to 422.5(A) for GFCI requirements for appliances.

- New prescriptive text now clarifies how to measure distance where required in 210.8, sinks measured from the top inside edge of the bowl of the sink.

- New 210.8(E) requires GFCI protection for lighting outlets (120 volt) in all crawl spaces.

FR: 333
SRs: 316, 317

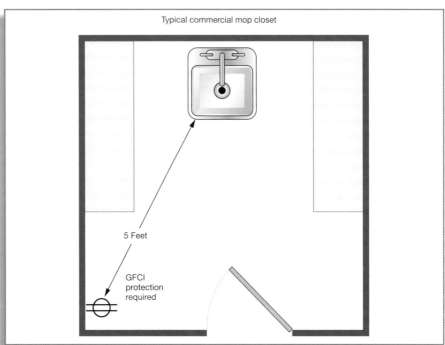

Typical commercial mop closet

5 Feet

GFCI protection required

Significance of the Change

A new informational note has been added below the parent text of 210.8 to direct *Code* users to 422.5(A) for the GFCI requirements for appliances. This reminds the *Code* user that appliances including but not limited to automotive vacuum machines, drinking water coolers, high-pressure washers, tire inflation machines, and vending machines require GFCI protection. A new last sentence is added in 210.8 to provide clarity on how to measure distance where required in this section. For example 210.8(A)(7) and 210.8(B)(5) require GFCI protection where a receptacle is installed within six feet of the outside edge of a sink. New prescriptive text now clarifies that distance is measured as the shortest path the cord of an appliance connected to the receptacle would follow without piercing a floor, wall, ceiling, or fixed barrier, or passing through a door, doorway, or window. This provides significant clarity for installers and the AHJ. Clarity is provided as sinks are to be measured from the "top inside edge of the bowl of the sink," not the "outside edge of the sink." A new 210.8(E) now requires GFCI protection for lighting outlets supplied at not more than 120-volts in crawl spaces. This applies to all locations (dwelling units and other than dwelling units) and recognizes that while many crawl spaces may not contain a receptacle, spaces that contain equipment will have lighting installed.

GFCI Protection for Personnel, Other than Dwelling Units

Courtesy of Square D

Code Language

210.8 GFCI Protection for Personnel

(B) Other Than Dwelling Units. All single phase receptacles rated 150 volts to ground or less, 50 amperes or less; and three phase receptacles rated 150 volts to ground or less, 100 amperes or less, installed in the following locations, shall have ground fault circuit interrupter protection for personnel.

(9) Crawl spaces — at or below grade level.

(10) Unfinished portions or areas of the basement not intended as habitable rooms.

(See NEC for actual text)

Significance of the Change

The parent text of 210.8(B) for GFCI protection for personnel in other than dwelling units is expanded beyond the previous requirement of only 125-volt, 15/20 amp receptacles. The revised text includes:

(1) All single phase receptacles rated 150 volts to ground or less, 50 amperes or less and

(2) All three phase receptacles rated 150 volts to ground or less, 100 amperes or less

This significantly expands installation requirements for receptacles in other than dwelling units that are addressed in 210.8(B). This will require permanent GFCI protection in the form of a receptacle, circuit breaker or other device for personnel protection. The list of locations in 210.8(B) are expanded to include receptacle outlets in crawl spaces at or below grade level and unfinished portions of basements that are not intended to be habitable rooms. This action now aligns the requirements in 210.8(B) for "other than dwelling units" with the requirements in 210.8(A) for dwelling units. The hazards are the same, this safety driven revision is long overdue. The revised parent text in 210.8 for measuring distance applies in both (A) Dwelling Units and (B) Other than Dwelling Units. List item 210.8(B)(5) is modified to clarify that the measurement for sinks is to be measured from the "top inside edge of the bowl of the sink," not the "outside edge of the sink."

Change Summary

- 210.8(B) now applies to all single phase receptacles rated 150 volts to ground or less, 50 amperes or less, and three phase receptacles rated 150 volts to ground or less, 100 amperes or less.

- The list of locations is expanded to include receptacle outlets in crawl spaces and receptacles in unfinished basements in 210.8(B)(10).

FR: 347

SRs: 321, 322

SCR: 117

Garage Branch Circuits

Code Language

210.11 Branch Circuits Required

(C) Dwelling Units

(4) Garage Branch Circuits. In addition to the number of branch circuits required by other parts of this section, at least one 120-volt, 20-ampere branch circuit shall be installed to supply receptacle outlets in attached garages and in detached garages with electric power. This circuit shall have no other outlets.

Exception: This circuit shall be permitted to supply readily accessible outdoor receptacle outlets.

(See NEC for actual text)

20 Amp branch circuit for garage 210.11(C)(4)

Receptacle required in each vehicle bay 210.52(G)(1)

Readily accessible outdoor receptacle is permitted on required garage branch circuit 210.11(C)(4) *Exception*

Change Summary

- A new second level subdivision 210.11(C)(4) has been added to require at least one 20-amp branch circuit to supply garage receptacle outlet(s).
- The text in 210.11(C)(3) is editorially revised to clarify that the required 20-amp branch circuit is permitted to serve the receptacle outlets in more than one bathroom.
- The previous prohibition to supply an outdoor receptacle from the garage circuit is deleted in 210.52(G)(1).

FR: 330
SRs: 324, 326

Significance of the Change

First level subdivision 210.11(C) addresses required branch circuits in dwelling units. This includes small appliance, laundry and bathroom branch circuits. A new second level subdivision 210.11(C)(4) has been added to require at least one 20-amp branch circuit to supply attached and detached garage receptacle outlet(s). This revision recognizes that many appliances and tools used in dwelling unit garages are rated at 12 to 16 amperes or higher and demand at least a 20-ampere rated branch circuit. While some installers may supply the garage with a 20-amp branch circuit, the 2014 *NEC* did not require it. In addition to appliances and tools being used, many garages may contain a refrigerator or freezer, and requiring at least one 20-amp branch circuit is a step in the right direction. A 15-amp rated branch circuit in the modern dwelling unit garage is typically not sufficient.

An exception is included to permit this required branch circuit to supply readily accessible outdoor receptacle outlets. This is correlated with a revision in 210.52(G)(1) to permit this branch circuit to supply a receptacle located outside of the garage. This is limited in the exception to a readily accessible outdoor receptacle outlet.

The text in 210.11(C)(3) is editorially revised to clarify that the required 20-amp branch circuit is permitted to serve the receptacle outlets in more than one bathroom.

210.12(B) & (D)

Article 210 Branch Circuits

Part I General Provisions

REVISION

Branch Circuit Extensions or Modifications

Code Language

210.12(B) Dormitory Units... *(bathrooms added)*

210.12(D) Branch Circuit Extensions or Modifications — Dwelling Units and Dormitory Units. In any of the areas specified in 210.12(A) or (B), where branch-circuit wiring is modified, replaced, or extended, the branch circuit shall be protected by one of the following:

(1) A listed combination-type AFCI located at the origin of the branch circuit

(2) A listed outlet branch-circuit type-AFCI located at the first receptacle outlet of the existing branch circuit

Exception: AFCI protection shall not be required where the extension of the existing conductors is not more than 1.8 m (6 ft.) and does not include any additional outlets or devices.

(See NEC for actual text)

Significance of the Change

Requirements for AFCI protection of branch circuit extensions and/or modifications are expanded to include both dwelling units and dormitories. The AFCI requirement for dormitories is in 210.12(B) and applies to all 120-volt single-phase 15- and 20-amp branch circuits supplying outlets "and devices" in bedrooms, living rooms, hallways, closets, "bathrooms" and similar rooms. The remainder of this section remains unchanged. The general requirement in 210.12(D) is that all modifications and/or extensions be AFCI protected. The existing exception permits installers to make necessary repairs and modifications, such as the replacement of a panelboard, in existing facilities without requiring AFCI protection provided extensions are not more than 6 feet, and no additional outlets or devices are added.

First level subdivisions 210.12(B) and (D) are editorially reversed in order and "bathrooms" has been added to the required list of areas requiring AFCI protection in 210.12(B).

Change Summary

- The existing requirements for AFCI protection of branch circuit extensions and/or modifications in dwelling units are expanded to include dormitories. The same hazards exist in dormitories.

- AFCI protection in dormitories is expanded to include all outlets and "devices" in dormitory "bathrooms."

FRs: 350, 351
SRs: 320, 328

AFCI Protection in Guest Rooms and Guest Suites

Code Language

210.12(C) Guest Rooms and Guest Suites. All 120-volt, single phase, 15- and 20-ampere branch circuits supplying outlets and devices installed in guest rooms and guest suites of hotels and motels shall be protected by any of the means described in 210.12(A) (1) through (6).

(See NEC for actual text)

Significance of the Change

A new first level subdivision 210.12(C) now requires that all 120-volt, single phase, 15- and 20-ampere branch circuits supplying outlets and devices installed in guest rooms and guest suites of hotels and motels to be protected by a listed arc-fault circuit interrupter meeting the requirements of 210.12(A)(1) through (6). This AFCI requirement applies to all guest rooms and guest suites without regard to whether or not there are provisions for cooking in the guest room or guest suite. A guest room without permanent provisions for cooking is not by definition a dwelling unit. It is interesting to note that the requirements for extensions and/or modifications apply to dwelling units and dormitories but not to guest rooms and guest suites.

Any of the methods permitted in 210.12(A)(1) through (6) are permitted to provide the AFCI protection required in guest rooms and guest suites.

Change Summary

• All 120-volt, single phase, 15- and 20-ampere branch circuits supplying outlets and devices installed in guest rooms and guest suites of hotels and motels are now required to be protected by any of the AFCI methods listed in 210.12(A)(1) through (6).

• This AFCI requirement applies to *all* guest rooms and guest suites without regard to provisions for cooking.

FR: 352
SR: 328

Dwelling Unit Receptacle Outlets, Wall Space

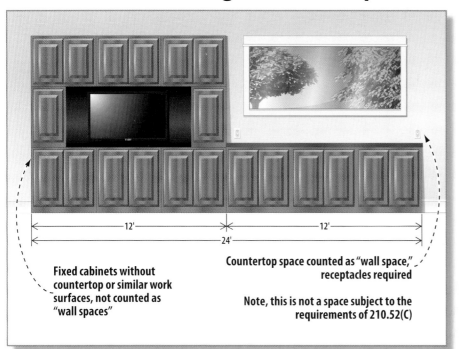

Fixed cabinets without countertop or similar work surfaces, not counted as "wall spaces"

Countertop space counted as "wall space," receptacles required

Note, this is not a space subject to the requirements of 210.52(C)

Code Language

210.52 Dwelling Unit Receptacle Outlets

(A) General Provisions

(2) Wall Space. (See *NEC* text)

(1) Any space 600 mm (2 ft) or more in width (including space measured around corners) and unbroken along the floor line by doorways and similar openings, fireplaces, and fixed cabinets that do not have countertops or similar work surfaces

(2) The space occupied by fixed panels in walls, excluding sliding panels

(3) Countertop and Similar Work Surfaces. Receptacles installed for countertop and similar work surfaces… (See *NEC* text)

(See NEC for actual text)

Significance of the Change

This revision addresses cabinets installed with countertop surfaces and similar work surfaces in areas other than those covered in 210.52(C). The requirements for wall space calculation to determine receptacle placement in 210.52(A) previously omitted any space with fixed cabinets. This revision recognizes that dwelling units may have fixed cabinets and similar work surfaces that will occupy a substantial length of wall space without any requirement for receptacles. The previous text addressed only "fixed cabinets." This revision now addresses fixed cabinets that do not have countertops and similar work surfaces. Where fixed cabinets are installed with countertops or in a similar work surface, those spaces are subject to the requirements for wall space and receptacles are required in accordance with 210. 52(A)(1). This will require that receptacles be installed in wall spaces and countertops or similar work surfaces so that no point measured horizontally along the floor line is more than six feet from a receptacle. Spaces with fixed cabinets without countertops or similar work surfaces are still exempt from the wall space calculation.

The previous text in 210.52(A)(2) included "space occupied by fixed panels in exterior walls, excluding sliding panels" as "wall space." The term *exterior* is deleted. This revision recognizes that interior walls may also contain fixed panels.

Change Summary

- Where fixed cabinets are installed with countertops in dwelling units, in other than areas addressed in 210.52(C), the countertop space is subject to the requirements for wall space, and receptacles are required in accordance with 210.52(A)(1).

- This revision also expands the requirements of 210.52(A)(2) and (A)(4) to similar work surfaces.

- The term *exterior* is deleted in 210.52(A)(2)(2) recognizing that interior walls may also contain fixed panels.

FR: 324
SR: 307

210.52(B)(1)

Dwelling Unit Receptacle Outlets, Small Appliances

Code Language

210.52 Dwelling Unit Receptacle Outlets

(B) Small Appliances.

(1) Receptacle Outlets Served. In the kitchen, pantry, breakfast room, dining room, or similar area of a dwelling unit, the two or more 20-ampere small-appliance branch circuits required by 210.11(C)(1) shall serve all wall and floor receptacle outlets covered by 210.52(A), all countertop outlets covered by 210.52(C), and receptacle outlets for refrigeration equipment.

Exception No. 2: In addition to the required receptacles specified by 210.52, a receptacle outlet to serve a specific appliance shall be permitted to be supplied from an individual branch circuit rated 15 amperes or greater.

(See NEC for actual text)

Change Summary

- Exception No. 2 for 210.52(B)(1) previously permitted only refrigeration equipment to be supplied by an individual branch circuit 15-amps or greater.
- This eliminates potential conflict with 210.22 which provides general permission for individual branch circuits.
- This expands this permissive exception to other appliances that may be supplied from a receptacle outlet such as dishwashers, garbage disposals, microwaves and more.

FR: None
SR: 308

Significance of the Change

Second level subdivision 210.52(B)(1) requires two or more 20-ampere small-appliance branch circuits to supply receptacle outlets in the kitchen, pantry, breakfast room, dining room, or similar area of a dwelling unit. It is further clarified that the two small appliance branch circuits (required by 210.11(C)(1)) must serve all wall and floor receptacle outlets covered by 210.52(A) (general receptacle outlet location in dwelling unit walls etc.), all countertop outlets covered by 210.52(C) (all countertops and similar work surfaces in dwellings), and receptacle outlets for refrigeration equipment. The existing exception provides relief by allowing an individual branch circuit rated at 15 amps or greater to supply a receptacle outlet (typically installed in a wall) for a refrigerator. The revised exception provides significant clarity and permits the installation of individual branch circuits to supply other appliances in addition to a refrigerator, including but not limited to a dishwasher, garbage disposal or a permanently installed microwave. This revision now correlates with the general permission in 210.22 to install individual branch circuits. The applicable Article 100 definition applies: **Branch Circuit, Individual.** A branch circuit that supplies only one utilization equipment.

Peninsular Countertop Spaces

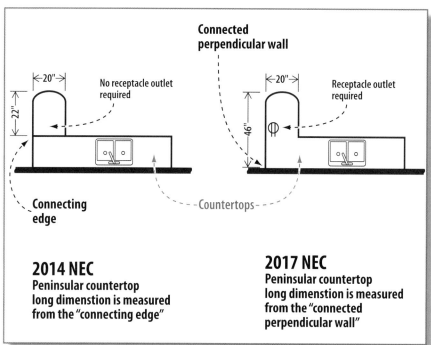

Connected perpendicular wall

←20"→ No receptacle outlet required

22"

Connecting edge

Countertops

←20"→ Receptacle outlet required

46"

2014 NEC
Peninsular countertop long dimenstion is measured from the "connecting edge"

2017 NEC
Peninsular countertop long dimenstion is measured from the "connected perpendicular wall"

Code Language

210.52 Dwelling Unit Receptacle Outlets.

(C) Countertops and Work Surfaces.

(3) Peninsular Countertop Spaces. At least one receptacle outlet shall be installed at each peninsular countertop long dimension space with a long dimension of 600 mm (24 in.) or greater and a short dimension of 300 mm (12 in.) or greater. A peninsular countertop is measured from the connected perpendicular wall.

(See NEC for actual text)

Significance of the Change

First level subdivision 210.52(C) is revised to apply to Countertops and "Work Surfaces". In some cases, a work surface in a kitchen area may not be considered as a "countertop." The general requirement in 210.52(C)(3) is modified to clarify that the long dimension of a peninsular countertop is measured from the "connected perpendicular wall." Previous *Code* text required measuring from the "connecting edge" of a peninsular countertop, which meant that a wall receptacle was not on the peninsular countertop, it was serving the countertop to which the peninsular countertop was connected. This new text infers that a wall receptacle may serve the peninsular countertop, but the change in how the measurement is made makes that impossible. In fact, this revision now requires a receptacle outlet in all peninsular countertops because the typical width of the connecting countertop is typically 24 inches deep.

A wall mounted receptacle on the perpendicular countertop to serve the peninsular countertop provided the long dimension was not over 6 feet was considered but failed. The reasoning was to address peninsular countertops that may serve as kitchen tables without cabinets installed under the peninsular countertop, making it difficult to locate a receptacle on what is essentially a tabletop.

Change Summary

- 210.52(C) is revised to apply to Countertops and "Work Surfaces."
- Peninsular countertops are no longer measured from the "connecting edge," they are measured from the "connected perpendicular wall."
- The width of the connecting countertop is now added to the peninsular countertop long dimension.

FR: 356
SR: 309
SCR: 67

Basements, Garages, and Accessory Buildings

Code Language

210.52 Dwelling Unit Receptacle Outlets.

(G) Basements, Garages, and Accessory Buildings. For one- and two-family dwellings, at least one receptacle outlet shall be installed in the areas specified in 210.52(G)(1) through (3)...

(G)(1) Garages. In each attached garage and in each detached garage with electric power, at least one receptacle outlet shall be installed in each vehicle bay and not more than 1.7 m (5½ ft) above the floor.

(See NEC for actual text)

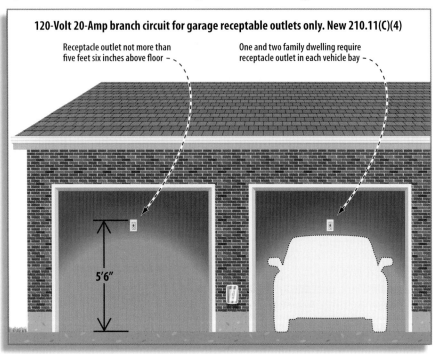

120-Volt 20-Amp branch circuit for garage receptable outlets only. New 210.11(C)(4)

Receptacle outlet not more than five feet six inches above floor

One and two family dwelling require receptacle outlet in each vehicle bay

5'6"

Change Summary

- The parent text in 210.52(G) is revised to include both one and two-family dwelling units expanding this requirement to two-family dwelling units.

- The sentence prohibiting this branch circuit supplying outlets outside of the garage is deleted to correlate with new 210.11(C)(4) requiring a garage branch circuit.

- The term *car space* is deleted. At least one "receptacle outlet" is now required in "each vehicle bay" and the outlet is not permitted to be more than 5½ feet above the floor.

FRs: 310, 317
SR: 326

Significance of the Change

The parent text in 210.52(G) is revised to include both one and two-family dwelling units expanding this requirement to two-family dwelling units. This expansion now includes two-family dwelling units with respect to 210.52(G)(1) Garages, (G)(2) Accessory Buildings and (G)(3) Basements. The requirement in 210.52(G)(1) is modified to delete the term *car space* and replace it with *vehicle bay*. This provides clarity by requiring a receptacle outlet for each vehicle bay. The previous wording would allow a single receptacle outlet with multiple receptacles to serve more than one car space. The term *receptacle outlet* is defined in Article 100 as "An outlet where one or more receptacles are installed." At least one "receptacle outlet" is now required in "each vehicle bay" and the outlet is not permitted to be more than 5½ feet above the floor. Installers must now identify each "vehicle bay" and install a receptacle outlet in each. A maximum height of 5½ feet above the floor, is added to ensure ready access to the receptacle for the homeowner.

The text prohibiting the garage branch circuit in 210.52(G)(1) from supplying outlets outside of the garage is deleted to correlate with new 210.11(C)(4) which now requires a garage branch circuit. New 210.11(C)(4) requires a 20-amp branch circuit to supply only garage receptacle outlets. The exception in 210.11(C)(4) permits the garage branch circuit to supply readily accessible outdoor receptacle outlets.

Electrical Service Areas, Required Receptacle

Code Language

210.64 Electrical Service Areas.
At least one 125-volt, single-phase, 15- or 20-ampere-rated receptacle outlet shall be installed within in an accessible location within 7.5 m (25 ft) of the indoor electrical service equipment. The required receptacle outlet shall be located within the same room or area as the service equipment.

Exception No. 1: The receptacle outlet shall not be required to be installed in one- and two-family dwellings.

Exception No. 2: Where the service voltage is greater than 120 volts to ground, a receptacle outlet shall not be required for services dedicated to equipment covered in Articles 675 and 682.

(See NEC for actual text)

Significance of the Change

The requirement for a 125-volt, single-phase, 15- or 20-ampere-rated receptacle outlet to be installed in the area of electrical service equipment is revised and must now be within 25 feet of, and in the same room or area as the electrical service equipment. The requirement is now limited to only indoor electrical service equipment. The revisions recognize that a typical extension cord used by installer/maintainers may not reach a receptacle that is 50 feet from the electrical service equipment; and the maximum distance to the required receptacle outlet is now limited to 25 feet. The substantiation for this requirement (new in 2014) recognized that installer/maintainers need power for some tasks when working in or on the service equipment. The requirement is limited to indoors as that is where monitoring equipment and other equipment is most likely to be used. The limitation to indoor only also recognizes that the use of cordless tools, vehicle power inverters, and mobile generators, make the need for an outdoor receptacle less likely.

Exception 2 was added for those service locations dedicated to electrically driven or controlled irrigation machines and natural and artificially made bodies of water where 120 volts to ground is not present.

Change Summary

- Receptacle outlets required by 210.64 must now be in an accessible location, within 25 feet, and in the same room or area.
- The requirement is now limited to only indoor electrical service equipment.
- A new exception No. 2 relieves the requirement for electrically driven or controlled irrigation machines and natural and artificially made bodies of water where 120 volts to ground is not present.

FR: 323
SR: None

Lighting Outlets Required, Dwelling Units

Code Language

210.70 Lighting Outlets Required.

(A) Dwelling Units.

(1) Habitable Rooms. At least one wall switch–controlled lighting outlet shall be installed in every habitable room, kitchen, and bathroom.

(2) Additional Locations. Additional lighting outlets shall be installed in accordance with…(See *NEC* text)

List items (1), (2) & (3) no changes… (See *NEC* text)

List Item (4) Lighting outlets controlled in accordance with 210.70(A)(2)(3) shall not be controlled by use of dimmer switches unless they provide the full range of dimming control at each location.

(See NEC for actual text)

Change Summary

- Kitchens are added to the required lighting outlets in 210.70(A)(1).
- Interior stairways are not permitted to be dimmer controlled, unless there is a full range of dimming control at each switch location.

Significance of the Change

First-level subdivision 210.70(A) contains requirements for required lighting outlets in dwelling units. The general rule for habitable rooms in 210.70(A)(1) is for each room to contain a lighting outlet. Kitchens have been added to the habitable room requirement. Previous *Code* text for habitable rooms included bathrooms but not kitchens. The existing exceptions remain unchanged and allow a switched receptacle in lieu of a lighting outlet in habitable rooms other than kitchens or bathrooms. Where a lighting outlet is installed for interior stairways, 210.70(A)(2)(c) requires a wall switch at each floor level, and landing level that includes an entryway, to control the lighting outlet where the stairway between floor levels has six risers or more. A new list item 210.70(A)(2)(d) is added to prohibit the use of dimmers for these interior stairways unless there is the ability to control the full range of dimming control at each location. This is necessary to ensure an adequate level of lighting for the interior stairway without regard to switching location. Dimmers are permitted where there is a full range of dimming control at each switch location.

FRs: 354, 355
SR: 325

Meeting Rooms, Required Receptacles

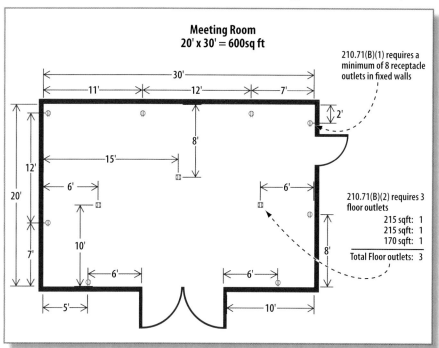

Meeting Room
20' x 30' = 600sq ft

210.71(B)(1) requires a minimum of 8 receptacle outlets in fixed walls

210.71(B)(2) requires 3 floor outlets

215 sqft:	1
215 sqft:	1
170 sqft:	1
Total Floor outlets:	**3**

Code Language

210.71 Meeting Rooms.

(A) General. Each meeting room of not more than 93 m² (1000 ft²) in other than dwelling units shall have outlets for nonlocking-type, 125-volt, 15- or 20-ampere receptacles. The outlets shall be installed in accordance with 210.71(B). Where a room or space is provided with movable partition(s), each room size shall be determined with the partition in the position that results in the smallest size meeting room.

(B) Receptacle Outlets Required.

   (B)(1) Receptacle Outlets in Fixed Walls

   (B)(2) Floor Receptacle Outlets

(See NEC for actual text)

Significance of the Change

Previous editions of the *NEC* do not require any receptacle outlets in meeting rooms. 210.71(A) requires that all meeting rooms of not more than 1000 ft² in other than dwelling units be provided with 125-volt, 15- and 20-ampere receptacles in accordance with 210.71(B). Where the meeting room or space is provided with movable partition(s), the room size must be determined with the partition in the position that results in the smallest size meeting room. An IN explains that meeting rooms are typically designed or intended for the gathering of seated occupants for such purposes as meetings where portable electronic equipment is likely to be used. 210.71(B) contains requirements for the required receptacle outlets and permits the location of the receptacle outlets to be determined by the designer or building owner. 210.71(B)(1) requires receptacle outlets installed in accordance with 210.52(A)(1) through (A)(4). 210.71(B)(2) requires at least one receptacle outlet located in the floor for meeting rooms that are at least 12 feet wide, with a floor area of at least 215 ft². The floor outlet must be installed not less than 6 feet from any fixed wall with one floor outlet for each of 215 ft² or major portion of floor space.

Change Summary

- All meeting rooms of not more than 1000 ft² in other than dwelling units are now required to have receptacle outlets installed.

- Where movable partitions exist, room size is determined with partitions resulting in the smallest size meeting room(s).

- A minimum number of receptacle outlets are required, and location is permitted to be determined by the owner or designer.

FR: 7517
SR: 329

Feeder Minimum Rating and Size

Code Language

215.2 Minimum Rating and Size.

(A) Feeders Not More Than 600 Volts.

(1) General. (a)...(No changes)

Exception No. 1 & 3: (Relocated for clarity, no change)

Exception No. 2: Where a portion of a feeder is connected at both its supply and load ends to separately installed pressure connections as covered in 110.14(C)(2), it shall be permitted to have an allowable ampacity not less than the sum of the continuous load plus the noncontinuous load. No portion of a feeder installed under the provisions of this exception shall extend into an enclosure containing either the feeder supply or the feeder load terminations, as covered in 110.14(C)(1).

(See NEC for actual text)

Change Summary

- Existing exceptions No. 1 and No. 3 are relocated for clarity.
- New exception No. 2 permits portions of a feeder (not the full length) to have an allowable ampacity not less than the sum of the continuous load plus the noncontinuous load under prescriptive conditions.

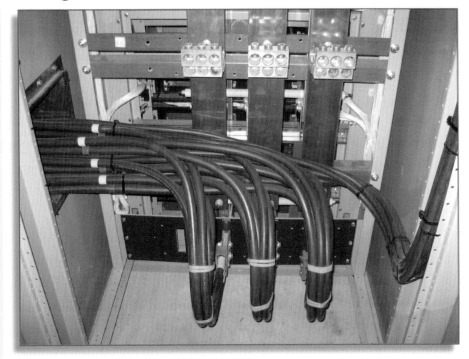

Significance of the Change

Existing exceptions No. 1 and No. 3 are relocated directly below 215.2(A)(1)(a), for clarity as they do not apply to the requirements in 215.2(A)(1)(b). Exception No. 1 retains that number and existing exception No. 2 is now No. 3. The previous location of these exceptions may have caused confusion. A new exception No. 2 is added to permit portions of a feeder (not the full length) to have an allowable ampacity of not less than the sum of the continuous load plus the noncontinuous load, relieving the requirement for 125% of the continuous load. In order to apply this exception, these portions of a feeder must be connected at both the supply and load ends to separately installed pressure connections as covered in 110.14(C)(2). These portions of the feeder are not permitted to extend into an enclosure containing either the feeder supply, or the feeder load terminations, as covered in 110.14(C)(1). The full-size conductor in accordance with 215.2(A)(1)(a) is required at terminations as the larger conductor acts as a heat sink for connected devices to accommodate continuous loading. This exception allows installers to consider cost effective options.

FR: 337

SR: None

Lighting Loads, Offices and Banks

Significance of the Change

This revision will reduce the lighting load calculation in banks and office buildings by over 28%. This will have a significant impact on the sizing of service conductors and feeders in occupancies with large lighting loads such as large office buildings. ASHRAE and IECC lighting power allowance standards are adopted in many areas as an energy code. However, prior to this new exception, service conductors, equipment and feeders had to be sized to the minimum *NEC* requirements. The 3.5 watts per square foot allowance for offices and banks in the 2014 *NEC* has been outdated for many years, and the reduction seen here is extremely conservative. It is typical to see office lighting design based on a nationally recognized lighting power density of 1.2 watts per square foot or less. This reduction to 2.5 watts per square foot for office buildings and banks is very conservative based upon the energy standards in place and provides a 200% safety factor.

Illumination standards in the 1980s required 70 foot-candles with 2'x4' fixtures using 4 fluorescent lamps, and an electromagnetic ballast at approximately 180 watts. Today, those same illumination standards have been reduced downward in the 40/50 foot-candle ranges with 2'x4' LED fixtures with equivalent lumen output at approximately 38 watts per fixture. This revision is long overdue.

Code Language

220.12 Lighting Load for Specified Occupancies. A unit load of not less than that specified in Table 220.12 for occupancies specified shall constitute the minimum lighting load. The floor area for each floor shall be calculated from the outside dimensions of the building, dwelling unit, or other area involved. For dwelling...(See *NEC* text)

Exception No. 2: Where a building is designed and constructed to comply with an energy code adopted by the local authority and specifying an overall lighting density of less than 13.5 volt-amperes/13.5 m^2 (1.2 volt-amperes/ 1.2 ft^2), the unit lighting loads in Table 220.12 for office and bank areas within the building shall be permitted to be reduced by 11 volt-amperes/11 m^2 (1 volt-amperes/1 ft^2).

(See NEC for actual text)

Change Summary

- A new exception to 220.12 permits reduced lighting load calculations in banks and office buildings.

- Illumination standards in the 1980's required 70 foot-candles with 2'x4' fixtures using 4 fluorescent lamps, and an electromagnetic ballast at approximately 180 watts.

- Illumination standards have been reduced downward in the 40/50 foot-candle ranges with 2'x4' LED fixtures with equivalent lumen output at approximately 38 watts per fixture.

FR: 326
SR: 313

Raceway Seals

Code Language

225.27 Raceway Seal. Where a raceway enters a building or structure from outside, it shall be sealed. Spare or unused raceways shall also be sealed. Sealants shall be identified for use with the cable insulation, conductor insulation, bare conductor, shield, or other components.

(See NEC for actual text)

Change Summary

- All raceways containing outside branch circuits and feeders that enter a building or structure from the outside, are now required to be sealed.
- The reference to 300.5(G) is deleted, this section no longer requires a determination to be made on the possibility of moisture making contact with live parts.

Significance of the Change

All raceways containing outside branch circuits and feeders that enter a building or structure from the outside, are now required to be sealed. This includes all spare raceways. The previous text mandated raceway seals in compliance with the general rule in 300.5(G) which only required seals, or plugs, where there was the possibility of moisture making contact with live parts. This revision is independent of 300.5(G), and there is no need for an installer/maintainer or AHJ to make a determination as to whether or not the possibility of moisture in contact with live parts exists, seals are required in all cases. The previous requirement also applied only to those raceways that were part of "an underground distribution system." The previous text created confusion as it applied only to both underground and to raceways that were part of the "distribution system." Where branch circuit conductors were installed, one could argue that it was not part of the "distribution system." The requirement is now clear and will apply to all raceways that enter a building or structure from outside.

FR: 920
SR: None

Number of Supplies, EV Charging Systems & Dwelling Units

Code Language

225.30 Number of Supplies.

(A) Special Conditions. *(List items (1) through (6), (No change)*

(7) Electric vehicle charging systems listed, labeled, and identified for more than a single branch circuit or feeder

(See NEC for actual text)

Significance of the Change

A new list item (7) is added to first level subdivision 225.30(A) to permit more than one branch circuit or feeder to supply listed electric vehicle charging systems that are identified and labeled for use with more than a single branch circuit or feeder. Free-standing electrical equipment installed outdoors was considered as a structure in the 2014 *NEC*, and this revision was necessary to permit more than one branch circuit or feeder. The defined term *Structure* has been modified in the 2017 *NEC* and does not include equipment. There is electric vehicle supply equipment that is listed, labeled, and identified to be fed by more than one branch circuit or feeder. This revision is necessary to permit more than one branch circuit or feeder to supply these listed car chargers.

This section saw significant action in this revision cycle with a proposed new first-level subdivision that would have permitted more than one feeder to supply one- or two-family dwelling units. The proposed revision failed to make it through the complete NFPA process and will most certainly be considered again for the 2020 *NEC*.

Change Summary

- Free standing electrical equipment installed outdoors is considered a structure.

- Listed electric vehicle charging systems, identified for more than a single branch circuit or feeder may be supplied with more than a single branch circuit or feed.

FR: 921
SR: 902

Supports over Buildings

Code Language

230.29 Supports over Buildings.
Service conductors passing over a roof shall be securely supported by substantial structures. For a grounded system, where the substantial structure is metal, it shall be bonded by means of a bonding jumper and listed connector to the grounded overhead service conductor. Where practicable, such supports shall be independent of the building.

(See NEC for actual text)

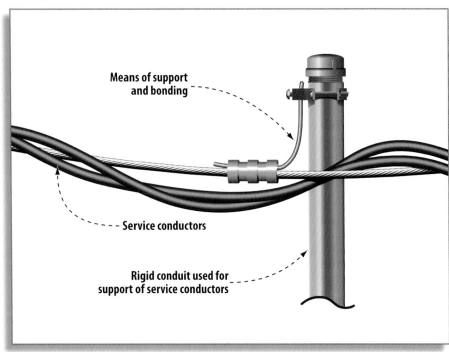

Means of support and bonding

Service conductors

Rigid conduit used for support of service conductors

Change Summary

- Where service conductors, of a grounded system, pass over a roof and are supported by a metal structure, the grounded overhead service conductor must be bonded to the support structure.
- A bonding jumper and listed connector to the grounded overhead service conductor are required.

Significance of the Change

This revision requires that where service conductors of a grounded system pass over a roof and are supported by metal structures, the grounded service conductor must be bonded to the metal structure. A listed connector is required for the connection of the bonding jumper and the grounded overhead service conductor. The previous text of section 230.29 required only that where service conductors pass over a roof, they must be securely supported by substantial structures and, that where possible, such supports must be independent of the building. In some cases, a metal structure is mounted on an adjacent building to securely support overhead service conductors as required by section 230.29. These may be referred to as a supplemental mast or a roof jack. Where they are made of metal, they must now be bonded to the grounded service conductor. Section 250.92(A) for bonding of equipment for services requires that normally non-current-carrying metal parts of equipment be bonded. This includes, but is not limited to raceways, cable trays, cable armor, enclosures, fittings, etc. but support structures are not in the list.

The bonding jumper must be installed in accordance with section 250.102 and sized as a "supply-side bonding jumper" in accordance with 250.102(C)(1).

FR: 936

SR: 909

SCR: 58

Cable Trays, Permitted Methods

Courtesy of Bill McGovern, City of Plano, TX

Code Language

230.44 Cable Trays. Cable tray systems shall be permitted to support service-entrance conductors. Cable trays used to support service-entrance conductors shall contain only service-entrance conductors and shall be limited to the following methods: *(No change in list items (1) through (4))*

(5) Single conductors 1/0 and larger that are listed for use in cable tray

(See NEC for actual text)

Significance of the Change

The use of single 1/0 and larger conductors are revised for clarity and consistency with both the product standards and the *NEC*. Previous text in 230.44(5) permitted only conductors with a "CT rating" which is not used elsewhere or defined in the *NEC*. Product standards use that acronym for such cable when evaluated for use in cable trays. The product standards use the markings "for cable tray use," "for CT use" or "for use in cable trays." The revised text deletes the reference to "CT rating" and replaces it with "that are listed for use in cable tray" providing clarity. Cables marked with a CT rating are still permitted because they are "listed for use in cable tray."

A new list item (6) was added in the second revision stage to recognize Power Control Cable (Type TC) provided the cable is "evaluated for use as service entrance conductors." This action was overturned by the Correlating Committee because the new permission to use Type TC cable was in direct conflict with the requirements for Type TC cable in Article 336. It is important to note that list item 230.44(5) references only "*single conductors* 1/0 and larger that are listed for use in cable tray." The reference to "single conductors" does not infer a cable assembly.

Change Summary

- The reference to "CT rating" is deleted, the phrase "listed for use in cable tray" provides additional clarity.
- Single conductors 1/0 and larger that are "listed for use in cable tray" are permitted. Product standards may use the marking "CT" to inform the installer and AHJ the cable is "listed for use in cable tray."

FR: 933
SR: 911
SCR: 60

Marking of Service Equipment

Code Language

230.66 Marking. Service equipment rated at 1000 volts or less shall be marked to identify it as being suitable for use as service equipment. All service equipment shall be listed or field labeled. Individual meter socket enclosures shall not be considered service equipment but shall be listed, and rated for the voltage and ampacity of the service.

Exception: Meter sockets supplied by and under the exclusive control of an electric utility shall not be required to be listed.

(See NEC for actual text)

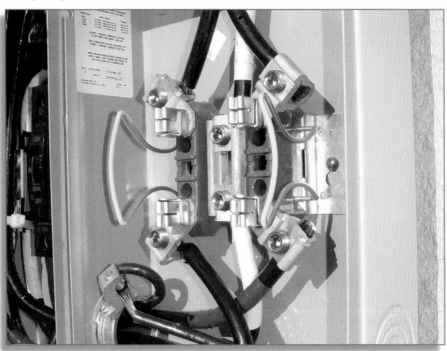

Change Summary

- Individual meter sockets are not considered to be service equipment but must now be "listed and rated for the voltage and ampacity of the service."
- Meter sockets are not considered to be "service equipment" but must be listed.
- A new exception is added for meter sockets supplied by and under the exclusive control of an electric utility that relieves the new requirement to be "listed."

FR: 935

SR: 913

SCR: 61

Significance of the Change

The general requirement in section 230.66 is that all service equipment must be listed. The previous text in this section as well as the revised text mandates that individual meter socket enclosures are not considered service equipment. This relieved the individual meter sockets from the general listing requirement. This revision now mandates that while individual meter sockets are not considered to be service equipment, they must now be "listed, and rated for the voltage and ampacity of the service." The general intent of the *NEC* text that does not consider the individual meter sockets as "service equipment" is to recognize that the meter sockets may be supplied by and maintained under the exclusive control of an electric utility. While these meter sockets are supplied by, and under the exclusive control of an electric utility, these enclosures are part of the premises wiring and must meet the general rules for service equipment in the *NEC*.

A new exception is added for meter sockets supplied by and under the exclusive control of an electric utility. This exception relieves these utility owned meter sockets from the new requirement that all individual meter sockets must now be "listed, and rated for the voltage and ampacity of the service."

Equipment Connected to the Supply Side of Service Disconnect

Courtesy of PDE Total Energy Solutions

Code Language

230.82 Equipment Connected to the Supply Side of Service Disconnect. Only the following equipment shall be permitted to be connected to the supply side of the service disconnecting means: *(List items (1) through (5) editorial changes only. No change in (7) through (9))*

(6) Solar photovoltaic systems, fuel cell systems, wind electric systems, energy storage systems, or interconnected electric power production sources.

(See NEC for actual text)

Significance of the Change

Section 230.82 provides the *Code* user with a prescriptive list of equipment that is permitted to be connected on the supply side of the service disconnecting means. Editorial revisions are made in list items (2) and (3) for clarity. List item (6) has been expanded to include both equipment that is part of wind electric systems or energy storage systems. The previous text in this list item included only equipment associated with solar photovoltaic systems (Article 690), fuel cell systems (Article 692) and interconnected electric power production sources (Article 705). This revision now includes permission for equipment associated with wind energy systems in Article 694 to be connected on the supply side of the service disconnecting means. This recognizes that these wind electric systems are designed and permitted to be connected in this manner. Additionally, list item (6) is expanded to include energy storage systems which are now recognized in a new Article 706. Energy storage systems are new to the *NEC* and recognize that emerging technologies and an aging transmission and distribution infrastructure, need to be addressed through onsite energy storage. This new article is a significant expansion of the *NEC,* and this revision is necessary to facilitate their inclusion ahead of service equipment.

Change Summary

- Equipment associated with wind electric systems and energy storage systems are now permitted to be connected to the supply side of the service disconnecting means.

- Inclusion of energy storage systems in 230.82 prescriptively recognizes new Article 706 for Energy Storage Systems.

- List item (6) now includes PV systems, fuel cell systems, wind electric systems, energy storage systems, and interconnected electric power production sources.

FR: 939
SR: None

Location of SE Overcurrent Protection

Code Language

230.91 Location. The service overcurrent device shall be an integral part of the service disconnecting means or shall be located immediately adjacent thereto. Where fuses are used as the service overcurrent device, the disconnecting means shall be located ahead of the supply side of the fuses.

(See NEC for actual text)

Courtesy of Eaton's Bussmann Business

Change Summary

- Clarity is provided for the location of the SE disconnecting means.
- Where the OCPD is a CB, the disconnecting means is integral.
- New text requires that where fuses are the SE OCPD, the disconnecting means must be on the line side of the fuses.

FR: 948
SR: None

Significance of the Change

The previous requirement in section 230.91 required that the disconnecting means for the service equipment (SE) overcurrent protective device (OCPD) be (1) an integral part of the disconnecting means or (2) the disconnect had to be immediately adjacent to the OCPD. This literally permitted the disconnecting means for SE fuses to be located immediately adjacent to the disconnecting means but they could be located on the line or load side and still comply with section 230.91. The general rule in section 240.40 however, requires fuses to be supplied "with a disconnecting means on their supply side so that each circuit containing fuses can be independently disconnected from the source of power." This revision resolves potential problems with a new last sentence that prescriptively mandates that where the OCPD's are fuses, the disconnect "be located ahead of the supply side of the fuses." This revision allows an installer/maintainer to remove and replace the fuses in a deenergized condition significantly enhancing safety. Removal and replacement of fuses while energized exposes personnel to shock, arc flash and arc blast hazards. While it would not be typical to see an installation in which SE fuses are located ahead of the SE disconnecting means, it is imperative that the *NEC* provide a clear, prescriptive requirement to prohibit such an installation.

Performance Testing, GFPE

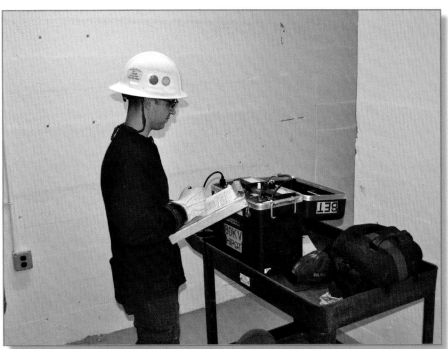

Courtesy of Burlington Electrical Testing

Code Language

230.95 Ground-Fault Protection of Equipment

(C) Performance Testing. The ground-fault protection system shall be performance tested when first installed on site. This testing shall be conducted by a qualified person(s) using a test process of primary current injection, in accordance with instructions that shall be provided with the equipment. A written record of this testing shall be made and shall be available to the authority having jurisdiction.

(Informational Notes 1, 2, 3 & 4, no changes)

(See NEC for actual text)

Significance of the Change

Section 230.95 requires ground-fault protection of equipment (GFPE) be provided for solidly grounded wye electric services of more than 150 volts to ground but not exceeding 1000 volts phase-to-phase for each service disconnect rated 1000 amperes or more. For example, consider a service rated at 480/277-volts with a circuit breaker that has a continuous current trip setting at 1000-amps. Section 230.95 requires that this service be provided with GFPE and that the performance of the GFPE be tested when first installed. It is prudent for the equipment owner to have the GFPE tested and maintained in accordance with the manufacturer's instructions and NFPA 70B. This revision mandates that a "qualified person" perform the required testing. The *NEC* defines *qualified person* in Article 100, but this requirement implies that the individual performing the test be qualified for the task and the equipment used. This would require a level of certification such as a NETA certified test technician. This revision also mandates the type of testing as "primary current injection." This type of testing consists of a "qualified person" using test equipment to inject a test current into an overcurrent or ground fault trip relay that operates with a current transformer to determine the performance of the GFPE.

Change Summary

- The *NEC* now requires that GFPE performance testing (230.95(C)) be by done by a "qualified person."

- GFPE performance testing (230.95(C)) is now required to use a test process of primary current injection.

- The required primary current injection testing must be performed in accordance with instructions provided with the test equipment.

FR: 941
SR: 915

240.24(A)

REVISION

Accessibility of Overcurrent Devices

Code Language

240.24 Location in or on Premises

(A) Accessibility. Switches containing fuses and circuit breakers shall be readily accessible and installed so that the center of the grip of the operating handle of the switch or circuit breaker, when in its highest position, is not more than 2.0 m (6 ft 7 in.) above the floor or working platform, unless one of the following applies... *(no change to four list items)*

Exception: The use of a tool shall be permitted to access overcurrent devices located within listed industrial control panels or similar enclosures.

(See NEC for actual text)

Change Summary

- This revision clarifies that "switches containing fuses and circuit breakers," not "overcurrent devices," must be readily accessible with operating handles not more than 6' 7" high.

- Fuses installed in a fused disconnect and CB's in panelboards etc. are readily accessible.

- A new exception clearly permits the use of a tool to access overcurrent devices within listed industrial control panels or similar enclosures.

FR: 2705
SR: 2701

Significance of the Change

In the 2014 revision cycle of the *NEC*, the definition of the term *readily accessible* was modified. The revised text clarified that where tools are necessary to gain access, the equipment is not considered "readily accessible." This revision of an Article 100 definition had a global effect in the *NEC* and created a conflict with the accessibility requirements for overcurrent devices in 240.24(A). An AHJ or installer applying the modified definition of *readily accessible* along with the accessibility requirements in 240.24(A) for industrial control panels quickly realized that the *NEC* now prohibited the use of tools to gain access. The accessibility requirements for overcurrent devices in Article 240 never intended to prohibit the use of tools to gain access into industrial control panels or similar enclosures. This revision clarifies that "switches containing fuses and circuit breakers," not "overcurrent devices," must be readily accessible with operating handles not more than 6' 7" high. A new exception now provides additional clarity for listed industrial control panels and similar enclosures to provide the AHJ and installers with prescriptive text permitting the use of tools to gain access.

Arc Energy Reduction, Fuses Rated 1200 Amps or Higher

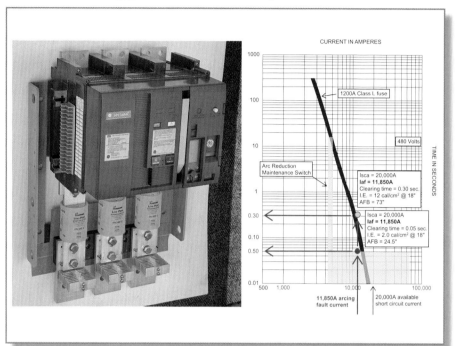

Courtesy of Eaton's Bussmann Business

Code Language

240.67 Arc Energy Reduction.
Where fuses rated 1200 A or higher are installed, 240.67(A) and (B) shall apply. This requirement shall become effective January 1, 2020.

(A) Documentation. (same as 240.87(A))

(B) Method to Reduce Clearing Time. A fuse shall have a clearing time 0.07 seconds or less at the available arcing current, or one of the following shall be provided:

(1) Differential relaying

(2) Energy-reducing maintenance switching with local status indicator

(3) Energy-reducing active arc flash mitigation system

(4) An approved equivalent means

(See NEC for actual text)

Significance of the Change

A means to reduce "arc energy" now applies to both fuses and circuit breakers with a threshold of 1200 amps and higher. This new requirement for fuses mirrors the existing requirement for circuit breakers in 240.87 in many ways. This new requirement will result in the use of fuses with a clearing time of 0.07 seconds, or less or a means to open the circuit to reduce arc energy with or without the fuse opening. For example, an energy-reducing maintenance switching with local status indicator could be used to open a switch before the opening of the fuse element. This requirement also permits a fuse that would open the circuit in 0.07 seconds or less, at or below the available arcing current. It is extremely important to recognize that the opening time of 0.07 seconds or less, is to be determined at the available arcing current. Circuit breakers utilizing ZSI to meet the requirements of 240.87 can take up to 0.07 seconds to open the circuit, therefore, a maximum fuse opening time of 0.07 seconds is also permitted. Three informational notes are included to address energy reduction maintenance switches, active arc flash mitigation systems and IEEE 1584.

Change Summary

- A means of "arc energy reduction" applies to all fuses rated 1200 A or higher.

- This requirement has a delayed implementation of January 1, 2020, to permit the industry to develop feasible solutions.

- 240.67 methods to reduce arc energy are similar to those in 240.87 with an additional provision permitting a fuse that would open the circuit in 0.07 seconds or less, at or below the available arcing current.

FR: 2707
SR: 2702

Method to Reduce Clearing Time

Code Language

240.87 Arc Energy Reduction

(B) Method to Reduce Clearing Time. One of the following means shall be provided: *(two new means permitted)...no other changes*

(5) An instantaneous trip setting that is less than the available arcing current

(6) An instantaneous override that is less than the available arcing current

Informational Note No. 3: An instantaneous trip is a function that causes a circuit breaker to trip with no intentional delay when currents exceed the instantaneous trip setting or current level. If arcing currents are above the instantaneous trip level, the circuit breaker will trip in the minimum possible time.

(See NEC for actual text)

Change Summary

• Two new means to reduce arc energy are added in 240.87 for circuit breakers rated at or capable of being adjusted to 1200 amps or higher.

• (5) An instantaneous trip setting that is less than the available arcing current *and* (6) An instantaneous override that is less than the available arcing current.

• New Informational Note No. 3 explains that where arcing currents are above the instantaneous trip level, the circuit breaker will trip in the minimum possible time.

FR: 2706
SR: None

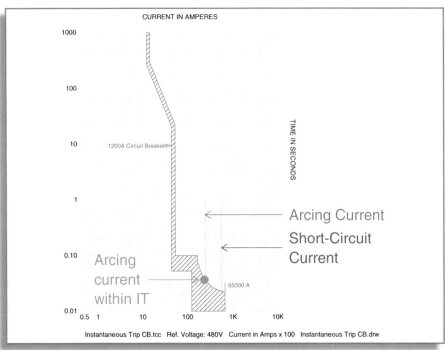

Courtesy of Eaton's Bussmann Business

Significance of the Change

Two new means to reduce the clearing time of circuit breakers rated at or adjustable to 1200 amps or larger are added in list items (5) and (6). These new means address circuit breakers that will open instantaneously at values below the available arcing current. The available arcing current is a factor of the available short circuit current. A low voltage power circuit breaker can be applied without an instantaneous trip. Where an instantaneous trip is installed, it can be set with an intentional delay for up to 0.5 seconds or 30 cycles. This is the reason section 240.87 requires a means to reduce arc energy through a reduction in clearing time. This revision recognizes that under specific conditions, an instantaneous trip device installed in a circuit breaker may meet the requirements for arc energy reduction because the device will trip as fast as possible due to the instantaneous setting being less than the available arcing current. Where a circuit breaker is provided with an instantaneous trip and the instantaneous trip setting is less than the available arcing current or there is an instantaneous override that is less than the available arcing current, no additional means of arc energy reduction is required. Two new informational notes are provided. Informational Note No. 3 explains that where arcing currents are above the instantaneous trip level, the circuit breaker will trip in the minimum possible time. Informational Note No. 4 references IEEE 1584.

250.4(A)(1) & 250.4(B)(1)

Lightning Protection System Grounding and Bonding

Significance of the Change

The added informational note and revisions to the existing informational note within this section provide increased emphasis that the *NEC* is not a lightning protection *Code* or standard. The *NEC* includes only requirements to bonding the normal power grounding electrode system to the grounding system installed for lightning protection. NFPA 780 *Standard for the Installation of Lightning Protection Systems* includes the prescriptive and performance requirements that must be applied to installations of lightning protection systems on buildings or structures. The additional wording in the informational notes provides the clarification about which standard contains the rules that must be applied to installed lightning protection equipment and systems. The scope of the *NEC* is clear that the purpose of the *Code* is the "practical safeguarding of persons and property from hazards that arise from the use of electricity." Lightning is not included in such use. The *NEC* contains rules that provide for connections to the earth for power and communications systems; lightning events are often dissipated through the power and communications systems grounding electrodes. For this reason, the ground terminals of lighting protection systems must be bonded to the grounding electrode(s) for power and communications systems installed on buildings and structures. The *NEC* addresses these bonding requirements.

Change Summary

- The words "installation of grounding and bonding for" were added to Informational Note No. 2 in Section 250.4(A)(1).
- A new informational note was added following 250.4(B)(1) and references NFPA 780 *Standard for the Installation of Lightning Protection Systems*.
- Appropriate references to NFPA 780 are now provided with the performance requirements related to grounded and ungrounded electrical systems.

FRs: 1203, 1204
SRs: 1202, 1201
SCRs: 48, 49

Circuits Not Permitted to Be Grounded

Code Language

250.22 Circuits Not to Be Grounded. The following circuits shall not be grounded:

(1) Circuits...(See 2014 *NEC* text)

(2) Circuits...(See 2014 *NEC* text)

(3) Circuits...(See 2014 *NEC* text)

(4) Secondary circuits...(See 2014 *NEC* text)

(5) Secondary circuits...(See 2014 *NEC* text)

(6) Class 2 load side circuits for suspended ceiling low-voltage power grid distribution systems as provided in 393.60(B).

(See NEC for actual text)

Change Summary

- A new list item (6) has been added to Section 250.22.

- The revision clarifies that Class 2 load side circuits for suspended ceiling low-voltage power grid distribution systems shall not be grounded.

- A reference to Section 393.60(B) provides a correlation between Section 250.22 and 393.60.

FR: 1208
SR: 1203

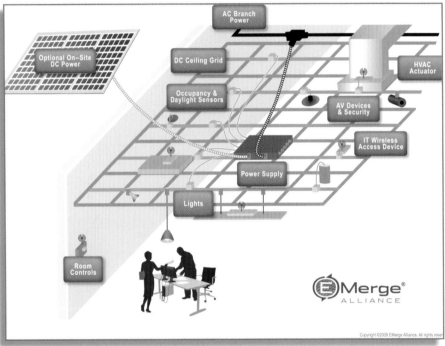

Courtesy of EMerge Alliance

Significance of the Change

Article 393 titled *Low-Voltage Suspended Ceiling Power Distribution Systems*, was added to Chapter 3 in the 2014 *NEC* development cycle. Like most of the other chapter 3 articles, the arrangement of this article includes three parts. Part I provides the general requirements, Part II includes the specific rules related to installing this wiring system, and Part III provides the construction specifications for this wiring and equipment. A critical provision of Article 393 is that the wiring, power supplies, and equipment must all be listed as a complete system and include installation instructions. A key operating and safety characteristic of low-voltage suspended ceiling power distribution systems is that they will include a listed Class 2 power supply, and the operating voltage is limited to 30 volts ac and 60 volts dc. As with many other chapter 3 articles the grounding rules are contained in Section 363.60. There are two key requirements in this section. The first addresses requirements to connect an equipment-grounding conductor to the supply side of the Class 2 power supply. Follow the manufacturer's installation instructions for grounding requirements for conductive parts of this type of system. The Subdivision (B) provides the key restriction on system grounding. The load side of the power supplies must not be grounded.

Size of Grounded Conductor in Raceway or Cable

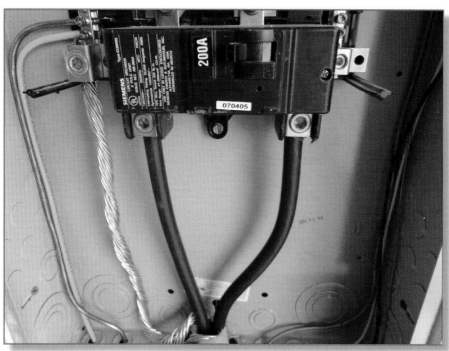

Significance of the Change

Section 250.24(C) contains critical requirements for installation and minimum sizing of grounded service conductors. The revisions to list items (1) and (2) of this section are to insert the words "or cable(s)." The change clarifies that the requirements in 250.24 apply to all grounded conductors installed with the service conductors, whether installed in raceway(s) or cable(s). The previous text clearly only addressed grounded service conductors in raceways, but was always intended to apply to grounded conductors that are part of a cable assembly. Services are sometimes installed using service cable in accordance with *NEC* Article 338. The grounded conductor installed to the service disconnect must perform two essential functions. It first must be sized to carry the maximum unbalanced neutral load served, and second, it must be sized with the capacity to effectively facilitate the operation of overcurrent devices in the event of a ground fault on the premises wiring system. By including both raceways and cables in the provisions of (1) and (2), it is clear that the minimum sizing requirements for service grounded conductors installed as a single conductor or in a parallel arrangement must be applied.

Code Language

250.24(C) Grounded Conductor Brought to Service Equipment. Where an ac...(See *NEC* text)

(1) **Sizing for Single Raceway or Cable.** The grounded conductor shall not be smaller than specified in Table 250.102(C)(1).

(2) **Parallel Conductors in Two or More Raceways or Cables.** If the ungrounded service-entrance conductors are installed in parallel in two or more raceways or cables, the grounded conductor shall also be installed in parallel. The size of the grounded conductor in each raceway or cable shall be based on the total circular mil area of the parallel ungrounded conductors in the raceway or cable, as indicated in 250.24(C)(1), but not smaller than 1/0 AWG.

(See NEC for actual text)

Change Summary

- The words "or cable(s)" have been added to list items (1) and (2).

- The revision clarifies that the minimum sizing requirements for service grounded conductors apply whether installed in a raceway or cable assembly.

- The sizing rule applies to service grounded conductors in a single raceway or cable and those installed in parallel arrangements.

FRs: 1209, 1210

SR: None

Electrode for Separately Derived System

Code Language

(4) Electrode. The building or structure grounding electrode system shall be used as the grounding electrode for the separately derived system. If located outdoors, the grounding electrode shall be in accordance with 250.30(C).

Exception: If a separately derived system originates in equipment that is listed and identified as suitable for use as service equipment, the grounding electrode used for the service or feeder equipment shall be permitted to be used as the grounding electrode for the separately derived system.

(See NEC for actual text)

Change Summary

- Section 250.30(A)(4) has been revised and simplified, and Exception No. 1 was deleted.
- The revision clarifies that the building grounding electrode system must be used when establishing a grounding electrode for a separately derived system.
- If installed outdoors, the grounding electrode for the separately derived system must comply with 250.30(C).

Significance of the Change

The revisions to list item (4) clarify that the electrodes present at the building or structure served must be used as the grounding electrode for a separately derived system. The former hierarchy of mandated electrodes (metal water pipe electrode and metal building frame electrode) for the separately derived systems has been removed. The revised text allowed exception No. 1 to be deleted as those options are covered by the referenced sections. For separately derived systems located outdoors, the reference to 250.30(C) triggers the requirement for use of the electrodes present at the building or structure served as indicated in 250.50. These revisions provide clear direction about the required grounding electrode(s). It should be noted that metal water piping and metal building frames that are above the ground are conductive paths to the electrode and perform the functions of a grounding electrode conductor. The revisions to this section recognize the water pipe and the structural metal frame as covered in 250.68(C) that are not grounding electrodes by definition, but rather are conductors or conductive paths that extend the grounding electrode connection. The service equipment addressed in the exception must be both listed and identified as revised.

FR: 1219
SR: 1210

Common Grounding Electrode Conductor

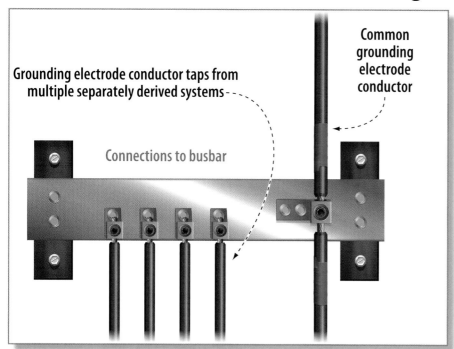

Grounding electrode conductor taps from multiple separately derived systems

Common grounding electrode conductor

Connections to busbar

Significance of the Change

The list of items that can function as common grounding electrode conductors installed and used for multiple separately derived systems has been expanded. Both a metal building frame that is connected to a grounding electrode as provided in 250.68(C)(2) and, as revised, a metal water pipe that ultimately is connected to a grounding electrode in accordance with 250.68(C)(1) can be used as a common grounding electrode conductor. This revision aligns with the definition of the term *grounding electrode* and recognizes that metal building frames and metal water piping above ground (the earth) are both conductive paths to the actual electrode. They perform the role of a conductive path to the electrode(s) just like a common grounding electrode conductor of the wire type. List item (2) to 250.30(A)(6) (c) has been revised to clarify the required length of a ¼-in. thick × 2-inch wide copper busbar used for making connections of grounding electrode conductor taps to the common grounding electrode conductor of the wire type. While that actual length is not specified for the busbar, it must be long enough to accommodate all conductors that have to be connected to it. This is consistent with the provisions in 250.64(D)(1)(3) as revised in the 2014 *NEC* cycle.

Code Language

250.30(A)(6)(a) *Common Grounding Electrode Conductor.* The common grounding electrode conductor shall be permitted to be one of the following:

(1) A conductor of the wire type not smaller than 3/0 AWG copper or 250 kcmil aluminum

(2) A metal water pipe that complies with 250.68(C)(1)

(3) The metal structural frame of the building or structure that complies with 250.68(C)(2) or is connected to the grounding electrode system by a conductor...(See *NEC* text)

250.30(A)(6)(c)(2) Listed connections to aluminum or copper busbars not smaller than 6 mm thick × 50 mm wide (¼ in. thick × 2 in. wide) and of sufficient length to accommodate the number of terminations...(See *NEC* text)

(See NEC for actual text)

Change Summary

- List item (6) addresses grounding electrode conductors for multiple systems.

- List item (6)(a) has been revised to clarify items that can serve as a common grounding electrode conductor.

- List item (6)(c)(2) now indicates the length of the busbar shall be of sufficient length to accommodate the number of terminations necessary for the installation.

FR: 1218

SR: 1206

Metal In-Ground Support Structure(s)

Code Language

(2) Metal In-Ground Support Structure(s). One or more metal in-ground support structure(s) in direct contact with the earth vertically for 3.0 m (10 ft) or more, with or without concrete encasement. If multiple metal in-ground support structures are present at a building or a structure, it shall be permissible to bond only one into the grounding electrode system.

Informational Note: Metal in-ground support structures include, but are not limited to, pilings, casings, and other structural metal.

(See NEC for actual text)

Change Summary

- Section 250.52(A)(2) has been revised and simplified to apply metal in-ground building or structure supports that function as grounding electrodes.

- The previous text related to structural metal building frames above the earth has been removed.

- The revision aligns this section with the definition of the term *grounding electrode* in Article 100.

FR: 1217
SR: None

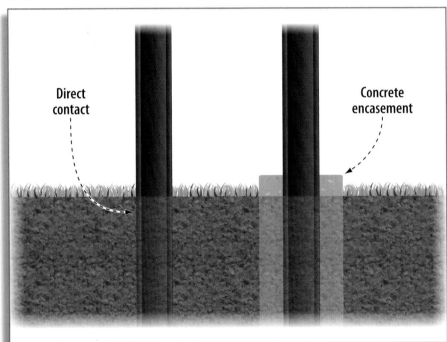

Direct contact

Concrete encasement

Significance of the Change

The revised title and text provides clarity by more accurately describing what a metal building framing and structural steel electrode actually is. The section is now titled "Metal In-Ground Support Structure(s)." The material regarding "hold-down" bolts was relocated to 250.68. In reality, metal frames of buildings or structures do not extend into the ground. Metal or concrete reinforced pilings or similar objects are either driven into the earth, or a hole is bored and the structural support placed into the hole. Often, concrete is poured around the metal piling at or near the surface of the earth. Usually, the metal or concrete piling is capped where a transition is made from the piling to the metal frame of the building. It is recognized that the definition of *Grounding Electrode* states it is "A conducting object through which a direct connection to earth is established." As a result, a metal frame of a building or structure that is above ground cannot be a grounding electrode. It may function as a grounding electrode conductor by providing a conductive path to the grounding electrode. This conductive path to the electrode is recognized and addressed by 250.68(C)(2). If a metal frame of a building or structure is driven into the ground and extends above the ground for any length, a transition from grounding electrode to grounding electrode conductor is made at the point of emergence from the earth.

Concrete In-Ground Pools Not Permitted as Electrodes

Code Language

(B) Not Permitted for Use as Grounding Electrodes. The following systems and materials shall not be used as grounding electrodes:

(1) Metal underground gas piping systems

(2) Aluminum

(3) The structures and structural reinforcing steel described in 680.26(B)(1) and (B)(2)

Informational Note: See 250.104(B) for bonding requirements of gas piping.

(See NEC for actual text)

Significance of the Change

The term *grounding electrode* is defined as "A conducting object through which a direct connection to earth is established." An in-ground pool typically meets the criteria in this definition. Information in the substantiation to Public Input 4809 indicated that detached buildings or structures with electrical power from a feeder such as detached garages, workshops, and so forth often require a grounding electrode system installed per the requirements of 250.32(A). Occasionally, these detached structures are located near in-ground permanently installed in-ground swimming pools. In certain areas of the country, the electrical installer will run a grounding electrode conductor from the electrical subpanel at the detached structure to the reinforcing steel of the conductive pool shell (belly steel) or to the structural steel of the perimeter surfaces (deck steel) and classify the pool reinforcing steel as an "other local metal underground system or structure" as described at 250.52(A)(8). Sometimes, this action is at the requirement of the local AHJ. List item (3) in 250.52(B) makes it clear that structures and reinforcing steel for in-ground pools are not permitted in the grounding electrode system for a building or structure. While an in-ground pool structure may be performing the function of an electrode, it is not permitted in the grounding electrode system.

Change Summary

- Section 250.52(B) provides a list of items that are not permitted for use as grounding electrodes.
- A new list item (3) has been added to Section 250.52(B).
- The structures and reinforcing steel for in-ground pools are not permitted to be used in the required grounding electrode system of a building or structure.

FR: 1220
SRs: 1208, 1209

Bonding to Create an Electrically Parallel Path

Code Language

(1) General. Ferrous metal raceways and enclosures for grounding electrode conductors shall be electrically continuous from the point of attachment to cabinets or equipment to the grounding electrode and shall be securely fastened to the ground clamp or fitting. Ferrous metal raceways and enclosures shall be bonded at each end of the raceway or enclosure to the grounding electrode or grounding electrode conductor to create an electrically parallel path. Nonferrous metal raceways and enclosures shall not be required to be electrically continuous.

(See NEC for actual text)

Change Summary

- The words "an electrically" have been incorporated into the second sentence of this section.
- The revision clarifies the type of electrical conductivity between the wire and the surrounding conduit or raceway.
- The conductor and the conduit must be electrically bonded to each other at each end to form a parallel path for any imposed current.

FR: 1225
SR: 1214

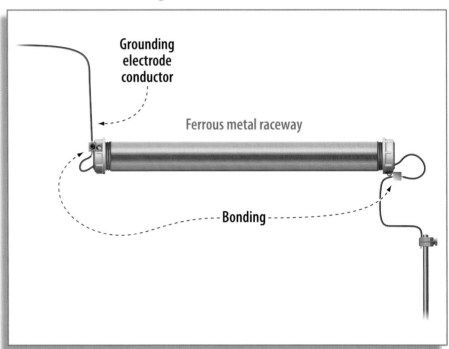

Grounding electrode conductor

Ferrous metal raceway

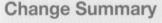

Bonding

Significance of the Change

Ferrous metal raceways are required to be bonded (electrically) to the contained grounding electrode conductor (GEC) to reduce the effects of magnetic fields. The GEC for an AC system or service is an alternating current carrying conductor. Varying amounts of current are present in this conductor during normal operation. This current can also rise and fall significantly depending on events such as ground faults, short circuits, or line surges. As the current rises and falls, the magnetic field of the contained GEC gets larger and smaller accordingly. This means stresses on the contained grounding electrode conductor increase and decrease as the current rises and falls. If a ferrous metal raceway encloses this conductor, there is an inductive reactance between the ferrous metal raceway and the contained GEC. This inductive reactance is one component of impedance and actually impedes current in the GEC. The magnetic field and the capacitance results in a coupling effect between the current in the conductor and the surrounding ferrous metal raceway. In actuality, the majority of the current would be present in the ferrous raceway rather than the contained GEC. This condition is often referred to as the *choke effect* because this condition is actually restricting the GEC from performing its essential function.

Length of Busbar for GEC Connections

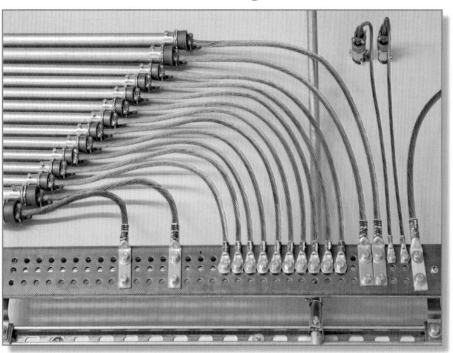

Photo from iStock

Code Language

(3) Bonding jumper(s) from grounding electrode(s) shall be permitted to be connected to an aluminum or copper busbar not less than 6 mm thick × 50 mm wide (1/4 in. thick × 2 in. wide) and of sufficient length to accommodate the number of terminations necessary for the installation. The busbar shall be securely fastened and shall be installed in an accessible location. Connections shall be made by a listed connector or by the exothermic welding process. The grounding electrode conductor shall be permitted to be run to the busbar. Where aluminum busbars are used, the installation shall comply with 250.64(A).

(See NEC for actual text)

Significance of the Change

Section 250.64(F)(1) provides methods of installing grounding electrode conductors and bonding jumpers that interconnect electrodes. The methods are to route the GEC to any convenient electrode in the grounding electrode system and connect the others with bonding jumpers or to run the grounding electrode conductor individually to one or more electrodes. List item (3) includes an allowance for connecting bonding jumpers from the grounding electrodes to an aluminum or copper busbar not less than 1/4 in. thick and not less than 2 in. wide. The length is not included which implied that if this method were used, the bar needed to be long enough for all conductors intended to be connected to the bar. List item (3) has been revised by simply including information about the required length, but no dimension is given. The bar must be long enough for the number of terminations connected to it. Some manufacturers of grounding and bonding equipment have produced grounding busbars specifically for this purpose, and these are produced in specific lengths. It should be noted that one could field construct a copper or aluminum busbar to meet the provisions of this section. The additional language included in this section clarifies the busbar length requirements in this section and correlates with 250.64(D)(1)(3).

Change Summary

- The words "and of sufficient length to accommodate the number of terminations necessary for the installation" have been added to the first sentence.
- The words "thick" and "wide" have been added following the numeric values of size.
- To correlate with 250.64(D), the length has to be sufficient for the number of terminations connected to it.

FR: 1226
SR: None

250.66(A)(B)(C)

REVISION

Connection to the Same Type of Electrode

Code Language

250.66(A)...(See *NEC* text)

250.66(B) Connections to Concrete-Encased Electrodes. If the grounding electrode conductor or bonding jumper connected to a single or multiple concrete-encased electrode(s), as described in 250.52(A)(3), does not extend on to other types of electrodes that require a larger size of conductor, the grounding electrode conductor shall not be required to be larger than 4 AWG copper wire.

250.66(C)...(See *NEC* text)

(See NEC for actual text)

Change Summary

- The text related to the concept of "sole connection" has been removed from this section.
- The wording "that does not extend on to other types of electrodes that require a larger size of conductor" have been added to subdivisions in 250.66.
- The revision clarifies when the maximum sizes in this section could be applied.

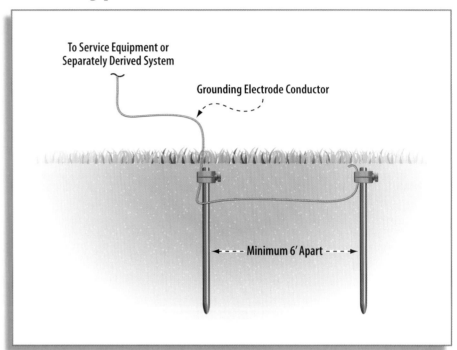

To Service Equipment or Separately Derived System

Grounding Electrode Conductor

Minimum 6' Apart

Significance of the Change

The revisions to all three subdivisions in this section build on the changes that were incorporated in the 2014 *NEC*. The maximum size provisions of this section are intended and allowed to be applied if the grounding electrode conductor and any bonding jumpers do not extend to another type of electrode that would require a larger grounding electrode conductor. The substantiation with Public Input 4196 indicated that additional clarity was necessary in this section to address what was meant by the phrase "sole connection" formerly used in this section. The revised text clarifies the intent to permit the practice of "daisy chaining" grounding electrodes to form a grounding electrode system and that as long as any downstream electrode would not require a larger grounding electrode conductor or bonding jumper the provisions of 260.66(A), (B), and (C) would apply for sizing of these conductors. The revised text removes the term *sole connection* that has caused confusion in the industry as to the intended application of these provisions. As revised, the relief from the sizes specified in Table 250.66 can be utilized in cases where the GEC or bonding jumper does not extend to electrodes such as a metal building frame or a metal water pipe electrode.

FR: 1227
SR: 1215

Grounding of Metal Components

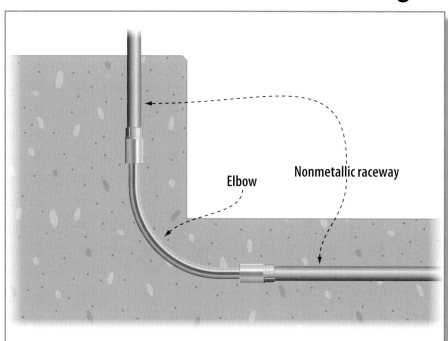

Elbow

Nonmetallic raceway

Code Language

250.80 Service Raceways and Enclosures.

Exception: Metal components that are installed in a run of underground nonmetallic raceway(s) and are isolated from possible contact by a minimum cover of 450 mm (18 in.) to all parts of the metal components shall not be required to be connected to the grounded system conductor, supply-side bonding jumper, or grounding electrode conductor.

(See NEC for actual text)

Significance of the Change

The revisions to Exception clarify that no part of the metal elbow or other metal components be covered by less than 18 inches of earth or other material to prevent inadvertent contact. The revised text clarifies that all metal components installed in non-metallic raceways, such as short lengths of metal conduit, adaptors or other fittings, and so forth are required to be covered and not just an elbow. The revision clarifies the intent is to require all portions of an isolated metal elbow or other metal component be below 18 inches. Information in the substantiation with Public Input pointed out that the exception could be misinterpreted and misapplied. As an example, if a three foot radius elbow were installed it could be possible to be at the correct burial depth and yet have a portion of the elbow exposed above grade. As the text requires it be "isolated from possible contact" this would not be the case, and therefore, the elbow would be required to be grounded. As revised, this exception applies to more than just metal elbows isolated from contact by burial depth or concrete-encasement.

Change Summary

- The exception to 250.80 has been rewritten and expanded to apply to other metal components in addition to just metal elbows.
- The term *metal elbow* has been removed and replaced with the term *metal components*.
- The revision expands the exception to apply to more than just buried or encased metal elbows.

FR: 1206
SR: None

Grounding of Metal Components

Code Language

250.86 Other Conductor Enclosures and Raceways.

Exception No. 3: Metal components shall not be required to be connected to the equipment grounding conductor or supply side bonding jumper where either of the following conditions exist:

(1) The metal components are installed in a run of nonmetallic raceway(s) and isolated from possible contact by a minimum cover of 450 mm (18 in.) to any part of the metal components.

(2) The metal components are part of an installation of nonmetallic raceway(s) and are isolated from possible contact to any part of the metal components by being encased in not less than 50 mm (2 in.) of concrete.

(See NEC for actual text)

Change Summary

• Exception No. 3 has been rewritten into a list format in accordance with the *NEC Style Manual* to improve usability.

• The term *metal elbow* has been removed from Exception No. 3 and replaced with the term *metal components*.

• The revision expands the exception to apply to more than just buried or encased metal elbows.

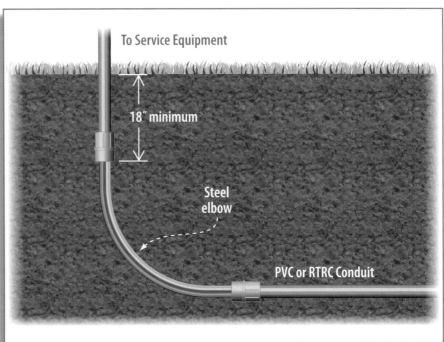

Significance of the Change

The revisions to Exception No. 3 include arrangement into a list format and clarifying that no part of the metal elbow or other metal components be covered by less than 18 inches of earth or other material to prevent inadvertent contact. The revised text clarifies that all metal components installed in non-metallic raceways, such as short lengths of metal conduit, adaptors or other fittings, and so forth are required to be covered and not just an elbow. The revision clarifies the intent is to require all portions of an isolated metal elbow or other metal component be below 18 inches. Information in the substantiation with Public Input pointed out that the exception could be misinterpreted and misapplied. As an example, if a three foot radius elbow were installed it could be possible to be at the correct burial depth and yet have a portion of the elbow exposed above grade. As the text requires it be "isolated from possible contact," this would not be the case, and therefore, the elbow would be required to be grounded. As revised, this exception applies to more than just metal elbows isolated from contact by burial depth or concrete-encasement.

FR: 1208
SR: 1217

Intersystem Bonding Termination (IBT) Requirements

Significance of the Change

Subdivision (A) in this section applies to intersystem bonding terminations and (B) provides other means for the bonding connections. Information provided with Public Input 702 indicated that the text in 250.94 works well for single-family dwelling unit. It does not take into account how a commercial or industrial building may bond the other systems. Many commercial buildings commonly utilize a common grounding bar for the connection of multiple electrodes and bonding of other systems such as water piping systems, building steel, internal antenna systems, and so forth, in addition to providing a means for connection of the other systems such as communication, satellite dish systems, network powered broadband systems. This revision allows the user to install other than the one device for the purposes of bonding all systems within a structure whether or not the structure is a single family dwelling or other type of structure. As a result, this section now recognizes connections to an aluminum or copper busbar not less than ¼ in. thick × 2 in. wide, and of sufficient length to accommodate at least three terminations for communication systems, in addition to other connections. The new informational note informs users of IBTs potentially reducing noise on the grounding system.

Code Language

250.94 Bonding for Other Communication Systems. Communications system bonding terminations shall be connected in accordance with (A) or (B).

(A) The Intersystem Bonding Termination Device. An intersystem bonding termination (IBT) for connecting the intersystem bonding conductors...(see *NEC* text)...and at the disconnecting means for any additional buildings or structures...(See *NEC* text)

(B) Other Means. Connections to an aluminum or copper busbar not less than 6 mm thick × 50 mm wide (¼ in. thick × 2 in. wide) and of sufficient length to accommodate at least three terminations for communication systems in addition to other connections. The busbar shall be securely...(See *NEC* text)

(See NEC for actual text)

Change Summary

- Section 250.94 has been reformatted into two subdivisions including a new exception and informational note.
- Subdivision (A) contains the previous requirements and has been titled "Intersystem Bonding Termination Device."
- Subdivision (B) is titled "Other Means" and recognizes use of a listed ¼ × 2 inch copper busbar.

FR: 1215
SR: None

Bonding Metal Piping and Metal Building Frames

Code Language

(A) Metal Water Piping. The metal water piping system shall be bonded... (See *NEC* text)

(1) General. Metal water piping... (See *NEC* text)...shall be bonded to any of the following:

(1) Service equipment enclosure

(2) Grounded conductor at the service

(3) Grounding electrode conductor if of sufficient size

(4) One or more grounding electrodes used...(See *NEC* text)

The bonding jumper(s) shall be sized...(See *NEC* text)

The bonding jumper(s) shall be sized in accordance with Table 250.102(C)(1)...(See *NEC* text)

(See NEC for actual text)

Change Summary

- Section 250.104(A) has been revised by adding the wording "if of sufficient size" to (A)(3) and (A)(4).

- The wording "that is interconnected to form a building frame" has been added in subdivisions (C) and (D).

- The minimum sizes of the bonding conductor or jumper must be in accordance with Table 250.102(C)(1) rather than Table 250.66.

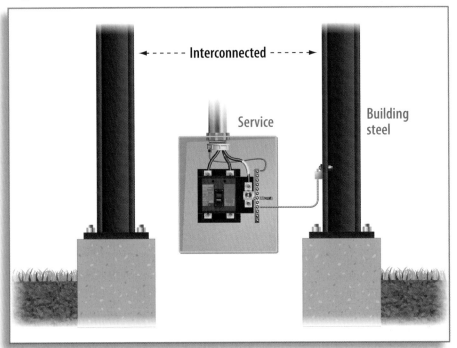

Significance of the Change

The first change of significance in this section clarifies that the grounding electrode conductor or bonding jumper referred to in (A)(4) must be of sufficient size. The revision clarifies that if the grounding electrode conductor or bonding jumper is to perform as both a grounding electrode conductor and a bonding jumper, it must be of sufficient size for both functions. The additional text in subdivision (C) clarifies that the structural metal referenced from this section must be interconnected to form a building frame as opposed to being isolate structural metal members. The most significant revision in this section is the change in sizing requirements for the bonding conductors. The previous requirement was to use Table 250.66 for sizing the water pipe bonding conductor and the bonding conductor for interconnected structural metal building framing. This is no longer the case. Table 250.102(C)(1) must now be used for sizing which triggers the 12.5% rule for larger installations. The main reason for the change is that the conductors addressed in this section are often not only grounding electrode conductors but serve as bonding jumpers or conductors.

FR: 1216
SR: 1220

Flexible Metal Conduit as EGC

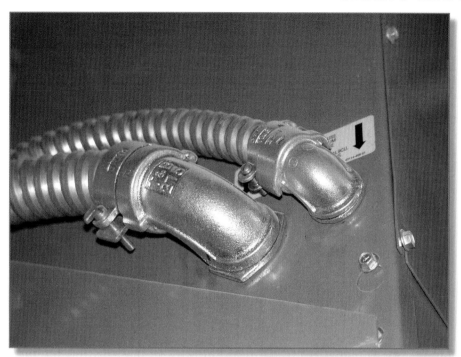

Code Language

(5) Listed flexible metal conduit meeting all the following conditions:

a. The conduit is terminated in listed fittings.

b. The circuit conductors contained in the conduit are protected by overcurrent devices rated at 20 amperes or less.

c. The size of the conduit does not exceed metric designator 35 (trade size 1¼).

d. The combined length of... (See *NEC* text)

(See NEC for actual text)

Significance of the Change

List item (5) in 250.118 has been revised to include a conduit size limitation. The UL listing for equipment grounding of Flexible Metal Conduit and the associated fittings have only been listed up to the metric designator 35 (Trade size 1¼) for a number of years, see UL category code DXUZ. This revision aligns the equipment grounding conductor rules in 250.118(5) for flexible metal conduit line up with changes with the limitations first published in the 2012 edition of the UL Guide Information for Electrical Equipment (White Book). Effective with that publication, there is now an upper limit of 1¼ trade size on the permitted size of flexible metal conduit that can be used as an equipment-grounding conductor. For flexible metal conduit, the *NEC* has always traded off the larger overcurrent device sizing limits for liquid-tight flexible metal conduit against the unlimited sizing permission for flexible metal conduit. For over 40 years, the *NEC* previously recognized flexible metal conduit in any trade size as an acceptable equipment-grounding conductor as long as the overcurrent protection was limited to 20 amperes. This *NEC* requirement as revised by CMP 5 will align with requirements in UL 1, the standard for Flexible Metal Conduit.

Change Summary

- A new list item (c) has been added to 250.118(5).
- The revision provides a size limitation not to exceed metric designator 35 (trade size 1¼).
- The change is consistent with the UL standard for flexible metal conduit and fittings and is consistent with the size limitations provided in 250.118(6).

FR: 1229
SR: None

250.122(B)

Article 250 Grounding and Bonding

Part VI Equipment Grounding and Equipment Grounding Conductors

REVISION

Increases in Size of Equipment Grounding Conductors

Code Language

(B) Increased in Size. If ungrounded conductors are increased in size to account for voltage drop, wire-type equipment grounding conductors shall be increased in size. The increase in size shall be at least in the same proportion as the increase in the size of the ungrounded conductors using their circular mil area.

(See NEC for actual text)

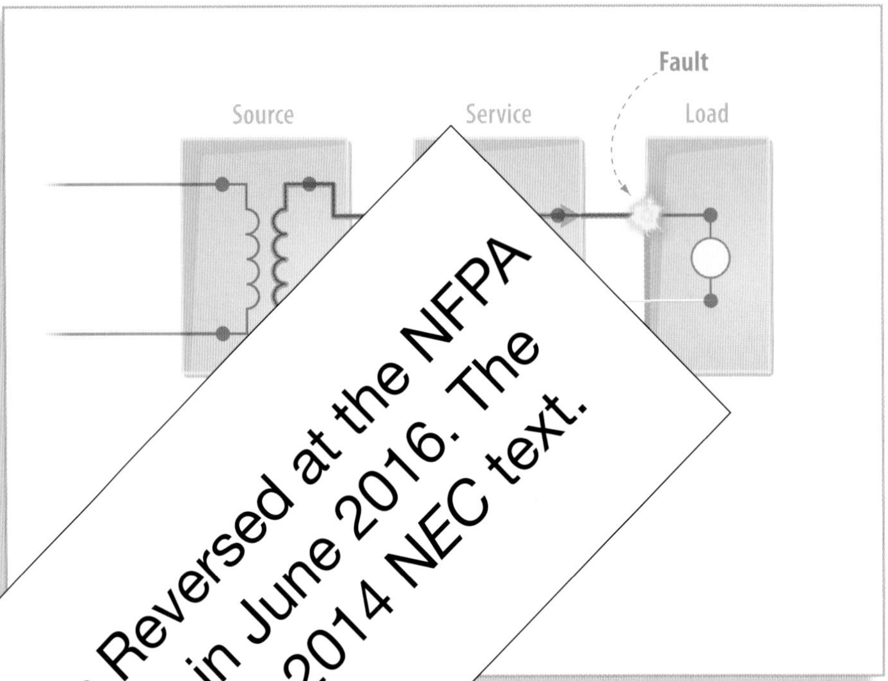

This Revision was Reversed at the NFPA Technical Meeting in June 2016. The NEC reverts back to 2014 NEC text.

Change Sum

- This revision ment to p crease of voltage
- Increases siz adjustment fac tion factors are un due to the short dura ground-fault event.
- This revision reverts back t the requirements in the 1999 *NEC* relative to required proportionate size increases.

ge

favorably to reverting back to the *EC* relative to required proportionate size grounding conductors only for reasons of multiple cycles of revisions to this rule, the ent evolved to overly restrictive and confusing essarily. Equipment grounding conductors perform functions. They ground equipment connected to the uit or feeder, they perform bonding functions through connections, and they facilitate the operation of overcurrent ctive devices during a ground fault or short circuit event. CMP-5 ovided a clarifying statement that increasing the size of a wire-type equipment-grounding conductor due to adjustment or correction factors is not necessary because of the short duration of a ground fault or short circuit condition. The resulting change leaves this section requiring a proportionate size increase of wire-type equipment grounding conductors only if the ungrounded circuit conductors are increased for reasons related to voltage drop. The previous requirement to increase the EGC size if the ungrounded circuit conductors were increased in size for any reason has been removed as it was determined to be overly restrictive and created confusion. The revision solves these issues.

FR: 1236

SR: 1223

Conductors Installed in Parallel Arrangements

Code Language

(1) Conductor Installations in Raceways, Auxiliary Gutters, or Cable Trays

(a) Single Raceway or Cable Tray... (See *NEC* text)

(b) Multiple Raceways. If conductors are installed in parallel in multiple raceways, wire-type equipment grounding conductors, where used, shall be installed in parallel in each raceway. The equipment grounding conductor installed in each raceway shall be sized in compliance with 250.122 based on the overcurrent protective device for the feeder or branch circuit. Metal raceways or auxiliary gutters in accordance with 250.118 or cable trays complying with 392.60(B), shall be permitted as the equipment grounding conductor.

(See NEC for actual text)

Significance of the Change

Section 250.122(F) provides the requirements for equipment grounding conductors installed with paralleled branch circuit or feeder conductors. The previous text has been reorganized into a list format to meet the *NEC Style Manual* requirements and to improve clarity. The revision provides a demarcation between the rules for a single equipment grounding conductor installed with a parallel arrangement in a single raceway or cable tray and multiple equipment grounding conductors installed in multiple raceways. The additional wording "based on the overcurrent protective device for the feeder or branch circuit" has been added in both list items (a) and (b). This added text improves EGC sizing accuracy and makes it clear that the wire-type equipment grounding conductor must be sized in accordance with 250.122 based on the rating of the overcurrent protective device for the branch circuit or feeder in the parallel arrangement. The revisions to the last sentences in each list item provide clearer wording relative to auxiliary gutters and wireways that are required to perform as equipment grounding conductors.

Change Summary

- The words "based on the overcurrent protective device for the feeder or branch circuit" have been added in (a) and (b).
- The last sentence has been revised to more clearly address metal wire-ways and auxiliary gutters.
- The revision in this section improves clarity and usability relative to accuracy of the equipment grounding conductor minimum sizes.

FR: 1246
SR: 1226
SCR: 52

250.122(F)(2)

Article 250 Grounding and Bonding

Part VI Equipment Grounding and Equipment Grounding Conductors

REVISION

Multi-Conductor Cables Installed in Parallel Arrangements

Code Language

250.122(F)(2) Multiconductor Cables. (in part)

(b) If multi-conductor cables are installed in parallel in the same raceway, auxiliary gutter, or cable tray, a single equipment grounding conductor that is sized in accordance with 250.122 shall be permitted in combination with the equipment grounding conductors provided within the multi-conductor cables and shall all be connected together.

(c) Equipment grounding...(See *NEC* text)

(d) Except as provided...(See *NEC* for actual text)

(See NEC for actual text)

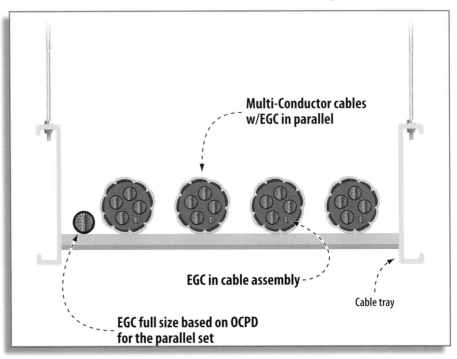

Multi-Conductor cables w/EGC in parallel

EGC in cable assembly

Cable tray

EGC full size based on OCPD for the parallel set

Change Summary

- Section 250.122(F)(2) has been revised and arranged in a list format.
- The revisions address minimum sizes for equipment grounding conductors in multi-conductor cables in parallel arrangements.
- A single EGC in each cable can be connected in parallel at each end and connected to a full-size EGC sized based on the OPCD for the entire circuit.

FR: 1246

SR: 1224

SCR: 53

Significance of the Change

Section 250.122(F)(2) provides the requirements for equipment grounding conductors installed with paralleled multi-conductor cables. The text has been reorganized into a list format to meet the *NEC Style Manual* requirements and to improve clarity. As indicated in list item (d), the equipment grounding conductors in each multi-conductor cable installed in a parallel arrangement shall generally be sized using 250.122 based on the rating of the overcurrent device protecting the entire circuit. For example, if (6) multi-conductor MC cables were installed in parallel to create a 1000-ampere feeder, the equipment grounding conductor in each cable assembly must be sized at 2/0 copper or 4/0 aluminum. As revised, list items (b) and (d) allow an EGC sizing alternative. Accordingly, a separately installed single equipment-grounding conductor that is sized in accordance with 250.122 for the entire feeder in the parallel installation shall be permitted in combination with the smaller equipment grounding conductors provided within each multi-conductor cable and shall all be connected together at each end of the run. Even though MC cable assemblies can be manufactured with larger EGCs as part of the assembly, the revision provides a nice alternative to usee cable assemblies with standard size EGCs in parallel arrangements, in cable tray for example.

82 Chapter 2 • Articles 210–250

EGC Continuity and Connections to Boxes

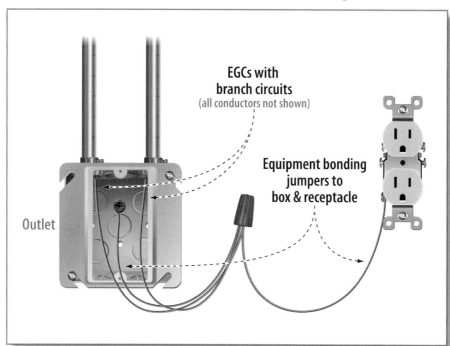

EGCs with branch circuits
(all conductors not shown)

Equipment bonding jumpers to box & receptacle

Outlet

Code Language

250.148 Continuity and Attachment of Equipment Grounding Conductors to Boxes. If circuit conductors are spliced within a box, or terminated on equipment within or supported by a box, all equipment grounding conductor(s) associated with any of those circuit conductors shall be connected within the box or to the box with devices suitable for the use in accordance with 250.8 and 250.148(A) through (E).

Exception: The equipment grounding conductor permitted in 250.146(D) shall not be required to be connected to the other equipment grounding conductors or to the box.

(See NEC for actual text)

Significance of the Change

Code-Making Panel 5 responded favorably to the concepts, revision, and substantiation provided with Public Input 1331. This section is frequently misunderstood to mean that where multiple circuits are present in a box the EGS's for each circuit are to be connected together but not connected to the EGC's of other circuits that are present. Consequently, this frequent misunderstanding has resulted in misapplication of the requirements to meet what was intended. This change clarifies that all of the wire-type equipment grounding conductors present in the box are required to be connected together regardless of which circuit they are associated. While the change reduces the possibilities of misconnecting the appropriate ECG with its associated branch circuit conductors, it does introduce the additional challenges for connecting all the EGCs together. This would be especially true when several branch circuits installed in the same box, some of which could be supplied by different voltages or systems. The resulting change requires all wire-type EGCs to be connected together and to the box, typically by using a single equipment-bonding jumper.

Change Summary

- The words "all" and "any of" have been added in Section 250.148.
- As revised, all equipment grounding conductors associated with any and all branch circuits in the box must be connected together and to the box.
- The change clarifies that connecting the EGCs together and to the box is not just for each associated circuit.

FR: 1237
SR: 1227

Chapter 3

Articles 300–396
Wiring Methods and Materials

Significant Changes
TO THE *NEC*® 2017

300.5(D)(4)

REVISION

Emerging from Grade

Code Language

300.5 Underground Installations

(D) Protection From Damage

(4) Enclosure or Raceway Damage.
Where the enclosure or raceway is subject to physical damage, the conductors shall be installed in electrical metallic tubing, rigid metal conduit, intermediate metal conduit, RTRC-XW, Schedule 80 PVC conduit, or equivalent.

(See NEC for actual text)

Change Summary

- Electrical metallic tubing (EMT) is added to the list of raceways permitted to provide physical protection direct-buried conductors and cables emerging from grade.

- EMT and associated elbows, couplings, and fittings are permitted to be installed in concrete, in direct contact with the earth, approved as suitable for the condition.

- 358.10(B) requires that where EMT is used in this manner, it must be where protected by corrosion protection and approved as suitable for the condition.

FR: 606
SR: None

Significance of the Change

First level subdivision 300.5(D) requires that "direct-buried conductors and cables" be protected from damage in accordance with 300.5(D)(1) through (4). This requirement applies only to "direct-buried conductors and cables" as seen in Table 300.5 Columns 1 and 4. Second level subdivision 300.5(D)(1) requires that direct-buried conductors and cables emerging from grade, as seen in Columns 1 and 4 of Table 300.5, be protected by enclosures or raceways extending from the minimum cover distance below grade, not less than 18 inches, required by 300.5(A) to a point at least eight feet above finished grade. Second level subdivision 300.5(D)(4) provides requirements for the enclosure or raceway used to protect these "direct-buried conductors and cables" where they emerge from the ground.

Electrical metallic tubing (EMT) is added by this revision to the list of raceways permitted to provide this protection. EMT and associated elbows, couplings, and fittings are permitted to be installed in concrete, in direct contact with the earth, or in areas subject to severe corrosive influences where protected by corrosion protection and approved as suitable for the condition. See 358.10(B).

Raceway Seals, Underground Conduits/Raceways

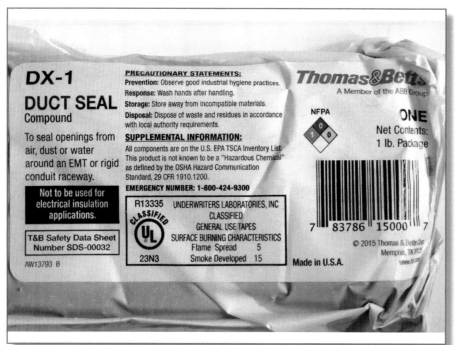

Courtesy of Thomas & Betts a member of the ABB Group

Code Language

300.5 Underground Installations.

(G) Raceway Seals. Conduits or raceways through which moisture may contact live parts shall be sealed or plugged at either or both ends. Spare or unused raceways shall also be sealed. Sealants shall be identified for use with the cable insulation, conductor insulation, bare conductor, shield, or other components.

Informational Note: Presence of hazardous gases or vapors may also necessitate sealing of underground conduits or raceways entering buildings.

(See NEC for actual text)

Significance of the Change

This revision provides necessary correlation for the requirements and application of raceway seals where conduits or raceways enter equipment from underground. There are existing requirements in section 225.27 for outside branch circuits and feeders, along with section 230.8 for service conductors that must be correlated with first level subdivision 300.5(G). This revision achieves correlation by adding two new general requirements. The first new general requirement adds a new sentence to address spare or unused raceways. This adds clarity by explaining that where moisture may contact live parts through spare raceways, they must also be sealed. The second new general requirement mandates that the type of sealant applied must be identified for use with the cable insulation, conductor insulation, bare conductor, shield, or other components. This is necessary to prevent the sealant material from damaging the insulation or the conductor.

Change Summary

- The general requirements of first level subdivision 300.5(G) is correlated with sections 225.27 and 230.8.

- Where necessary, spare or unused raceways shall also be sealed.

- The type of sealants applied must be identified for use with the cable insulation, conductor insulation, bare conductor, shield, or other components.

FR: 608
SR: None

Minimum Cover Requirements, Low Voltage Lighting

Code Language

Table 300.5 Minimum Cover Requirements, 0 to 1000 Volts, Nominal, Burial in Millimeters (Inches)

Column 5 Circuits for Control of Irrigation and Landscape Lighting Limited to Not More Than 30 Volts and Installed with Type UF or in Other Identified Cable or Raceway

[a]A lesser depth shall be permitted where specified in the installation instructions of a listed low voltage lighting system.

[b]A depth of 150 mm (6 inches) shall be permitted for pool, spa, and fountain lighting, installed in a nonmetallic raceway, limited to not more than 30 volts where part of a listed low-voltage lighting system.

(See NEC for actual text)

Photo from iStock

Change Summary

- Listed low voltage lighting systems that include installation instructions that permit burial depths less than 6 inches are now permitted.

- Clarity is provided for required burial depth of nonmetallic raceways that are part of a listed low voltage lighting system for pool, spa, and fountain lighting (6 inches).

Significance of the Change

Column 5 "Circuits for Control of Irrigation and Landscape Lighting Limited to Not More Than 30 Volts and Installed with Type UF or in Other Identified Cable or Raceway" in Table 300.5 is modified to provide clarity for burial depths of listed low voltage lighting systems. Low voltage lighting systems are not typically installed in trenches below concrete, streets, roads, driveways or airport runways and always fall under the row for "all locations not specified below." Column 5 lists the burial depth for "all locations not specified below" at 6-inches. This burial depth of 6-inches in the table is now supplemented with superscript "6[ab]" for the *Code* user to read additional information on required burial depth. Table 300.5 is now supplemented to allow listed low voltage lighting systems to be installed at a depth less than 6-inches where specified in the installation instructions. Additionally, clarity is provided for listed low voltage lighting systems installed with a pool, spa, or fountain to be installed at a depth of 6-inches where the conductors are installed in a nonmetallic raceway and are limited to not more than 30 volts.

FRs: 603, 604
SR: 623

Expansion Fittings for Raceways

Courtesy of Thomas & Betts a member of the ABB Group

Code Language

300.7 Raceways Exposed to Different Temperatures.

(B) Expansion, Expansion-Deflection, and Deflection Fittings. Raceways shall be provided with expansion, expansion-deflection, or deflection fittings where necessary to compensate for thermal expansion, deflection, and contraction.

Informational Note. (No changes)

(See NEC for actual text)

Significance of the Change

Section 300.7 has contained requirements for sealing raceways where condensation is possible and for expansion/contraction of raceways for many *Code* cycles. The previous text recognized only "expansion fittings" which work only where there is straight (axial) expansion and contraction. Two new types of fittings are now recognized along with expansion fittings. They are expansion-deflection and deflection fittings. This revision makes it clear to inspectors, designers, and contractors that expansion-deflection and deflection fittings are acceptable to be used with raceways to address straight thermal expansion, as well as installations which may require flexibility due to deflection, and contraction.

Standard expansion fittings work very well where raceways are aligned in a straight or axial manner. These new fitting types allow for thermal expansion or contraction when the raceways are off-set or misaligned.

Change Summary

• Long standing requirements for expansion type fittings on raceways are modified to include expansion-deflection, and deflection type fittings.

• Standard expansion fittings are designed for axial expansion and contraction only.

• Expansion-deflection, and deflection type fittings allow for axial deflection as well as parallel and angular deflection.

FR: None
SR: 602

Ducts Specifically Fabricated for Environmental Air

Code Language

300.22(B) Ducts Specifically Fabricated for Environmental Air.

(New exception. No change to the existing requirements)

Exception: Wiring methods and cabling systems, listed for use in other spaces used for environmental air (plenums), shall be permitted to be installed in ducts specifically fabricated for environmental air-handling purposes under the following conditions:

(1) The wiring methods or cabling systems shall be permitted only if necessary to connect to equipment or devices associated with the direct action upon or sensing of the contained air, and

(2) The total length of such wiring methods or cabling systems shall not exceed 1.2 m (4 ft).

(See NEC for actual text)

Change Summary

- A new exception in 300.22(B), correlates requirements for wiring in ducts specifically fabricated for environmental air between the *NEC* and NFPA 90A.
- NFPA 90A permits cables that are "directly associated with the air distribution system" and not to "exceed four feet."
- This revision correlates existing requirements within the *NEC*. For example, in Chapter 8, first level subdivision 800.113(B) contains the same permission.

FR: 614
SR: None

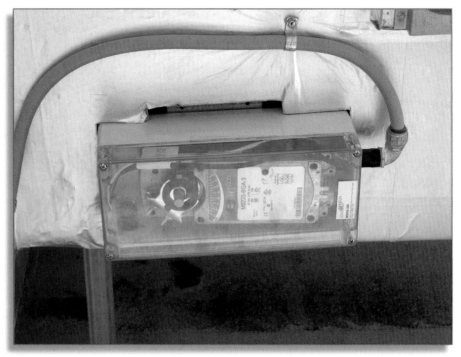

Significance of the Change

A new exception is added in first level subdivision 300.22(B) to correlate requirements for wiring in ducts specifically fabricated for environmental air between the *NEC* and NFPA 90A *Standard for Installation of Air-Conditioning and Ventilating Systems*. First level subdivision 300.22(B) covers all spaces that are constructed primarily for moving air such as metal duct. First level subdivision 300.22(C) covers "other spaces" used to move air that are not built for that purpose alone such as the space above a lay-in type ceiling used for return air. NFPA 90A has purview over all products installed in ducts or plenums. Requirements in NFPA 90A permit very limited amounts of cabling inside a duct for only cables that are "directly associated with the air distribution system and does not exceed four feet." Additionally, NFPA 90A requires such cabling to be "as short as practicable." This new exception permits only cable/wiring methods listed for the use in lengths not to exceed a total amount of four feet only where connected to equipment or devices associated with the movement of air.

This new exception is necessary to correlate between the *NEC* and NFPA 90A and to correlate existing requirements within the *NEC*. For example, in Chapter 8, first level subdivision 800.113(B) already permits the limited amount of cabling inside of ducts in correlation with NFPA 90A.

Ampacity Adjustment Factors

Photo from iStock

Significance of the Change

The requirements for derating ampacity of conductors exposed to direct sunlight on rooftops has been significantly revised. Table 310.15(B)(3)(c) is deleted and the requirement to derate for ampacity on rooftops is revised to apply only to raceways or cables that are closer to the roof surface than 7/8 inch. There was significant technical substantiation in a public input provided to support this revision by a task group appointed by the *NEC* Correlating Committee. The substantiation provided significant data to prove that the original acceptance of this requirement was flawed. The data submitted to support this revision included: (1) the fact that the existing ampacity tables (310.16) were developed (1890s) prior to the introduction of modern insulation types currently being used, (2) proof that the heat inside a raceway insulates it from solar radiation, the thermal effects of rooftop installations are not additive. A raceway placed directly on the rooftop will have higher internal temperatures.

The ampacity values we use today are extremely conservative. New insulation types perform far better than the old "code grade rubber" upon which the original ampacity values were based. It is also significant that there has never been any data submitted that there was damage or failure of conductors exposed to sunlight on rooftops.

Code Language

310.15(B) Tables

(3) Adjustment Factors

(c) Raceways and Cables Exposed to Sunlight on Rooftops. Where raceways or cables are exposed to direct sunlight on or above rooftops, raceways or cables shall be installed a minimum distance above the roof to the bottom of the raceway or cable of 23 mm (7/8 in.). Where the distance above the roof to the bottom of the raceway is less than 23 mm (7/8 in.), a temperature adder of 33°C (60°F) shall be added to the outdoor temperature to determine the applicable ambient temperature for application of the correction factors in Table 310.15(B)(2)(a) or Table 310.15(B)(2)(b).

Exception: Type XHHW-2 insulated conductors shall not be subject to this ampacity adjustment.

Informational Note: One source for the ambient temperatures in various locations is the ASHRAE Handbook — Fundamentals.

Table 310.15(B)(3)(c) is *DELETED*

(See NEC for actual text)

Change Summary

- Table 310.15(B)(3)(c) for rooftop temperature adders is deleted.
- Raceways or cables must be installed a minimum distance of 7/8 inch above the roof.
- Where less than 7/8 inch above the roof to the bottom of the raceway or cable add a temperature adder of 60°F.

FR: 1503

SR: None

Single-Phase Dwelling Services and Feeders

Code Language

310.15(B) Tables

(7) Single-Phase Dwelling Services and Feeders.

For one-family dwellings and the individual dwelling units of two-family and multifamily dwellings, single-phase feeder conductors consisting of 2 ungrounded conductors and the neutral conductor from a 208Y/120 volt system shall be permitted to be sized in accordance with 310.15(B)(7)(1) through (3).

(No change (1) through (4))

Where correction or adjustment factors are required by 310.15(B)(2) or (3), they shall be permitted to be applied to the ampacity associated with the temperature rating of the conductor.

(See NEC for actual text)

Change Summary

- 310.15(B)(7) is no longer limited to 120/240-volt systems, single-phase 120/208-volt systems are now included.
- Single-phase feeders from a 208Y/120-volt system are permitted to use 310.15(B)(7)(1) through (3).
- Correction or adjustment factors in 310.15(B)(2) or (3) are permitted to be applied to the ampacity associated with the temperature rating of the conductor.

FR: 1503
SR: 1505

Significance of the Change

Second level subdivision 310.15(B)(7) permits the installation of reduced ampacity service and feeder conductors under specified conditions in dwelling units. Service/feeder conductors supplying the entire load associated with a one-family dwelling, or the service/feeder conductors supplying the entire load associated with an individual dwelling unit in a two-family or multifamily dwelling, are permitted to have an ampacity not less than 83 percent of the service or feeder rating. This permissive requirement is no longer limited to single-phase 120/240-volt systems. This revision will permit a reduction in conductor size where single-phase 208Y/120-volt services and feeders are installed. Correlation is now achieved with the *Canadian Electrical Code*, which allows reduced conductor sizes for single dwellings, apartments and similar buildings for both 120/240- and 208Y/120-volt service/feeder conductors. The load diversity in residential applications is similar whether the residence is fed with 120/240- or 208Y/120-volts.

A new last sentence is added to clarify that temperature and correction factors in 310.15(B)(2) and 310.15(B)(3)(a), should be applied to the conductor temperature rating and not the ampacity in the temperature column associated with the equipment termination values. Informational note No. 1 is revised for clarity referencing standard ampacity ratings from 240.6(A).

Power Monitoring Equipment

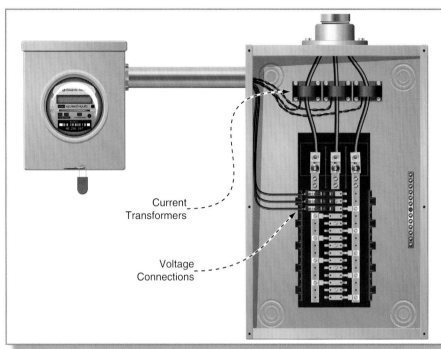

Current Transformers

Voltage Connections

Code Language

312.8 Switch and Overcurrent Device Enclosures

(B) Power Monitoring Equipment. The wiring space of enclosures for switches or overcurrent devices shall be permitted to contain power monitoring equipment where all of the following conditions are met:

(1) The power monitoring equipment is identified as a field installable accessory as part of the listed equipment or is a listed kit evaluated for field installation in switch or overcurrent device enclosures.

(2) The total area of all conductors, splices, taps, and equipment at any cross section of the wiring space does not exceed 75 percent of the cross-sectional area of that space.

(See NEC for actual text)

Significance of the Change

Section 312.8 is separated into two first level subdivisions. The previous requirement addressed only switch and overcurrent device enclosures with splices, taps, and feed-through conductors and permitted them to be installed provided they met the fill and marking requirements. This revision recognizes that there is power monitoring equipment listed for use in switch or overcurrent device enclosures. This would include but not be limited to equipment for automation, monitoring, controlling, metering, and energy management.

New first level subdivision 312.8(A) addresses devices and equipment installed in switch and overcurrent device enclosures used for splices, taps, and feed-through conductors.

This new requirement in 312.8(B) mandates that the power monitoring equipment to be installed must be "identified as a field installable accessory as part of the listed equipment," or is a "listed kit evaluated for field installation in the specific equipment." This means that all power monitoring equipment for installation in a panelboard, for example, must be identified for that use and in a panelboard. The new requirement also mandates that where power monitoring equipment is installed in switch or overcurrent device enclosures, the total area of all conductors, splices, taps, and power monitoring equipment at any cross section of the wiring space cannot exceed 75 percent of the cross-sectional area of that space.

Change Summary

- Section 312.8 is separated into first level subdivisions for clarity.

- New 312.8(B) provides requirements for power monitoring equipment installed in switch and overcurrent device enclosures other than those used for splices, taps, and feed-through conductors.

- This equipment must be identified as a field installable accessory as part of the listed equipment, or is a listed kit evaluated for field installation in switch or overcurrent device enclosures.

FR: 2404
SR: 2401

314.15

Article 314 Outlet, Device, Pull, and Junction Boxes; Conduit Bodies;...

Part II Installation

REVISION

Damp or Wet Locations

Code Language

314.15 Damp or Wet Locations... Approved drainage openings not smaller than 3 mm (⅛ in.) and not larger than 6 mm (¼ in.) in diameter shall be permitted to be installed in the field in boxes or conduit bodies listed for use in damp or wet locations. For installation of listed drain fittings, larger openings are permitted to be installed in the field in accordance with manufacturer's instructions.

(See NEC for actual text)

Courtesy of Thomas & Betts a member of the ABB Group

Change Summary

- Approved drainage openings are permitted to be installed in boxes or conduit bodies that are listed for use in damp or wet locations.
- Approved drainage openings must not be smaller than ⅛ inch.
- Approved drainage openings must not be larger than ¼ inch.

Significance of the Change

Section 314.15 was revised in the 2014 *NEC* cycle with new text that recognized and permitted field installed drainage openings provided they were approved. This permitted the installer to create drainage openings in boxes or conduit bodies that are listed for use in damp or wet locations. Drainage holes may also be installed by the manufacturer in boxes or conduit bodies that are listed for use in damp or wet locations. In 2014, a maximum size drainage opening was provided at ¼ inch. This revision now places a minimum size drainage opening of ⅛ inch to comply with applicable standards because smaller holes can become blocked by debris over time and the necessary drainage openings get clogged. This section does permit a larger hole to be installed where listed drain fittings are installed in accordance with manufacturers instructions.

FR: 2405
SR: None

314.16(A)

Article 314 Outlet, Device, Pull, and Junction Boxes; Conduit Bodies;...

Part II Installation

REVISION

Box Volume Calculations

Code Language

314.16(A) Box Volume Calculations... (See *NEC* Text) Where a box is provided with one or more securely installed barriers, the volume shall be apportioned to each of the resulting spaces. Each barrier, if not marked with its volume, shall be considered to take up 8.2 cm³ (½ in³) if metal, and 16.4 cm³ (1.0 in³) if nonmetallic.

(B) Box Fill Calculations... Each space within a box installed with a barrier shall be calculated separately.

(See NEC for actual text)

Significance of the Change

This revision now addresses box volume calculations for boxes that contain internal barriers. Internal barriers are installed for multiple reasons such as to separate conductors of different systems or where required due to voltage between devices in 404.8(B) and 406.5(H). The revised text in first level subdivision 314.16(A) requires that a box with a barrier(s) installed have the volume calculated on the resulting spaces. For example, if six single-gang old work boxes are ganged together and two barriers are installed on both ends of the ganged box for single devices, there are three resulting spaces, two single-gang and a four-gang space. Additionally each barrier that is not marked with its volume (nonmetallic barriers typically are marked and steel are not) now has a required volume of ½ in³ for metal and 1 in³ for nonmetallic barriers. This revision now addresses resulting spaces in boxes without revisions to Table 314.16(A). A new last sentence in 314.16(B) for box fill calculations requires that each space within a box installed with a barrier, be calculated separately.

Box fill for conductors, clamps, fittings and devices must now be calculated on each resulting space where barriers are present. In the body of Table 314.16(A) the term *gang* is deleted to ensure that the *Code* user does not calculate on the total space of ganged boxes.

Change Summary

- 314.16 now specifically addresses box volume calculations for boxes that contain internal barriers.
- Barriers not marked with its volume, are calculated at ½ in³ for metal and 1 in³ for nonmetallic barriers.
- The term *gang* is deleted in Table 314.16(A) to ensure that the *Code* user does not calculate on the total space of ganged boxes.

FR: 2406
SR: None

Nails and Screws for Box Support

Code Language

314.23 Supports

(B) Structural Mounting.

(1) Nails and Screws. Nails and screws, where used as a fastening means, shall secure boxes by using brackets on the outside of the enclosure, or by using mounting holes in the back or in a single side of the enclosure, or they shall pass through the interior within 6 mm (¼ in.) of the back ends of the enclosure. Screws shall not be permitted to pass through the box unless exposed threads in the box are protected using approved means to avoid abrasion of conductor insulation. Mounting holes made in the field shall be approved.

(See NEC for actual text)

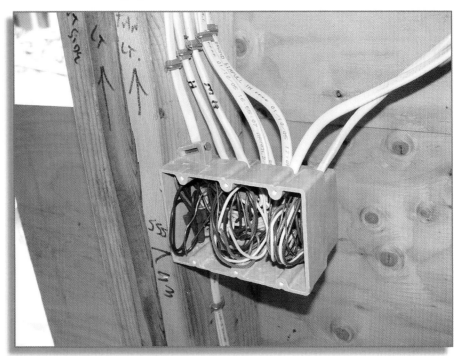

Change Summary

- Mounting holes made in the field shall be approved, the AHJ must evaluate for suitability.
- Brackets on the outside of boxes and manufacturer made mounting holes are required to be used.

Significance of the Change

The use of nails and screws to secure boxes is revised for clarity. The previous text required that the nails or screws be secured by brackets. The intent here is to secure the box, and the revised text corrects that error and provides additional clarity. Boxes are required to be secured by:

(1) brackets on the outside of the enclosure, typical for both plastic and metal boxes

(2) using mounting holes in the back or in a single side of the enclosure, note that these are holes provided by the box manufacturer

(3) passing through the interior within 6 mm (¼ in.) of the back ends of the enclosure, typical for a nail-on plastic box

The requirement to protect exposed threads passing through a box is retained in order to prevent abrasion to the conductor insulation. A new last sentence is added to require that mounting holes made in the field must be approved. This means the AHJ must evaluate the mounting holes to ensure that suitable support is provided. Drilling holes in metal boxes for support will not create much concern, but the manufacturers of plastic boxes discourage drilling your own mounting holes.

FR: 2410
SR: 2405

314.27(E)

Article 314 Outlet, Device, Pull, and Junction Boxes; Conduit Bodies;...

Part II Installation

NEW

Outlet Boxes with Separable Attachment Fittings

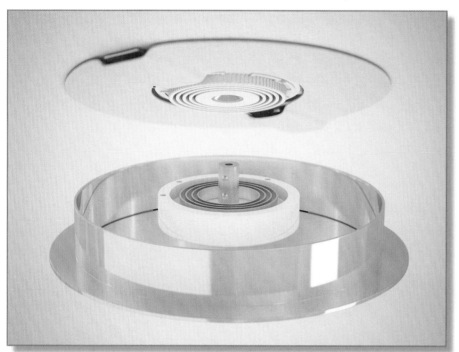

Courtesy of Safety Quick Lighting and Fans Corp.

Code Language

314.27 Outlet Boxes.

(E) Separable Attachment Fittings.
Outlet boxes required in 314.27 shall be permitted to support listed locking support and mounting receptacles used in combination with compatible attachment fittings. The combination shall be identified for the support of equipment within the weight and mounting orientation limits of the listing. Where the supporting receptacle is installed within a box, it shall be included in the fill calculation covered in 314.16(B)(4).

(See NEC for actual text)

Significance of the Change

A new first level subdivision 314.27(E) is added to recognize a new type of separable plug and receptacle assembly for fixed equipment mounted on outlet boxes. These new devices are listed; as power supply devices, listed locking support, through listed receptacles and supporting means. These devices are designed to be installed in or to boxes designed for the purpose and are now permitted to be used for all types of luminaires, ceiling-suspended paddle fans and more. This new product is designed to facilitate quick and easy interchange of luminaires or ceiling mounted paddle fans. As incorporated into section 314.27, this new requirement is permissive in nature. This revision now recognizes this new technology and permits the use of these listed devices but does not require they be installed.

It is not unusual for a new product to make it into the *NEC* before being made available to the public. In order for a manufacturer to sell an electrical product that incorporates new technology or methods there are multiple hurdles to overcome. Typically the product must be listed by a research and testing laboratory to ensure that it is safe for the intended use. In some cases it is also necessary to address one or more sections in the *NEC* to specifically permit the use of the product as seen with the new text in 314.27(E).

Change Summary

- New 314.27(E) permits a new product known as a "separable attachment fitting."
- This new product is a listed locking support and mounting receptacle used in combination with compatible attachment fittings designed for the support of luminaires, paddle fans and other utilization equipment.
- These new devices are designed to facilitate quick and easy interchange of luminaires or other equipment.

FR: 2411
SR: 2406

314.28(A)(3)

Article 314 Outlet, Device, Pull, and Junction Boxes; Conduit Bodies;...

Part II Installation

REVISION

Minimum Size of Pull and Junction Boxes and Conduit Bodies

Code Language

314.28 Pull and Junction Boxes and Conduit Bodies

(A) Minimum Size.

(3) Smaller Dimensions... For other conductor sizes and combinations, the total cross-sectional area of the fill shall not exceed the cross-section area of the conductors specified in the marking, based on the type of conductor identified as part of the product listing.

Informational Note: Unless otherwise specified, the applicable product standards evaluate the fill markings covered here based on conductors with Type XHHW insulation.

(See NEC for actual text)

Change Summary

- 314.28(A)(3) is modified to permit conductor installation in conduit bodies based on the total cross-sectional area of the fill.
- Markings on conduit bodies are based on how applicable product standards evaluate the fill.
- Markings covered here are typically based on conductors with Type XHHW insulation.

FR: 2412
SR: None

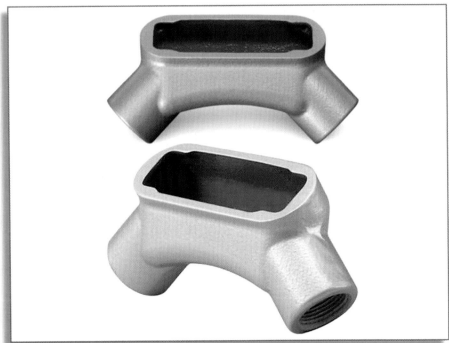

Courtesy of Thomas and Betts

Significance of the Change

Section 314.28 provides requirements for pull/junction boxes and conduit bodies. First level subdivision 314.28(A) provides minimum size requirements for pull/junction boxes and conduit bodies used for spices or straight, angle and U pulls. 314.28(A)(3) addresses minimum size requirements for listed boxes and conduit bodies with dimensions less than those required in 314.28(A)(1) & (2). This requirement was significantly modified in the 2014 *NEC* with respect to listed conduit bodies. These conduit bodies are typically marked for only one size of conductor and in most cases for a maximum of three conductors. This creates an issue for both the installer and AHJ where multiple circuits and three or four wire circuits with equipment grounding conductors result in four, five or more conductors exceeding the conduit body markings. Some conduit bodies are permitted by the manufacturer to be used for many other combinations of both the number and size of conductors in the listing for the conduit body. This revision now permits the installation of conductors in the conduit body where the total cross-sectional area of the fill does not exceed the cross-section area of the conductors specified in the marking, based on the type of conductor identified as part of the product listing. A new informational note informs the *Code* user that typical product standard evaluations and subsequent markings are based on the use of conductors with type XHHW insulation.

Power Distribution Blocks, Line Side of Service Equipment

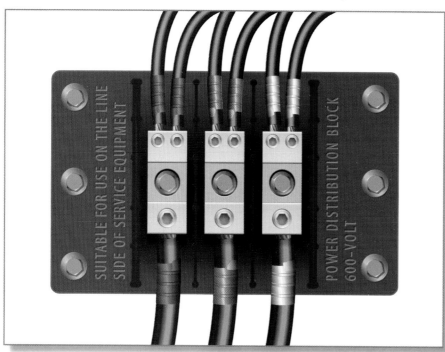

Code Language

314.28 Pull and Junction Boxes and Conduit Bodies

(E) Power Distribution Blocks.

(1) Installation. Power distribution blocks installed in boxes shall be listed. Power distribution blocks installed on the line side of the service equipment shall be listed and marked "suitable for use on the line side of service equipment" or equivalent.

(See NEC for actual text)

Significance of the Change

In the 2014 *NEC* revision cycle, a new requirement was added in first level subdivision 376.56(B) to mandate that power distribution blocks "installed on the line side of the service equipment shall be listed for the purpose." This revision only impacted power distribution blocks installed on the line side of the service in "metal wireways." Subsequent to that action, the Outline of Investigation for "Power Distribution Blocks", in the UL 1953 Standard, was modified to reflect the requirements necessary to apply power distribution blocks on the line side of service equipment. This revision to the product standard was not limited to the use of power distribution blocks installed on the line side of the service equipment in wireways only.

This revision will now require power distribution blocks installed on the line side of the service equipment in any pull or junction box to be listed and marked "suitable for use on the line side of service equipment" or equivalent. It is significant that in addition to the listing requirement that this revision mandates the power distribution blocks be marked for use on the line side of service equipment.

Electrical equipment that is listed must be labeled or marked to identify it is listed. In this case, the labeling or marking is expanded to clarify to the installer and AHJ the product is suitable for the application.

Change Summary

- The use of power distribution blocks for SE conductors in pull or junction boxes is modified.
- Power distribution blocks installed on the line side of the service equipment must be listed and marked accordingly.
- UL 1953 has been modified to reflect the requirements necessary to apply power distribution blocks on the line side of service equipment.

FR: 2413
SR: 2407

Listing Requirements

Code Language

3XX.6 Listing Requirements. Type AC, FC, MV, MC, MI, TC, & SE cable and associated fittings shall be listed. (Additional text in 330.6)

(See NEC for actual text)

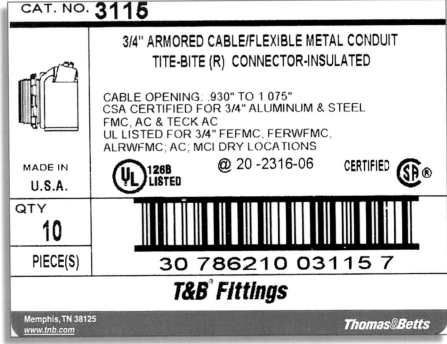

CAT. NO. **3115**

3/4" ARMORED CABLE/FLEXIBLE METAL CONDUIT
TITE-BITE (R) CONNECTOR-INSULATED

CABLE OPENING: .930" TO 1.075"
CSA CERTIFIED FOR 3/4" ALUMINUM & STEEL
FMC, AC & TECK AC
UL LISTED FOR 3/4" FEFMC, FERWFMC,
ALRWFMC; AC; MCI DRY LOCATIONS

MADE IN U.S.A.

UL 126B LISTED   @ 20 -2316-06   CERTIFIED (SA)®

QTY **10** PIECE(S)

30 786210 031157

T&B® Fittings

Memphis, TN 38125
www.tnb.com

Thomas&Betts

Courtesy of Thomas & Betts a member of the ABB Group

Change Summary

- Type AC, FC, MV, MC, MI, TC, & SE cables are now required to be listed.
- This includes all associated fittings used in the installation of these cable assemblies.
- The *NEC* does not require cable assemblies, raceways, fittings or other equipment to be listed unless a specific requirement exists.

Significance of the Change

The *NEC* does not require cable assemblies, raceways, fittings or other equipment to be listed unless a specific requirement exists. Cable assembly, raceway and other Articles in the *NEC* used a standard section numbering format. For example, 3XX.6 Listing Requirements, makes it easy for *Code* users to quickly find requirements. Types AC, FC, MV, MC, MI, TC, & SE cables and all associated fittings, are now required to be listed. While listed cable assemblies and fittings were common before this requirement, it was not mandated or enforceable by the AHJ. This permitted non-listed products to be installed creating potential problems with cable compatibility with fittings, insulation types, metal/nonmetallic jackets, terminations and construction of the cable. Additionally, the lack of listing allowed the use of associated fittings with non-listed cable assemblies that were not designed for the purpose, creating potential problems.

Listing of these cable assemblies means that they must comply with the recognized product standard. First level subdivision 110.3(B) requires all listed and labeled fittings to be installed in accordance with their listing and labeling. All listed products, without regard to an *NEC* requirement for listing, are subject to installation in accordance with listing/labeling per 110.3(B).

FRs: 1808, 1801, 1814, 1816, 1806, 1833, 1827
SR: None

Securing and Supporting

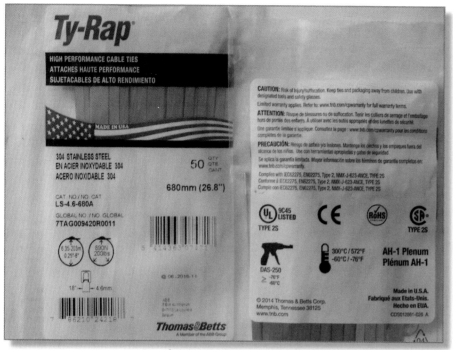

Courtesy of Thomas & Betts a member of the ABB Group

Code Language

3XX.30 Securing and Supporting

(A) General. Type AC cable shall be supported and secured by staples; cable ties listed, and identified for securement and support; straps, hangers, or similar fittings, or other approved means designed and installed so as not to damage the cable.

(See NEC for actual text)

Significance of the Change

This revision impacts the use of cable ties (ty-wraps) for multiple types of cable assemblies, flexible conduit and flexible tubing, including, Type AC in 320.30(A), Type MC in 330.30(A), Type NM in 334.30, FMC in 348.30(A), LFMC in 350.30(A), LFNMC in 356.30, and ENT in 362.30(A). The only type cable ties permitted for securing and supporting are listed cable ties identified as Type 2S or Type 21S. The "S" suffix for these cable ties means they are recognized for "securement and support." Additionally, the cable assemblies, flexible conduit and flexible tubing addressed in this revision may also be supported by "other approved means". This permits many other types of support acceptable to the AHJ.

The applicable product standard, *UL 62275 Cable Ties for Electrical Installations,* was recently published and became effective on 6/1/2014. This new product standard establishes a classification system of cable tie "Type designators" to assist those who specify, installers and AHJ's. Cable ties identified as Type 2S or Type 21S are recognized in the standard as capable of providing "securement and support" in accordance with the requirements of cable assemblies, flexible conduits, and flexible tubing at maximum spacing intervals as required by the *NEC*. The standard requires markings that identify what the cable tie is capable of and how it should be used. The markings include permitted operating temperatures, resistance to ultraviolet light for outdoor installations and securement and support capabilities.

Change Summary

- Cable ties used to support cable assemblies, flexible conduit and flexible tubing must be listed and identified for support.

- This includes types AC, MC, NM cable assemblies, types FMC, LFMC, and LFNMC flexible conduits and type ENT flexible tubing.

- Type 2S and Type 21S cable ties meet this requirement. The "S" suffix for these cable ties means they are recognized for "securement and support."

FRs: 1809, 1821, 1830, 2166, 2170, 2104, 2115
SRs: 1802, 1807, 1811

Listed and Labeling Requirements

Code Language

Proposed Revision:

324.6 Listing Requirements. Type FCC cable and associated fittings shall be listed and labeled.

Revision Reversal:

324.6 Listing Requirements. Type FCC cable and associated fittings shall be listed.

(See NEC for actual text)

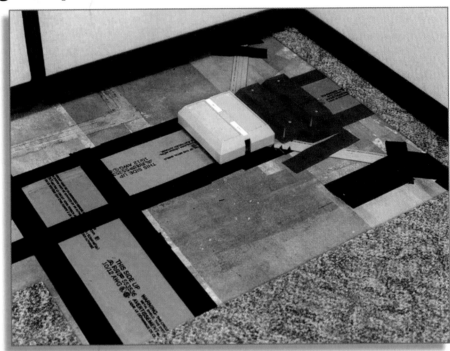

Change Summary

- Several public inputs and subsequent comments added the words "and labeled" after the word "listed" throughout the *NEC*.
- Some committees accepted the revisions and comments and some did not, which would have resulted in significant inconsistencies and confusion.
- The *NEC* Correlating Committee directed that the term *and labeled* after *listed* as proposed be deleted, returning to previous 2014 *NEC* text.

FR: CC 143
SCR: 119

Significance of the Change

In the first revision stage of the 2017 *NEC* development process several public inputs (revisions) and subsequent public comments were submitted to add the term *and labeled* after the word *listed* to existing listing requirements throughout the *NEC*. Such global revisions would have added more restrictive and impractical requirements that were inconsistent with product safety standards relative to how listed (certified) products could be marked or identified. Many small products are difficult to mark with product certification marks. Product safety standards allow for various methods to achieve evidence (marking) of certification or listing. Inconsistent actions of the *NEC* Code-Making Panels on these public inputs and subsequent comments would have created conflicts and several inconsistencies throughout the *NEC*. Another problem would have been the proper correlation with other NFPA standards that use the same term(s). The Correlating Committee recognizes that the terms *listed* and *labeled* are defined in Article 100, but are not used consistently throughout the *NEC*. Accordingly, an appropriately staffed task group has been assigned to review this issue as it impacts the entire *NEC* and potentially other NFPA standards, as well as other industry standards beyond the control of NFPA.

Installation of Type MV Cable

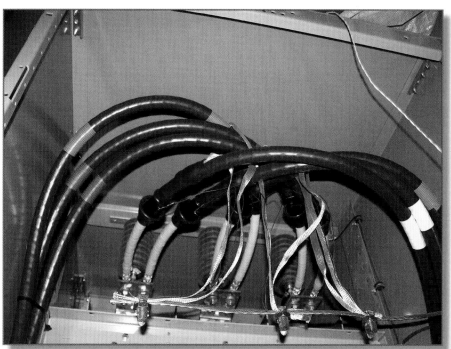

Code Language

328.14 Installation. Type MV cable shall be installed, terminated, and tested by qualified persons.

Informational Note: *Information about accepted industry practices and installation procedures for medium-voltage cable are described in ANSI/NECA/NCSCB 600-2014, Standard for Installing and Maintaining Medium-Voltage Cable and in IEEE 576-2000, Recommended Practice for Installation, Termination, and Testing of Insulated Power Cables as Used in Industrial and Commercial Applications.*

(See NEC for actual text)

Significance of the Change

Section 328.14 requires that type MV cable shall be installed, terminated, and tested by qualified persons.

A qualified person is one who has skills and knowledge related to the construction and operation of the electrical equipment and installations and has received safety training to recognize and avoid the hazards involved. Type MV cable requires specific methods of handling, installation and termination. This revision adds a reference to NECA 600-2014 to the existing informational note. NECA/NCSCB 600-2014 *Standard for Installing and Maintaining Medium Voltage Cable* contains essential installation requirements and guidelines for qualified installers. NECA/NCSCB 600-2014 is one standard that serves as a basis for cable splicing and termination certifications. This information is extremely useful to installers and those maintaining or testing Type MV cable installations. NECA 600 should be part of the required training for all "qualified persons" that install, terminate and test Type MV cable.

This revised informational note now references both NECA 600-2014 and IEEE 576-2000 to provide users with valuable information to assist in these types of installations.

Change Summary

- 328.14 requires that type MV cable shall be installed, terminated, and tested by qualified persons.

- NECA 600-2014, *Standard for Installing and Maintaining Medium-Voltage Cable* is added to the existing informational note.

- NECA 600-2014 provides the *Code* user with valuable information on installation requirements, guidelines for qualified installers, cable slicing, required termination certifications and cable testing criteria.

FR: 1819
SR: None

Support of Type MV Cable

Code Language

328.30 Support. Type MV cable terminated in equipment, or installed in pull boxes, or in vaults shall be secured and supported by metallic or nonmetallic supports suitable to withstand the weight, by cable ties listed and identified for securement and support, or other approved means, at intervals not exceeding 1.5 m (5 ft) from terminations or a maximum of 1.8 m (6 ft) between supports.

(See NEC for actual text)

Courtesy of Burlington Electrical Testing

Change Summary

- A new section 328.30 now provides support requirements for type MV cable.
- Type MV cable terminated in equipment, installed in pull boxes, or in vaults shall be secured and supported by metallic or nonmetallic supports suitable to withstand the weight, by listed cable ties or other approved means.
- Type MV cable must be supported at intervals not exceeding five feet from terminations or a maximum six feet between supports.

FR: 1815
SR: 1805

Significance of the Change

This new section now provides installers and the AHJ with requirements for support of type MV cable. Previous editions of the *NEC* did not provide any requirements for support of type MV cable. The only requirement that impacted support for type MV was installation in a neat and workmanlike manner in 110.12.

This new requirement mandates support of type MV cable at intervals not exceeding five feet from terminations or a maximum six feet between supports. This will impact all type MV cable installations in pull boxes, cable vaults, manholes and all other equipment. The required means of support is through cable ties listed and identified for securement and support or other approved means. The support must be suitable to withstand the weight of the cable. Where cable ties are used they must be listed and identified as Type 2S or Type 21S as these types are recognized in the new cable tie standard as being capable of providing "securement and support."

This requirement is necessary to ensure type MV installations are installed in a neat and workmanlike manner to ensure the performance of the cable and for safety. It is important to also note that section 328.14 requires that type MV cable, be installed by qualified persons. The informational note for 328.14 now references both NECA 600-2014 and IEEE 576-2000 to provide users with valuable information to assist in these types of installations.

Exposed Work, Type MC Cable

Code Language

330.15 Exposed Work. Exposed runs of cable, except as provided in 300.11(A), shall closely follow the surface of the building finish or of running boards. Exposed runs shall also be permitted to be installed on the underside of joists where supported at each joist and located so as not to be subject to physical damage.

(See NEC for actual text)

Significance of the Change

A new section 330.15 is added into Article 330 to address the installation of type MC cable where it is exposed. This new requirement correlates with similar provisions found in Article 320 for type AC cable and in Article 334 for type NM cable. This revised text now mandates that exposed runs of cable closely follow the surface of the building finish or of running boards except where installed as provided in 300.11(A), which permits independent support wires that are installed in addition to any supporting a ceiling where the support wires are secured at both ends. Additionally, this new requirement permits exposed runs, where not subject to physical damage, to be installed on the underside of joists where supported at each joist.

It is imperative to note that the term *exposed* (as applied to wiring methods) is defined in article 100 as follows:

Article 100: Exposed (as applied to wiring methods). On or attached to the surface or behind panels designed to allow access.

This revision provides necessary correlation for similar wiring methods with prescriptive requirements for exposed installations of type MC cable.

Change Summary

- New section 330.15 addresses exposed runs of type MC cable.
- Except as provided in 300.11(A), type MC cable must closely follow the surface of the building finish or of running boards.
- Exposed runs of type MC cable not to be subject to physical damage, are permitted to be installed on the underside of joists where supported at each joist.

FR: 1820
SR: None

Uses Permitted, Cable Tray and Industrial

Code Language

336.10 Uses Permitted. Type TC cable shall be permitted to be used as follows:

(2) In cable trays, including those with mechanically discontinuous segments up to 300 mm (1 ft)

(7) Between a cable tray and the utilization equipment or device(s), provided all of the following apply:

(Existing text of 336.10(7), along with modifications, is separated into six list items)

(See NEC for actual text)

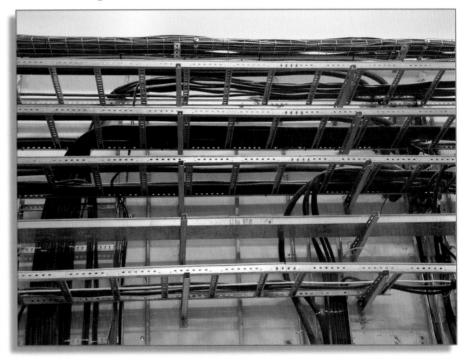

Change Summary

- Type TC cable is permitted to be installed in cable tray including those cable trays with mechanically discontinuous segments up to a distance of one foot.
- Only type TC-ER is permitted to be used for industrial installations in 336.10(7).
- The application of the existing exception is clarified and applies only to 336.10(7).

Significance of the Change

List item (2) section 336.10 is revised to clarify that type TC cable is now permitted to be installed in cable tray including those cable trays with mechanically discontinuous segments up to a distance of one foot. First level subdivision 392.18(A) requires cable tray to maintain electrical continuity but permits complete cable tray installations to have mechanically discontinuous segments between cable tray runs or between cable tray and equipment.

List item (7) in section 336.10 which addresses only industrial installations and permitted cable length from cable tray to utilization equipment is revised and also editorially separated into six list items for clarity. The first list item is new and requires that the cable be type TC-ER. The "ER" suffix stands for "exposed run" and identifies TC cables that meet additional crush and impact test requirements. The existing exception that allows Type TC-ER cable to transition between cable trays and between cable trays and utilization equipment or devices for a distance not to exceed six feet without continuous support is retained with added clarity due to placement and retitling as "Exception to (7)."

FR: 1832
SR: None

Uses Permitted, Dwelling Unit Generator Installations

Courtesy of Bob Cramer, Generac Power Systems Inc.

Code Language

336.10 Uses Permitted.

(9) In one- and two-family dwelling units, Type TC-ER cable containing both power and control conductors that is identified for pulling through structural members shall be permitted. Type TC-ER cable used as interior wiring shall be installed per the requirements of Part II of Article 334.

Exception: Where used to connect a generator and associated equipment having terminals rated 75°C (140°F) or higher, the cable shall not be limited in ampacity by 334.80 or 340.80.

Informational Note: TC-ER cable that is suitable for pulling through structural members is marked "JP."

Informational Note No. 2: See 725.136 for limitations on Class 2 or 3 circuits contained within the same cable with conductors of electric light, power, or Class 1 circuits.

(See NEC for actual text)

Significance of the Change

A new list item (9) is added to section 336.10 for permitted use of type TC-ER cable. This new list item recognizes the use of type TC-ER in only one and two family dwelling units where the cable contains both power and control conductors and is identified for pulling through structural members. This means that the TC-ER cable must be additionally marked with the acronym "JP." A new informational note is also added to clarify that type TC-ER cables marked with the acronym "JP" are suitable for pulling through structural members.

Where type TC-ER cable is installed as interior wiring, it must be installed per the requirements of Part II of Article 334 for type NM cable. Type TC-ER meets the crush and impact requirements of metal-clad cable. The suffix "ER" is for exposed run.

This revision recognizes a new UL listed Type TC-ER cable that contains both power and control conductors for generator feeder and control conductors for the installation of a standby generator in an optional standby system. The feeder and control conductors are permitted to occupy the same cable where they meet the requirements of 300.3(C)(1) which requires all conductors to be insulated for the maximum voltage applied to any conductor in the cable assembly.

Change Summary

- New list item (9) in 336.10 permits type TC-ER cable containing both power and control conductors to be used in one and two family dwelling units where marked with the acronym "JP"; suitable for pulling through structural members.

- Where used in accordance with the exception 334.80 or 340.80 do not apply to TC-ER cable as applied in 336.10(9).

FR: 1840
SR: 1808

NEW

Uses Permitted, Hazardous Locations

Code Language

336.10 Uses Permitted. Type TC cable shall be permitted to be used as follows:

(11) In hazardous (classified) locations where specifically permitted by other articles in this *Code*. For Class I, Division 1 and Zone 1 locations only, Type TC cable used for other than flexible connections shall also comply with the following:

a. The cable jacket and construction shall be evaluated and listed for the specific hazardous materials present in the location,

b. The hazardous material group(s) evaluated shall be marked on the cable,

c. The cable diameter shall be limited to 1" or smaller,

d. The cable shall be permitt[ed] for voltages of 150 volts [or less and currents of] less, and

e. The cable sha[ll] "-ER" and "-H[L"]

(See NEC [...])

Change Sum[mary]

- New 501.10(A)(1)(f) [...] use of Type TC-ER-HL [in] Class 1 Division 1 locatio[n]

- New list item (11) provides pre-scriptive limitations for the use of Type TC cable in hazardous locations.

[...]itted for use in Class 1 Division 1 and [...] 501.10(A)(1)(f) and 505.15(B)(1)(i). Ar-[...]nd Control Cable: Type TC, known as tray [...] designates the cable as meeting the crush and [...] of Type MC cable and "HL" designates permitted [...]s (classified) locations. The 2014 *NEC* permitted [...]HL in Class 1 Zone 1 locations and this is expanded to [...]vision 1 locations in 2017. This revision in 336.10 Uses Per-[...]s necessary to provide the *Code* user with prescriptive limita-[...] or safe use of TC cable. Cable jackets and construction must [...]isted for the specific hazardous materials present in the location [...]with the hazardous material group(s) evaluated marked on the cable. [...]The maximum TC-ER-HL cable diameter is 1-inch. Cables marked with the suffixes "-ER" and "-HL" have voltage limitations of 150 volts to ground or less with currents of 30 amps or less.

It is imperative that cable jackets be evaluated and listed for the specific hazardous materials present in the location because many hazardous materials that may be present can have an adverse effect on commercially available jacketing materials.

This was overturned by floor action.

FR: None
SR: 1809

Installation Methods for Branch Circuits and Feeders, Interior

Code Language

338.10(B) Branch Circuits or Feeders.

(4) Installation Methods for Branch Circuits and Feeders.

(a) *Interior Installations...* (See *NEC* text) For Type SE cable with ungrounded conductor sizes 10 AWG and smaller, where installed in thermal insulation, the ampacity shall be in accordance with 60°C (140°F) conductor temperature rating. The maximum conductor temperature rating shall be permitted to be used for ampacity adjustment and correction purposes, if the final derated ampacity does not exceed that for a 60°C (140°F) rated conductor.

(See NEC for actual text)

Significance of the Change

Second level subdivision 338.10(B)(4) provides requirements for type SE cable used as a branch circuit or feeder in an interior installation. The previous requirement limited the ampacity of SE cables installed in thermal insulation, without regard to conductor size, to the 60°C conductor temperature rating. Type SE cable is typically listed at 75°C and is constructed with 90°C insulated conductors. This revision now limits the requirement for type SE installed in insulation to conductors sizes 10 AWG and smaller only. Larger size SE cable installed in thermal insulation is no longer limited to an ampacity in the 60°C column and can be applied at 75°C rating. Type SE cable is commonly available in copper 8 AWG and larger and aluminum 6 AWG and larger. The smaller sizes of type SE cable, where used in interior installations, are often used in residential applications to feed large appliances such as stoves and dryers. Appliance receptacles sized 30 amps and larger are listed and marked for use at 75°C with both copper and aluminum. NM cable is frequently used for smaller devices such as lighting outlets, receptacles, and switches that are listed for use at 60°C. The restriction for type NM cable at 60°C was due primarily to the damage to conductor insulation in outlet boxes for luminaires that were in many cases used with lamps above the wattage rating.

Change Summary

- Type SE cable with ungrounded conductor sizes 10 AWG and smaller, installed in thermal insulation, is limited to ampacity rating at 60°C.

- Larger size SE cable installed in thermal insulation is no longer limited to an ampacity in the 60°C column and can be applied at 75°C rating.

FR: 1828

SR: None

Dissimilar Metals and Construction of IMC, RMC and EMT

Code Language

3XX.14 Dissimilar Metals.

Where practicable, dissimilar metals in contact anywhere in the system shall be avoided to eliminate the possibility of galvanic action. Aluminum fittings and enclosures shall be permitted to be used with galvanized steel IMC where not subject to severe corrosive influences. Stainless steel IMC shall only be used with stainless steel fittings and approved accessories, outlet boxes, and enclosures.

3XX.100 Construction...(See *NEC* text)

(See NEC for actual text)

Change Summary

• Requirements for dissimilar metals in 3XX.14 for IMC and RMC revised for clarity and to prevent issues with galvanic action on dissimilar metals.

• New 358.14 for EMT is added to prevent issues with galvanic action on dissimilar metals.

• The construction requirements in 3XX.100 are added and revised for IMC, RMC, and EMT.

Significance of the Change

Sections 342.14 and 344.14 are revised to clarify that aluminum fittings and enclosures are permitted to be used with galvanized steel IMC/RMC and that stainless steel IMC/RMC can only be used with stainless steel fittings and approved accessories, outlet boxes, and enclosures.

A new section 358.14 is added for dissimilar metals. This requirement mirrors existing requirements for both IMC and RMC. Both EMT and RMC may be constructed of aluminum. This requires text to clarify that aluminum fittings and enclosures are permitted to be used with galvanized steel RMC/EMT, and galvanized steel fittings and enclosures are permitted to be used with aluminum RMC/EMT where not subject to severe corrosive influences.

A new section 342.100 is added to permit steel with protective coatings and stainless steel IMC. Section 344.100 is revised to clarify that steel RMC is always made with protective coatings. 358.100 is revised to delete "threads" because EMT is not threaded and to clarify that EMT may be made of steel with protective coatings, aluminum, and stainless steel.

FRs: 2129, 2131, 2137, 2139, 2142, 2143
SR: None

Uses Permitted, EMT

Code Language

358.10 Uses Permitted.
(A) Exposed and Concealed
(B) Corrosive Environments
    (1) Galvanized Steel and Stainless Steel EMT, Elbows, and Fittings
    (2) Supplementary Protection of Aluminum EMT
(C) Cinder Fill
(D) Wet Locations

(See NEC for actual text)

Significance of the Change

Section 358.10 has been revised for clarity and consistency with other 3XX.10 sections for uses permitted. Section 358.12 for uses not permitted contained multiple permissive statements allowing the use of EMT under given conditions. That text has been removed from 358.12 and added to 358.10 in positive text.

358.10(A) Exposed and Concealed, is revised with three new list items to recognize the permitted use of EMT in: (1) In concrete, in direct contact with the earth or in areas subject to severe corrosive influences where installed in accordance with 358.10(B), (2) In dry, damp and wet locations and (3) In any hazardous (classified) location as permitted by other articles in this *Code*.

358.10(B) Corrosive Environments, is revised with two new second level subdivisions to address: (1) Galvanized Steel and Stainless Steel EMT, Elbows, and Fittings and (2) Supplementary Protection of Aluminum EMT, where it is encased in concrete or in direct contact with the earth.

A new first level subdivision 358.10(C) Cinder Fill, is added to provide requirements for EMT in contact with cinder concrete or cinder fill subject to moisture.

First level subdivision 358.10(D) Wet Locations, remains unchanged.

Change Summary

- Section 358.10 has been revised for clarity and consistency with other 3XX.10 sections for uses permitted.
- Permissive applications for EMT in 358.12 are relocated in 358.10 for clarity.
- Stainless steel EMT is now addressed in 358.10(B) for Corrosive Environments.

FR: 2144
SR: 2102

Conductors Connected in Parallel

Code Language

366/376/378.20 Conductors Connected in Parallel. Where single conductor cables comprising each phase, neutral, or grounded conductor of an alternating-current circuit are connected in parallel as permitted in 310.10(H), the conductors shall be installed in groups consisting of not more than one conductor per phase, neutral, or grounded conductor to prevent current imbalance in the paralleled conductors due to inductive reactance.

(See NEC for actual text)

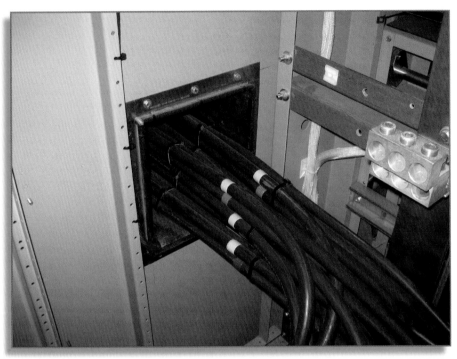

Change Summary

- New requirements for conductors connected in parallel are added in the 3XX.20 section to Articles, 366 Auxillary Gutters, 376 Metal Wireways, and 378 Nonmetallic Wireways.
- AC circuits, connected in parallel, must have conductors installed in groups consisting of not more than one conductor per phase, neutral, or grounded conductor.
- The intention is to prevent current imbalance that can create heat and subsequent failure in the paralleled conductors due to inductive reactance.

FRs: 2179, 2182, 2106
SR: None

Significance of the Change

A new section with requirements for conductors connected in parallel is added in the 3XX.20 section to Articles, 366 Auxillary Gutters, 376 Metal Wireways and 378 Nonmetallic Wireways. This new requirement mandates that where single conductor cables comprising each phase, neutral, or grounded conductor of an alternating-current circuit are connected in parallel, the conductors must be installed in groups consisting of not more than one conductor per phase, neutral, or grounded conductor.

This requirement intends to prevent current imbalance that can create heat and subsequent failure in the paralleled conductors due to inductive reactance. General requirements for conductors installed in parallel are located in 310.10(H) which permits conductors 1/0 AWG and larger (with very limited exceptions) to be installed in parallel. A similar requirement exists in 392.20(C) for conductors in parallel installed in cable tray. However, these requirements for conductors in parallel installed in cable trays also require that the conductors of each circuit be securely bound in circuit groups to prevent excessive movement due to magnetic forces imposed on the parallel conductors from fault current. There is no such secure binding of circuit groups in these new sections because the conductors are within an enclosure.

The substantiation for this revision noted multiple failures due to the lack of properly grouping conductors that are in parallel.

Feeder or Branch Circuits Tapped from Busway

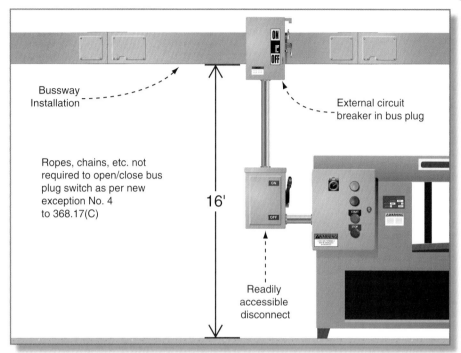

Bussway Installation

External circuit breaker in bus plug

Ropes, chains, etc. not required to open/close bus plug switch as per new exception No. 4 to 368.17(C)

16'

Readily accessible disconnect

Code Language

368.17(C) Feeder or Branch Circuits. ... (See *NEC* text) Where such devices are mounted out of reach and contain disconnecting means, suitable means such as ropes, chains, or sticks shall be provided for operating the disconnecting means from the floor.

(Exception No. 1 through 3, No Changes)

Exception No. 4: Where the branch-circuit overcurrent plug-in device is directly supplying a readily accessible disconnect, a method of floor operation shall not be required.

(See NEC for actual text)

Significance of the Change

A new exception No.4 is added to first level subdivision 368.17(C). The general requirement of this rule is that where a busway is used as a feeder, all devices or plug-in connections to the busway for tapping off the feeder must contain the required overcurrent protective device. The plug-in device must be an externally operable circuit breaker or an externally operable fusible switch. Additionally, where the plug-in switches or circuit breakers are mounted out of reach and contain disconnecting means, there must be suitable means such as ropes, chains, or sticks available to operate/open the disconnecting means.

The intent of the general requirement to provide a means to operate a disconnecting means that is mounted out of reach is to facilitate the ready access to deenergize or remove power to the equipment supplied.

New exception No.4 added in this revision recognizes that where the plug-in device on the busway supplies a readily accessible disconnect, there is a readily accessible means available to disconnect the equipment supplied. Therefore, the ropes, chains, or sticks for operating the "out of reach" disconnecting means from the floor are not required where the branch-circuit overcurrent plug-in device is directly supplying a readily accessible disconnect.

Change Summary

- A new exception No.4 is added to first level subdivision 368.17(C).
- Where there is a readily accessible means available to disconnect the equipment supplied, ropes, chains, or sticks for operating the "out of reach "disconnecting means from the floor are not required.
- Removal of a male cord cap from a receptacle supplied by the busway is permitted by this new exception.

FR: 2148

SR: None

Multiconductor Cables, Rated 2000 Volts or Less

Code Language

392.22(A) Number of Multiconductor Cables, Rated 2000 Volts or Less, in Cable Trays. The number of multiconductor cables, rated 2000 volts or less, permitted in a single cable tray shall not exceed the requirements of this section. The conductor sizes shall apply to both aluminum and copper conductors. Where dividers are used, fill calculations shall apply to each divided section of the cable tray.

(See NEC for actual text)

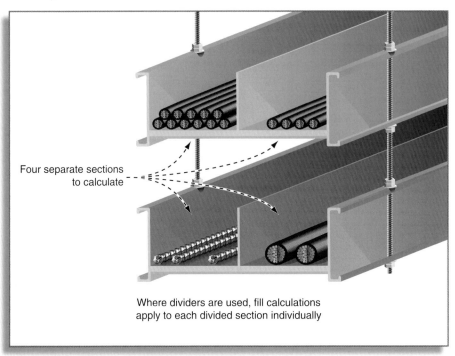

Four separate sections to calculate

Where dividers are used, fill calculations apply to each divided section individually

Change Summary

• Cable tray that contains dividers must have each divided section of the cable tray treated individually with respect to fill calculations.

• A ladder type tray that is divided with power on one side and control on the other side of the divider may now have the fill calculated by both 392.22(A)(1) and (A)(2) permitting a 50% fill calculation on the signal side of the tray.

FR: 2124

SR: None

Significance of the Change

First level subdivision 392.22(A) provides requirements for the permitted number of multiconductor cables, rated 2000 volts or less, permitted in a single cable tray. These requirements are separated into four second level subdivisions that separate the requirements based on the type of cable tray and the conductors within as follows: (1) Ladder or Ventilated Trough Cable Trays Containing Any Mixture of Cables, (2) Ladder or Ventilated Trough Cable Trays Containing Multiconductor Control and/or Signal Cables Only, (3) Solid Bottom Cable Trays Containing Any Mixture of Cables and (4) Solid Bottom Cable Tray Containing Multiconductor Control and/or Signal Cables Only. Where the tray contains multiconductor control and/or signal cables in 392.22(A)(2) and (4) the permitted fill is higher than where there is a mixture of power and control and/or signal cables.

This revision adds a new last sentence to address cable tray that contains dividers and requires that each divided section of the cable tray be treated individually with respect to fill calculations. A cable tray with a divider may contain power cables on one side and signal cables on the other. This revision now clarifies that cable tray fill is based upon each divided section. This will now permit a ladder type tray that is divided with power on one side and control on the other side of the divider to have the fill calculated by both 392.22(A)(1) and (A)(2) permitting a 50% fill calculation on the signal side of the tray.

Definition of "Insulated Conductor"

Significance of the Change

The existing definition of "Messenger Supported Wiring" in 396.2 mandates that this is an exposed wiring support system using a messenger wire to support "insulated conductors." This literally eliminated all use of triplex and quadruplex because the conductors are not insulated they are "covered" with a polymeric material. This new definition is added in an effort to permit extremely limited use of triplex and quadruplex.

The new definition now recognizes a conductor as insulated where: (1) the conductor is a type described in 310.104, and (2) overhead service conductors encased in a polymeric material that has been evaluated for the applied nominal voltage. The reference to "conductors encased in a polymeric material" is addressing multiplex cables utilizing a bare conductor, factory assembled and twisted with one or more insulated conductors, such as duplex, triplex, or quadruplex type of construction. A new informational note references ICEA S-76-474-2011, Standard for Neutral Supported Power Cable Assemblies with Weather-Resistant Extruded Insulation Rated 600 Volts. This standard is for overhead service conductors only.

This revision now clearly prohibits the use of these multiplex cables for use as outdoor feeders or branch circuits.

Code Language

396.2 Definition.

Insulated Conductor. For the purposes of this article, an insulated conductor includes the following:

(1) Conductor types described in 310.104, and

(2) Overhead service conductors encased in a polymeric material that has been evaluated for the applied nominal voltage.

> Informational Note: Evidence of evaluation for the applied nominal voltage can be given by certification that the conductors have met the requirements of ICEA S-76-474-2011, Standard for Neutral Supported Power Cable Assemblies with Weather-Resistant Extruded Insulation Rated 600 Volts.

(See NEC for actual text)

Change Summary

- A new definition of *insulated conductor* is added in Article 396 Messenger-Supported Wiring.
- Polymeric cables such as triplex and quadruplex are now clearly limited in application to only overhead service conductor applications.
- This clearly prohibits the use of triplex or quadruplex as overhead outdoor feeders.

FR: 1835
SR: 1814

Chapter 4

Articles 400–480
Equipment for General Use

Uses Not Permitted

Code Language

400.12 Uses Permitted. (Relocated from 400.7)

400.12 Uses Not Permitted. Unless specifically permitted in 400.10, flexible cords and cables, flexible cord sets, and power supply cords shall not be used for the following:

New exception to list Item No. 5

Exception to (5): Flexible cord and flexible cable shall be permitted if contained within an enclosure for use in Other Spaces Used for Environmental Air as permitted by 300.22(C)(3).

(See NEC for actual text)

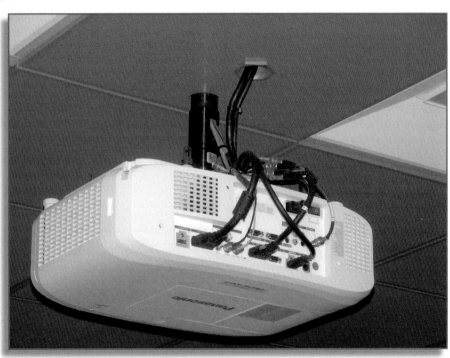

Change Summary

- Section 400.8 has been relocated to 400.12 for correlation with standard location of rules for "Uses Not Permitted."

- This revision clarifies that Article 400 covers "cord sets and power-supply cords" in addition to "flexible cords and cables."

- A new informational note in section 400.1 clarifies that Article 400 applies to both "cord sets and power-supply cords" and "flexible cords and cables."

Significance of the Change

Section 400.7 is relocated to 400.10 and Section 400.8 has been relocated to 400.12 for correlation with the format in Chapter 3 for wiring methods. The parent text of Section 400.12 is revised to clarify that "cord sets and power-supply cords" are covered in Article 400. There was a misconception due to the fact that the previous text in 400.8 addressed "flexible cords and cables" it was permissible to apply "cord sets and power-supply cords" in any manner whatsoever. This misconception was based upon the fact that "flexible cords and cables" are addressed in UL 62 and "cord sets and power-supply cords" are addressed in UL 817. This revision clarifies that Article 400 covers "cord sets and power-supply cords."

This will now provide clear text to prohibit cords for multimedia projectors, condensate pumps and more from being run through holes in walls, in structural ceilings, in suspended ceilings, in dropped ceilings/floors, attached to building surfaces, through doorways, windows, concealed by floors walls or ceilings, or where subject to physical damage. A new Informational Note is added to Section "400.1 Scope," to provide additional clarity.

FRs: 1514, 1519
SRs: 1504, 1502

Switches Controlling Lighting Loads

Significance of the Change

First level subdivision 404.2(C) requires that the grounded conductor of a branch circuit be installed at the switch location where the switch controls lighting loads. Where a switch controls lighting loads, it is likely a motion sensor or other electronic device to control the lighting loads will be installed initially or in the future. The parent text of this requirement is modified for clarity to explain that the general rule is to install the grounded conductor and lists rooms and a reference to the applicable building codes. The previous text provided exemption where the switch did not serve a "habitable" room or bathroom. This created problems for both installers and enforcers because the *NEC* did not define a "habitable room." The new requirement is for bathrooms, hallways, stairways and rooms suitable for human habitation with a reference to applicable building codes. New text now requires the grounded conductor be connected to switching devices that require line-to-neutral voltage to operate the electronics in the device. A new exception (1) makes the connection requirement effective on January 1, 2020, (2) exempts replacement or retrofit switches installed prior to local adoption of 404.2(C) and where the grounded conductor cannot be extended without removing finish materials, (3) limits the number of electronic lighting control switches on a branch circuit to five, and the number connected to any feeder on the load side of a system or main bonding jumper to not more than twenty-five.

Code Language

404.2(C) Switches Controlling Lighting Loads. The grounded circuit conductor... (See *NEC* text) shall be installed... (See *NEC* text) (in) bathrooms, hallways, stairways, or rooms suitable for human habitation or occupancy as defined in the applicable building code...(See *NEC* text)

The grounded conductor shall be extended to any switch location as necessary and shall be connected to switching devices that require line-to-neutral voltage to operate the electronics of the switch in the standby mode and shall meet the requirements of 404.22.

Exception: (See NEC text)... effective on January 1, 2020 shall not apply to replacement or retrofit switches installed in locations wired prior to local adoption of 404.2(C)... (not more than five on BC, 25 on feeder)...

(See NEC for actual text)

Change Summary

- "Habitable room" is deleted. Bathrooms, hallways, stairways and rooms suitable for human habitation (applicable building code) require the grounded conductor be installed.
- The section parent text is modified for clarity.
- Device connection must be made to device where required. New Exception and effective date of Jan. 1, 2020.

FR: 2416
SR: 2408
SCR: 54

Electronic Lighting Control Switches

Code Language

404.22 Electronic Lighting Control Switches. Electronic lighting control switches shall be listed. Electronic lighting control switches shall not introduce current on the equipment grounding conductor during normal operation. The requirement to not introduce current on the equipment grounding conductor shall take effect on January 1, 2020.

Exception: Electronic lighting control switches that introduce current on the equipment grounding conductor shall be permitted for applications covered by 404.2(C) Exception. Electronic lighting control switches that introduce current on the equipment grounding conductor shall be listed and marked for use in replacement or retrofit applications only.

(See NEC for actual text)

Change Summary

• All electronic lighting control switches are required to be listed.

• As of January 1, 2020, electronic lighting control switches (with exceptions) will not be permitted to introduce current on the equipment grounding conductor during normal operation.

• Manufacturers will still make devices that place current on the equipment grounding conductor during normal operation for only replacement/retrofit.

FR: 2423

SR: 2409

SCR: 55

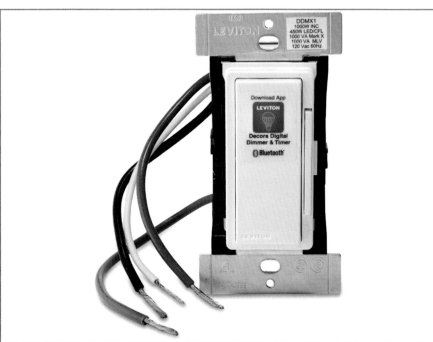

Courtesy of Leviton

Significance of the Change

This new section, located in *Part II Construction Specifications*, mandates that all types of "electronic lighting control switches" be listed and designed to not introduce current on the equipment grounding conductor (EGC) during normal operation. This is a significant revision that will address the present problem of allowing current flow on the EGC where electronic lighting control switches are installed. This new requirement will be phased in with a delayed implementation date of January 1, 2020. This will allow manufacturers of these devices to begin making electronic lighting control switches that do not put current flow on the EGC and to allow the inventory of devices in current production to be installed. An exception will permit devices that put current on the EGC for only replacements/retrofits in older installations. The 2014 *NEC* includes a general requirement to install a grounded conductor at switch locations that control lighting loads, but there was no requirement to use the grounded conductor. An installer could provide the grounded conductor at all switch locations controlling lighting loads and still use electronic lighting control switches that put current flow on the EGC because there is no requirement in the 2014 *NEC* to address the construction of these devices. This is corrected in 404.2(C) in 2017.

Definition of Outlet Box Hood

Code Language

406.2 Outlet Box Hood. A housing shield intended to fit over a faceplate for flush-mounted wiring devices, or an integral component of an outlet box or of a faceplate for flush-mounted wiring devices. The hood does not serve to complete the electrical enclosure; it reduces the risk of water coming in contact with electrical components within the hood, such as attachment plugs, current taps, surge protective devices, direct plug-in transformer units, or wiring devices.

(See NEC for actual text)

Significance of the Change

The *NEC* contains requirements for receptacles installed in damp or wet locations in section 406.9. The general rules for covers on receptacles installed in damp and wet locations are:

Damp Locations: Receptacles installed in damp locations must have an enclosure for the receptacle that is weatherproof when the receptacle is covered with an attachment plug cap not inserted and receptacle covers closed.

Wet Locations: Receptacles installed in wet locations require a cover that is weatherproof whether or not the attachment plug cap is inserted through a listed "outlet box hood" that is identified as "extra duty."

This new definition is necessary to provide clarity and usability for *Code* users to apply the term *outlet box hood*. This definition clarifies that the hood is simply a shield intended to fit over a faceplate for flush-mounted wiring devices, or an integral component of an outlet box or of a faceplate for flush-mounted wiring devices. The hood does not serve to complete the electrical enclosure; it reduces the risk of water coming in contact with electrical components. The "street term" for an "outlet box hood" is a "bubble cover" due to the physical shape of the hood.

See the revision in 406.9(B)(1) which clarifies that listed products, enclosures, or assemblies providing weatherproof protection, that do not utilize an outlet box hood need not be marked "extra duty."

Change Summary

- 406.2 now contains a new definition for *Outlet Box Hood* that applies where the term is used in Article 406.
- The hood does not serve to complete the electrical enclosure, it reduces the risk of water coming in contact with electrical components.
- "Outlet Box Hoods" are commonly known as a "bubble cover."

FR: 5111
SR: 55
SCR: 56

Markings on Controlled Receptacles

Code Language

406.3(E) Controlled Receptacle Marking. All nonlocking-type, 125-volt, 15- and 20-ampere receptacles that are controlled… (See *NEC* text) shall be permanently marked with the symbol shown in Figure 406.3(E) and the word "controlled."

For receptacles controlled by an automatic control device, the marking shall be located on the receptacle face and visible after installation.

In both cases where a multiple receptacle device is used, the required marking of the word "controlled" and symbol shall denote which contact devices are controlled.

Exception: (No changes)

(See NEC for actual text)

Change Summary

- Clarity is provided with a new requirement that the receptacle face be marked.
- Where more than one contact device exists on a receptacle, the controlled contact device must be marked.
- In addition to the required symbol marking, the receptacle must be marked as "controlled."

FR: 5102
SR: 5111

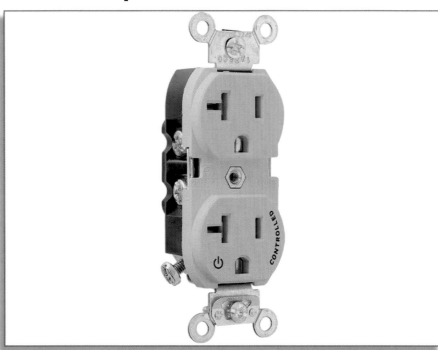

Courtesy of Leviton

Significance of the Change

The requirements for controlled receptacle marking are revised for clarity. The required symbol marking alone has created confusion and controversy. The symbol used is the universal marking for "power" and exists on many devices to turn them on or off. This is confusing to the average homeowner or end user. The symbol alone does not convey that the power available at that device is controlled automatically. This revision will provide significant clarity for homeowners and other end users by requiring the word "controlled" be marked under the symbol. The previous requirement was not very clear on where the marking was required, and many marked the receptacle while others marked the device faceplate. The receptacle face is now required to be marked with both the symbol and the word "controlled." Where a receptacle has more than one contact device, each controlled device must be marked. Receptacles controlled through energy management systems are often installed to align with the applicable energy code rules (such as those in the ICC Energy Code or ANSI/ASHRAE/IES Standard 90.1) adopted within a jurisdiction. The revisions in this section help the occupants more readily understand that certain receptacles within a facility are controlled and reduces possibilities of power interruption to loads that normally would be required to remain on and should not be interrupted through energy management control.

Receptacle with USB Charger

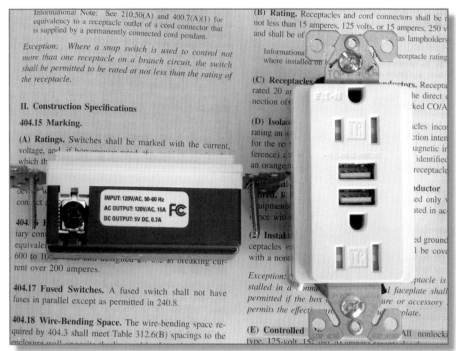

Courtesy of Eaton Corporation

Code Language

406.3(F) Receptacle with USB Charger. A 125-volt 15- or 20-ampere receptacle that additionally provides Class 2 power shall be listed and constructed such that the Class 2 circuitry is integral with the receptacle.

(See NEC for actual text)

Significance of the Change

A new first level subdivision is added to section 406.3 to provide requirements for receptacles that contain a USB charger. These types of receptacles are readily available in the market, and previous editions of the *NEC* did not contain any requirements for these devices. Devices that are charged through a USB connection such as cell phones, tablets, pads, e-readers and much more exist in every home and workplace in abundance. Each of these devices comes with a charger that is a Class 2 power supply for charging. Installing receptacles with built-in USB connections that have integral Class 2 power supplies and circuitry eliminates the need for the chargers and allows the user to plug directly into the USB to charge a device.

This new requirement permits receptacles with USB chargers provided that it is a listed device and constructed such that the Class 2 circuitry is integral with the receptacle. The listing requirement ensures that the receptacles with a built-in USB charger conform to ANSI/UL 498, which addresses the construction as well as the performance requirements to evaluate the suitability of a receptacle with an integral power supply and with Class 2 output connectors.

Change Summary

- Devices that are charged through a USB connection such as cell phones, tablets, pads, e-readers and much more exist in every home and workplace in abundance.
- New 406.3(F) Receptacle with USB Charger permits these devices provided they are listed and constructed such that the Class 2 circuitry is integral with the receptacle.
- These devices are listed to ANSI/UL 498.

FR: 5101
SR: None

406.4(D)(2)

REVISION

Replacement of Non–Grounding-Type Receptacles

Code Language

406.4 General Installation Requirements.

(D) Replacements.

(2) Non–Grounding-Type Receptacles. Where attachment to an equipment grounding conductor does not exist in the receptacle enclosure, the installation shall comply with (D)(2)(a), (D)(2)(b), or (D)(2)(c).

(b) ... (See *NEC* text) These receptacles or their cover plates shall be marked "No Equipment Ground."

(c) ... (See *NEC* text) shall be marked "GFCI Protected" and "No Equipment Ground," visible after installation.

> Informational Note No. 1: Some equipment or appliance manufacturers require that the branch circuit to the equipment or appliance includes an equipment grounding conductor.
>
> Informational Note No. 2: See 250.114 for a list of a cord-and-plug-connected equipment or appliances that require an equipment grounding conductor.

(See NEC for actual text)

Change Summary

- Marking is required on the receptacle or faceplate and be visible after installation.
- IN's explain some appliances are required to be grounded by connection to a circuit EGC and a reference to 250.114.

Significance of the Change

Non-grounding type receptacles, common in older homes, are permitted to be replaced with grounding type receptacles provided they are GFCI protected and marked to inform the end user that no equipment grounding conductor (EGC) exists. The required marking is clarified and must now be visible after installation.

First level subdivision 90.5(C) explains that informational notes are not enforceable as part of the *NEC*. Two new informational notes are added in 406.4(D)(2) that refer the *Code* user to other product standards and *NEC* requirements that have a significant impact on the replacement of non-grounding receptacles with grounding type receptacles. The first informational note infers 110.3(B) which requires that listed or labeled equipment must be used in accordance with any instructions in the listing or labeling. Many equipment and appliance manufacturers require that the branch circuit supplying equipment or an appliance must include an EGC. The second informational note refers the *Code* user to Section 250.114 for a list of cord-and-plug-connected equipment or appliances that require an EGC. Once these requirements are understood, it is clear that most replacements would require modification of or a new branch circuit to include an EGC.

FR: 5104
SR: 5104

Receptacle Mounting, Countertops and Work Surfaces

Courtesy of Thomas & Betts

Code Language

406.5 Receptacle Mounting.

(E) Receptacles in Countertops. Receptacle assemblies for installation in countertop surfaces shall be listed for countertop applications... (See *NEC* text)

(F) Receptacles in Work Surfaces. Receptacle assemblies and GFCI receptacle assemblies listed for work surface or countertop applications shall be permitted to be installed in work surfaces.

(G) Receptacle Orientation. Receptacles shall not be installed in a face-up position in or on countertop surfaces or work surfaces unless listed for countertop or work surface applications.

(See NEC for actual text)

Significance of the Change

Section 406.5 contains requirements for the mounting of receptacles. First level subdivision (E) is revised and now addresses only countertops. Additionally, the prohibition for mounting receptacles face-up in a countertop or work surface is relocated. A new sentence now requires receptacle outlets installed in countertops to be listed for countertop applications. A new first level subdivision (F) Receptacles in Work Surfaces is added to permit receptacle assemblies that are listed for either use in "work surfaces" or "countertops" to be installed in "work surfaces." There is a significant difference between receptacle outlet assemblies that are listed for use in "work surfaces" and those listed for use in "countertops." The UL standard for receptacle outlet assemblies that are listed for use in "work surfaces" address the spillage of liquid onto receptacle outlets mounted on a desk or table and require spillage of 8 oz (1 cup) of liquid. The UL standard for receptacle outlet assemblies that are listed for use in "countertops" address the spillage of up to 32 oz of liquid onto the installed receptacle outlet assembly. The difference is that work surfaces are not expected to see the same possible amount of spillage as a device mounted in a kitchen or bathroom countertop. A new first level subdivision (G) Receptacle Orientation, now prohibits the installation of receptacles in a face-up position in countertops or work surfaces unless they are listed for the application.

Change Summary

- Receptacle assemblies for installation in "countertops" are now required to be listed for countertop applications.

- Receptacle assemblies for installation in "work surfaces" are now required to be listed for use in work surfaces or countertop applications.

- Receptacle assemblies for installation in "countertops" are tested with spillage of 32 oz and "work surfaces" with spillage of only 8 oz.

FR: 5108
SR: 5106

NEW

Integral Night Light and/or USB Charger

Code Language

406.6 Receptacle Face Plates (Cover Plates)

(D) Receptacle Face plates (Cover Plates) with Integral Night Light and/or USB Charger. A flush device cover plate that additionally provides a night light and/or Class 2 output connector(s) shall be listed and constructed such that the night light and/or Class 2 circuitry is integral with the flush device cover plate.

(See NEC for actual text)

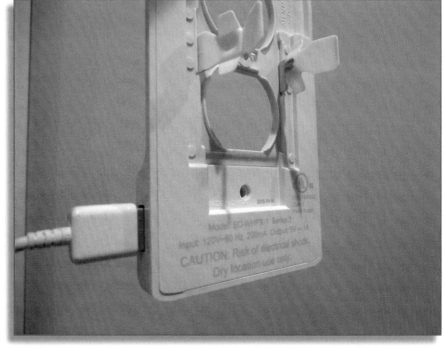

Change Summary

- A new 406.6(D) requires receptacle faceplates with integral night lights or USB chargers to have the night light and/or Class 2 circuitry integral with the flush device cover plate.

- Devices associated with receptacle outlets to provide a USB connection are now addressed in 406.3(F) and 406.6(D) for receptacles.

- The abundance of devices requiring USB connections for charging is driving these new devices.

Significance of the Change

Section 406.6 addresses requirements for receptacle faceplates commonly called "cover plates." A new first level subdivision (D) is added to address flush device cover plates that provides a night light and/or Class 2 output connector(s). This new requirement mandates that these faceplates be listed and constructed such that the night light and/or Class 2 circuitry is integral with the flush device cover plate. This new requirement is in addition to a new first level subdivision 406.3(F) that requires receptacles with a USB charger to be listed and constructed such that the Class 2 circuitry is integral with the receptacle. Faceplates with built-in night lights and USB chargers are readily available in the market and previous editions of the *NEC* did not contain any requirements for these devices. Devices that are charged through a USB connection such as cell phones, tablets, pads, e-readers and much more exist in every home and workplace in abundance. Each of these devices comes with a charger that is a Class 2 power supply for charging. Installing faceplates with built-in USB connections that have integral Class 2 power supplies and circuitry eliminates the need for the chargers and allows the user to plug directly into the USB to charge a device.

FR: 5109
SR: None

Receptacles of 15 and 20 Amperes in a Wet Location

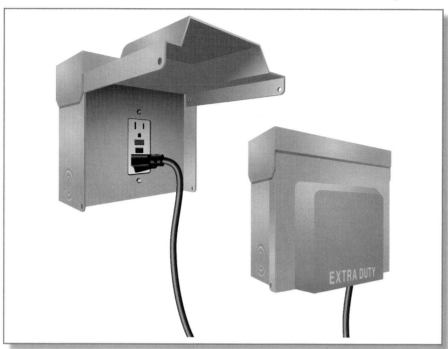

Significance of the Change

The general rule in 406.9(B)(1) mandates receptacles that are installed in wet locations have an enclosure that is weatherproof whether or not the attachment plug cap is inserted. A listed outlet box hood installed for this purpose must be marked as "extra-duty." A new sentence is added to follow the general rule to clarify that other listed products, enclosures, or assemblies providing weatherproof protection that do not utilize an outlet box hood need not be marked "extra duty." There are many types of listed enclosures and assemblies that are not required to have an "outlet box hood" and may be provided with a weatherproof hinged cover that is not marked "extra duty." A new sentence is added to informational note 1 to clarify that listed receptacles, faceplates, outlet boxes, enclosures, or assemblies that are identified as either being suitable for wet locations, or are rated as one of the outdoor enclosure type numbers of Table 110.28 are not required to have outlet box hoods or to be marked as "extra duty."

406.9(B)(1) requires all 15- and 20-ampere, 125- and 250-volt nonlocking-type receptacles to be listed and so identified as "weather-resistant" type, typically identified as "WR." This requirement is relocated after the exception for spray washing areas to clarify that "weather-resistant type" receptacles are required in a spray washing area.

FR: 5110
SR: 5102

NEW / **REVISION**

Tamper Resistant Receptacles

Code Language

406.12 Tamper Resistant Receptacles. All 15- and 20-ampere, 125- and 250-volt nonlocking-type receptacles in the areas specified in 406.12(1) through (7) shall be listed tamper-resistant receptacles.

(1) Dwelling units (2) Guest rooms and guest suites of hotels and motels (3) Child care facilities (4) Preschools and elementary education facilities (5) Business offices, corridors, waiting rooms and the like in clinics, medical, and dental offices and outpatient facilities (6) Subset of assembly occupancies described in 518.2 to include places of waiting transportation, gymnasiums, skating rinks, and auditoriums (7) Dormitories

(See NEC for actual text)

Change Summary

- 406.12 now addresses all 125- and 250-volt nonlocking-type, 15- and 20-ampere receptacles.

- New venues are added to the tamper resistant receptacles (TR) requirement.

- Preschools and elementary education, business offices, corridors, waiting rooms and the like in clinics, medical, and dental offices and outpatient facilities, assembly occupancies described in Section 518.2, dormitories.

FR: 5112
SR: 5107
SCR: 45

Significance of the Change

The parent text of 406.12 is revised for clarity with list items to identify venues impacted. The previous limitation to "125-volt" receptacles is deleted and tamper resistant receptacles (TR) are now required for all 125- and 250-volt nonlocking-type, 15- and 20-ampere receptacles in each of the venues addressed in list items (1) through (7).

New venues are now addressed in 406.12, to cover other areas where children will or could be present. These include; (4) preschools and elementary education facilities, which would include classrooms, hallways and any other area designed for children to occupy, (5) business offices, corridors, waiting rooms and the like in clinics, medical and dental offices and outpatient facilities, which includes waiting rooms, offices or any other space designed for children to occupy, (6) subset of assembly occupancies described in Section 518.2 to include places of waiting, transportation, gymnasiums, skating rinks, and auditoriums which includes the venues specifically mentioned along with "waiting areas" in all of the venues listed in 518.2 such as restaurants, and (7) dormitories to include all rooms designed for occupancy by persons that could include children.

An informational note is added to list the types of receptacles intended to be covered by this requirement. They are identified as 5-15, 5-20, 6-15, and 6-20 in ANSI/NEMA WD 6–2012, Wiring Devices — Dimensional Specifications.

Service Panelboards, Switchboards, and Switchgear

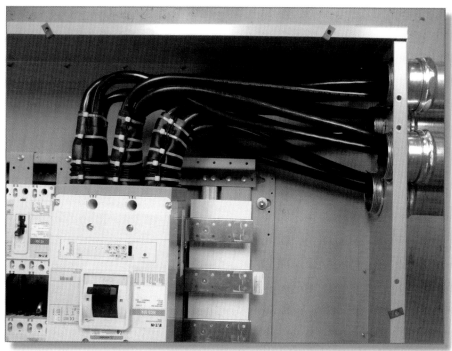

Courtesy of Eaton Corporation

Code Language

408.3(A)(2) Service Panelboards, Switchboards, and Switchgear. Barriers shall be placed in all service panelboards, switchboards, and switchgear such that no uninsulated, ungrounded service busbar or service terminal is exposed to inadvertent contact by persons or maintenance equipment while servicing load terminations.

Exception: This requirement shall not apply to service panelboards with provisions for more than one service disconnect within a single enclosure as permitted in 408.36, Exceptions 1, 2, and 3.

(See NEC for actual text)

Significance of the Change

This revision adds panelboards to first level subdivision 408.3(A)(2), which requires barriers for service equipment to prevent inadvertent contact with energized parts. Barriers are now required in all panelboards, switchboards, and switchgear so that "no uninsulated, ungrounded service busbar or service terminal is exposed to inadvertent contact by persons or maintenance equipment while servicing load terminations." This revision brings the *NEC* requirements a step closer to correlation with the *Canadian Electrical Code*, which requires physical barriers in panelboards used as service equipment. A new exception is added to exempt panelboards used as service equipment with more than one disconnect as permitted in the exceptions to section 408.36. Where multiple service disconnecting means are used, providing barriers becomes more difficult.

The general rule for electrical safe work practices in NFPA 70E, Section 130.2, is to create an "electrically safe work condition" (ESWC) where an employee is inside the limited approach boundary or interacting with equipment that increases the likelihood of an arc flash. This new requirement for a barrier, while limited to service equipment is a step in the right direction to isolate energized conductors and circuit parts.

Change Summary

- Panelboards used as service equipment now require barriers to prevent inadvertent contact with line side energized parts.
- An exception is provided for panelboards with more than one service disconnecting means.
- Barriers will likely be provided as a "field-installed kit" to be applied where they are used as service equipment.

FR: 2424
SR: 2410

Source of Supply, Markings

Code Language

408.4 Field Identification Required (B) Source of Supply. All switchboards, switchgear, and panelboards supplied by a feeder(s) in other than one- or two-family dwellings shall be permanently marked to indicate each device or equipment where the power originates. The label shall be permanently affixed, of sufficient durability to withstand the environment involved, and not handwritten.

(See NEC for actual text)

Feeder supplied switchboard, switchgear and panelboards in other than dwelling must be marked to indicate the source.

PANELBOARD LP-427 SUPPLIED FROM SW-L22 ON LOWER LEVEL 2 NORTHWEST

Label must be of sufficient durability for environment

Label must be permanently affixed

Not handwritten

Change Summary

- The source of supply for all switchboards, switchgear, and panelboards supplied by a feeder(s) is now required to be "permanently marked" on the equipment.
- The marking is now required to be "a label" of some type that is placed on the equipment.
- Labels must be of "sufficient durability" to withstand the environment involved, and "not handwritten."

Significance of the Change

This revision clarifies the required marking of the "source of supply" for all switchboards, switchgear, and panelboards supplied by feeder(s) in other than one- or two-family dwellings. This requirement does not apply to service supplied equipment. This is an installation requirement that provides the installer/maintainer who may work on the equipment after initial installation with readily accessible information to quickly determine the source of supply for troubleshooting and to create an electrically safe work condition. The marking is now required to be "a label" of some type that is placed on the equipment. The label is also now required to be "permanently affixed" to the equipment, and not handwritten. Previous interpretations of this rule permitted handwriting the source of supply for a panelboard on the panel schedule, which in many cases is easily removed and not permanently affixed. In some cases, the AHJ permitted a handwritten marking with a permanent marker. The label is also required to be of sufficient durability to withstand the environment involved. This will impact switchboards, switchgear, and panelboards that may be installed outdoors or in any environment that could negatively impact the label.

FR: 2427
SR: None

Available Fault Current, Documentation

Code Language

409.22 Short-Circuit Current Rating.

(A) Installation... (See *NEC* text)

(B) Documentation. If an industrial control panel is required to be marked with a short-circuit current rating in accordance with 409.110(4), the available short-circuit current at the industrial control panel and the date the short-circuit current calculation was performed shall be documented and made available to those authorized to inspect the installation.

(See NEC for actual text)

Significance of the Change

A new first level subdivision 409.22(B) is added to require documentation of the available short circuit current available at industrial control panels. This documentation is only required for an industrial control panel that is required to be marked with a short circuit current rating as required in 409.110(4). This requires all industrial control panels, "other than those containing only control circuit components," to be marked in a manner that is "plainly visible after installation" with the short-circuit current rating of the equipment and the date the calculation was performed.

This revision now requires documentation of the available short circuit current at the industrial control panel and the "date the short circuit current calculation was performed." The documentation is required to be made available to those authorized to inspect the installation. This means that the documentation must be "made available" which could be on drawings or simply "documented in a manner that is readily available." While the documentation is not required to be marked on the industrial control panel, it would be permitted.

Change Summary

- New first level subdivision 409.22(B) requires documentation of ASCC available at industrial control panels other than those that contain only control circuit components.
- The documentation must include the date of the calculation.
- The documentation must be made available to those authorized to inspect the installation, it is not required to be marked on the equipment.

FR: 3002
SR: 3003

Industrial Control Panel Marking

Code Language

409.110 Marking. ....(3) Industrial control panels supplied by more than one electrical source where more than one disconnecting means is required to disconnect all circuits 50-volts or more within the control panel shall be marked to indicate that more than one disconnecting means is required to de-energize the equipment. The location of the means necessary to disconnect all circuits 50-volts or more shall be documented and available.

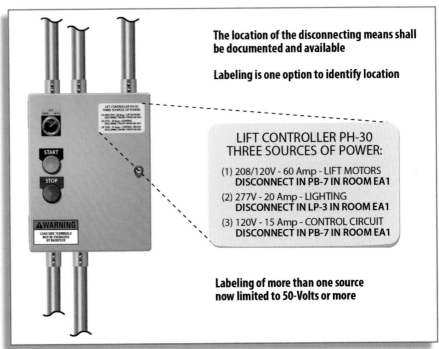

The location of the disconnecting means shall be documented and available

Labeling is one option to identify location

LIFT CONTROLLER PH-30 THREE SOURCES OF POWER:

(1) 208/120V - 60 Amp - LIFT MOTORS **DISCONNECT IN PB-7 IN ROOM EA1**

(2) 277V - 20 Amp - LIGHTING **DISCONNECT IN LP-3 IN ROOM EA1**

(3) 120V - 15 Amp - CONTROL CIRCUIT **DISCONNECT IN PB-7 IN ROOM EA1**

Labeling of more than one source now limited to 50-Volts or more

Change Summary

- 409.110(3) already requires marking for industrial control panels supplied by more than one source.
- 409.110(3) now requires the *location of the means necessary to disconnect* all circuits 50-volts or more be documented, and available.
- The parent text of 409.110 requires the information in all seven list items be marked on the industrial control panel.

Significance of the Change

Section 409.110 contains significant requirements for marking of industrial control panels. List item 409.110(3) previously required that where an industrial control panel is supplied by more than one electrical source and more than one disconnecting means would need to be opened to disconnect all power circuits within the control panel, the equipment needed to be marked to inform the installer/maintainer. While this information was critical to the worker there was no requirement to identify the location of those disconnecting means. A new last sentence is added to list item 409.110(3) to require documentation be made available to identify the location of all disconnecting means necessary to open all circuits 50-volts or more within the industrial control panel. The NEC contains many marking requirements that provide the installer/maintainer with the location of the disconnecting means supplying the equipment. These requirements include but are not limited to 225.52(F), 312.8(3) and 408.4(B) which require a label, plaque or directory placed on the equipment to identify the location of the disconnecting means supplying the equipment.

This new requirement for industrial control panels provides the installer/maintainer with information necessary to locate all sources of power at 50-volts or more supplying an industrial control panel.

FR: 3001
SR: 3004

Low-Voltage Lighting

Significance of the Change

Article 411 is significantly revised for clarity and to reverse many changes that occurred in the 2014 *NEC*. The title of the Article is changed from "Lighting Systems Operating at 30 Volts or Less and Lighting Equipment Connected to Class-2 Power Systems" to simply "Low-Voltage Lighting." The scope of the Article is revised in section 411.1 to include lighting systems and their associated components operating at no more than 30 volts ac or 60 volts dc and where wet contact is likely to occur, the limits are 15 volts ac or 30 volts dc. The previous scope limited all low voltage lighting to 30 volts or less and lighting equipment connected to a Class 2 power source. In the 2014 *NEC* listed Class 2 lighting equipment, is required to be rated in conformance with Chapter 9 Table 11(A) or Table 11(B). Referencing these tables for Class 2 lighting extended the provisions of Article 411 to Class 2 luminaires operating above 30 volts ac. Table 11(B) limits this Class 2 power supply to a nameplate rating of 100 volt-amps and 1.67 amps. Substantiation provided for this revision pointed out that there was no net benefit to this limitation, and requiring multiple power supplies did not result in a reduced risk of fire or shock.

A new informational note is added with the Article scope to inform the *Code* user to refer to Article 680 for applications involving immersion of low voltage lighting.

Change Summary

- Article 411 is now titled "Low-Voltage Lighting."
- The scope of Article 411 is revised to cover lighting systems and their associated components operating at no more than 30 volts ac or 60 volts dc.
- Class 2 lighting equipment is no longer required to conform to the limits in Tables 11(A) and 11(B).

FR: 5147
SR: None

GFCI Protection for Personnel

Code Language

422.5 Ground-Fault Circuit-Interrupter (GFCI) Protection for Personnel.

(A) General. Appliances identified in 422.5(A)(1) through (5) rated 250 volts or less and 60 amperes or less, single or 3-phase, shall be provided with GFCI protection for personnel. Multiple GFCI protective devices shall be permitted but shall not be required...(See *NEC* text) *List items (1) through (5)*

(B) Type. The GFCI shall be readily accessible, listed, and located in one or more of the following locations...(See *NEC* text) List items *(1) through (5)*

(See NEC for actual text)

Change Summary

- GFCI requirements that were spread throughout Article 422 are grouped for clarity and usability.
- Five different methods and locations to provide the required GFCI protection are provided.

FR: 4801

SR: None

SCR: 39

Significance of the Change

Previous GFCI requirements in Article 422 were spread throughout the Article with a general requirement in 422.5 that all GFCI devices protecting appliances be located in a readily accessible location. The GFCI requirements for appliances in Article 422 are relocated into one location in section 422.5 significantly increasing clarity and usability. Multiple GFCI protective devices are permitted but not required, meaning a vending machine, for example, could have an integral GFCI and be plugged into a GFCI type receptacle. The appliances listed in 422.5(A) are (1) Automotive vacuum machines provided for public use, relocated from 422.23, (2) Drinking water coolers, relocated from 422.52, (3) High-pressure spray washing machines — cord-and-plug-connected, relocated from 422.49, (4) Tire inflation machines provided for public use, relocated from 422.23 and (5) Vending machines, relocated from 422.51. New first level subdivision 422.5(B) addresses the type of GFCI device permitted, requires all GFCI's to be readily accessible, listed, and located in one or more of the following locations (1) Within the branch circuit overcurrent device, (2) A device or outlet within the supply circuit, (3) An integral part of the attachment plug, (4) Within the supply cord not more than 300 mm (12 in.) from the attachment plug and (5) Factory installed within the appliance.

Appliances, Listing Required

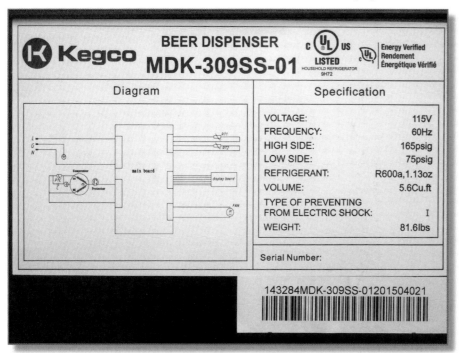

Code Language

422.6 Listing Required. All appliances operating at 50 volts or more shall be listed.

(See NEC for actual text)

Significance of the Change

New section 422.6 now requires all appliances operating at 50 volts or more to be listed. While most appliances are listed, new devices and technologies must be evaluated for safety. There are requirements throughout Article 422 that are related in many cases to specific appliances. This new requirement for listing ensures those requirements in the *NEC* are applied to the appliances through the applicable product standard. Using the *NEC* definition for *vending machines* or using marketing information or marketplace terms for other appliances could result in misapplication of requirements from Article 422. Listing of products will properly classify the equipment, and that listing will ensure application of proper installation requirements through installation instructions and product labeling. For example, the *NEC* definition of *vending machine* is very broad, and likely includes equipment not listed as appliances and probably not considered in the original development of requirements in existing 422.51, now relocated to 422.5. *NEC* requirements drive the product standards in many cases and requiring all appliances to be listed ensures that the construction and application requirements in Article 422 are applied to the applicable product standard.

Change Summary

- All appliances operating at 50 volts or more are now required to be listed.
- Listing ensures that the specific appliance construction conforms to the applicable product standard and the requirements in Article 422.

FR: 4802
SR: 4801

Built-in Dishwashers and Trash Compactors

Code Language

422.16 Flexible Cords

(B) Specific Appliances.

(2) Built-in Dishwashers and Trash Compactors. … (See *NEC* text)

(2) For a trash compactor, the length of the cord shall be 0.9 m to 1.2 m (3 ft to 4 ft)… (See *NEC* text)

(3) For a built-in dishwasher, the length of the cord shall be 0.9 m to 2.0 m (3 ft to 6.5 ft) measured from the face of the attachment plug to the plane of the rear of the appliance.

(6) The receptacle for a built-in dishwasher shall be located in the space adjacent to the space occupied by the dishwasher.

(See NEC for actual text)

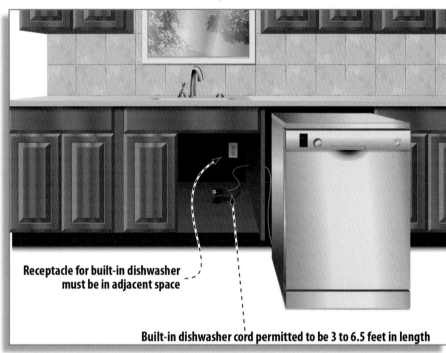

Receptacle for built-in dishwasher must be in adjacent space

Built-in dishwasher cord permitted to be 3 to 6.5 feet in length

Change Summary

- Flexible cords supplying trash compactors are permitted to be between 3 feet and 4 feet long.
- A longer flexible cord to facilitate connection for dishwashers in an adjacent space is permitted to be between 3 feet and 6 ½ feet long.
- The receptacle for a trash compactor must be located in the space occupied by the appliance or adjacent and the receptacle for a built-in dishwasher must be located in the space adjacent to the space occupied by the dishwasher.

FR: 4804
SR: 4804

Significance of the Change

Section 422.16 provides requirements for flexible cords that supply appliances. Requirements for flexible cords supplying built-in dishwashers and trash compactors are located in 422.16(B)(2) and have been revised for clarity and to correlate with product standards. Requirements for the installation of trash compactors are revised in changes to list items (2) and (5). 422.16(B)(2)(2) is revised and now applies only to trash compactors limiting the length of the flexible cord to between 3 and 4 feet. 422.16(B)(2)(4) is relocated to list item (5) and now permits the receptacle for a trash compactor to be located in the space occupied by the compactor or in an adjacent space. Multiple revisions have been made to requirements for flexible cords for built-in dishwashers to correlate with the applicable product standard. *UL 749 Household Dishwashers* prohibits the flexible cord on a built-in dishwasher to be plugged into a receptacle located in the space occupied by the dishwasher. UL 749 requires the receptacle to be installed in a location adjacent to the dishwasher. A new list item 422.16(B)(2)(3) is added to permit a longer flexible cord to facilitate connection for dishwashers in an adjacent space and allows the cord to be between 3 feet and 6½ feet long. Additionally, a new list item 422.16(B)(2)(6) is added to require that the receptacle for a built-in dishwasher be located in the space adjacent to the space occupied by the dishwasher.

Support of Ceiling-Suspended (Paddle) Fans

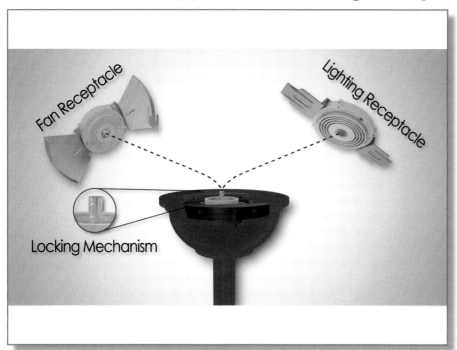

Courtesy of Safety Quick Lighting and Fans Corp.

Code Language

422.18 Support of Ceiling-Suspended (Paddle) Fans. Ceiling-suspended (paddle) fans shall be supported independently of an outlet box or by one of the following:

(1) A listed outlet box or listed outlet box system identified for the use and installed in accordance with 314.27(C).

(2) A listed outlet box system, a listed locking support and mounting receptacle, and a compatible factory installed attachment fitting designed for support, identified for the use and installed in accordance with 314.27(E)

(See NEC for actual text)

Significance of the Change

This revision correlates with a new type of separable plug and receptacle assembly for fixed equipment mounted on outlet boxes in 314.27(E). The requirement is separated into list items with the existing requirement for listed outlet box or listed outlet box system identified for the use and installed in accordance with 314.27(C) in list item (1). List item (2) now permits a listed outlet box system, a listed locking support, and mounting receptacle, and a compatible factory installed attachment fitting designed for support, identified for the use and installed in accordance with 314.27(E). These new devices are listed; as power supply devices, listed locking support, through listed receptacles and supporting means. These devices are designed to be installed in or to boxes designed for the purpose and are now permitted to be used for all types of luminaires, ceiling-suspended paddle fans and more. This new product is designed to facilitate quick and easy interchange of luminaires or ceiling mounted paddle fans. As incorporated into section 314.27 and here in 422.18, this new requirement is permissive in nature. This revision now recognizes this new technology and permits the use of these listed devices but does not require they be installed.

Change Summary

- 422.18 is revised and separated into list items for support of ceiling-suspended (paddle) fans.

- A new type of listed outlet box system, a listed locking support and mounting receptacle, and a compatible factory installed attachment fitting designed for support, identified for the use and installed in accordance with 314.27(E) is now permitted to support ceiling-suspended (paddle) fans.

FR: None
SR: 4806

Disconnection of Permanently Installed Appliances

Code Language

422.31(A) Rated at Not over 300 Volt-Amperes or ⅛ Horsepower. For permanently connected appliances rated at not over 300 volt-amperes or ⅛ hp, the branch-circuit overcurrent device shall be permitted to serve as the disconnecting means where the switch or circuit breaker is within sight from the appliance or is lockable in accordance with 110.25.

(C) Motor Operated Appliances Rated Over ⅛ Horsepower......

(See NEC for actual text)

Courtesy of Eaton Corporation

Change Summary

- Permanently connected appliances rated at not over 300 volt-amperes or ⅛ hp and motor operated appliances over ⅛ hp now require disconnects within sight or lockable in accordance with 110.25.
- The provisions for locking shall remain in place with or without the lock installed.
- This will require an identified accessory for circuit breakers.

Significance of the Change

422.31(A) in the 2014 NEC contains requirements for disconnecting means of appliances rated at not over 300 volt-amps or ⅛ horse-power and permits the branch circuit overcurrent protective device to serve as the disconnecting means. This requirement is revised to permit the overcurrent protective device as the required disconnecting means where it is within sight from the appliance or is lockable in accordance with 110.25. The intent of the requirement for the disconnecting means is safety driven. The previous requirement did not contain prescriptive text to ensure that the appliance could be maintained in a safe manner. In most cases the appliance is not within sight and a means to lock the disconnecting means in the open position was not previously required. This revision will now require that where the disconnecting means is not within sight from the appliance, the disconnect must be lockable in the open position in accordance with section 110.25 which also requires that the provisions for locking remain in place with or without the lock installed. Where a circuit breaker is the overcurrent protective device, an identified accessory device will be required to ensure that the provisions for locking remains in place with or without the lock installed.

A similar revision occurred in the positive text of 422.31(C) for motor operated appliances over ⅛ hp.

FRs: 4812, 4813

SR: None

Article 424 Part X
Article 424 Fixed Electric Space-Heating Equipment
Part X Low-Voltage Fixed Electric Space-Heating Equipment

NEW

Low-Voltage Fixed Electric Space-Heating Equipment

Code Language

Part X. Low-Voltage Fixed Electric Space-Heating Equipment

424.100 Scope. Low-voltage fixed electric space-heating equipment shall consist of an isolating power supply, low-voltage heaters, and associated equipment that are all identified for use in dry locations.

424.101(A) Power Unit. The power unit shall be an isolating type with a rated output not exceeding 25 amperes, 30 volts (42.4 volts peak) ac, or 60 volts dc under all load conditions.

(See NEC for actual text)

Significance of the Change

A new Part X is added to Article 424 to specifically address "Low-Voltage Fixed Electric Space-Heating Equipment." The term "low-voltage" in the title of this Part is addressed in 424.100. The scope of this Part recognizes low-voltage fixed electric space-heating equipment that consists of an isolating power supply, low-voltage heaters, and associated equipment that are all identified for use in dry locations. The "power unit" is addressed in 424.101(A) and is required to be an "isolating type" with a rated output not exceeding 25 amperes, 30 volts (42.4 volts peak) ac, or 60 volts dc under all load conditions. The voltage and current limitations in this new Part mirror those permitted in Article 411 as revised in the 2017 edition of the *NEC*.

Low voltage heating equipment is specifically permitted to be supplied by an alternate power source such as PV or Wind energy provided the alternate source and any power conversion equipment between the source and the heating equipment and its supply are listed and comply with all other applicable *NEC* requirements including the limitations for the "power unit" in 424.101(A). All low-voltage fixed electric space-heating equipment is required to be listed as a complete system and installed per the manufacturer's installation instructions. Branch circuits supplying this equipment are limited to 30 amps, secondary circuits are not permitted to be grounded, and GFCI protection is not required.

Change Summary

- Part X is added to Article 424 to specifically address "Low-Voltage Fixed Electric Space-Heating Equipment."

- "Power units" must be an isolating type with a rated output not exceeding 25 amperes, 30 volts (42.4 volts peak) ac, or 60 volts dc under all load conditions.

- Low-voltage fixed electric space-heating equipment is required to be listed as a complete system.

FR: 4843
SR: 4812

Extending Beyond the Room or Area

Code Language

424.38 Area Restrictions

(A) Extending Beyond the Room or Area. Heating cables shall be permitted to extend beyond the room or area in which they originate.

(See NEC for actual text)

Change Summary

- Heating cables are now permitted to extend beyond the room or area in which they originate.
- Multiple other revisions support this change including new 424.45 for cables installed under floor coverings and new 424.47 for labeling of panelboards.
- Clarity is provided throughout Part V for requirements in both floors and ceilings.

Significance of the Change

Section 424.38 addresses "area restrictions" for space heating cables installed in floors and ceilings. This revision now permits heating cables to extend beyond the room or area in which they originate. There have been significant advancements in design and the product standards that cover electric space heating cables since this requirement was first in the *NEC* and there is no practical reason to limit heating cables to the room or area in which they originate. For example, where there is a path from one room to another, such as a water closet to a vanity area in a bathroom, the floor can be warmed with one heating cable circuit without creating safety concerns if the manufacturer's installation instructions are followed and other applicable requirements including but not limited to GFCI protection, where required in Section 424.44 and 424.45 are applied.

There are also additional revisions throughout Part V to support this change. Two significant revisions include a new Section 424.45 with requirements for heating cables installed under floor coverings and new Section 424.47 which will require labeling of panelboards that supply electric heating cables. Additionally, 424.38(B) is revised for clarity on uses not permitted, 424.39 is revised to clarify it applies to ceiling installed cables, and 424.41 is revised to clarify it applies only to cables installed in ceilings.

FR: 4826
SR: None

Installation of Cables Under Floor Covering

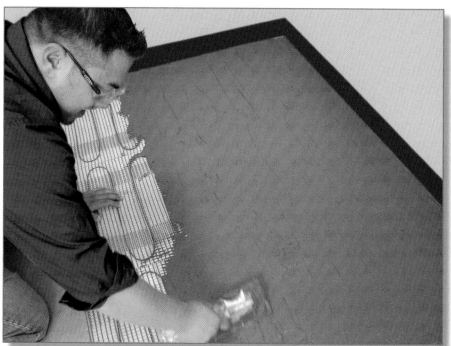

Significance of the Change

A new section 424.45 is added in Part V Electric Space-Heating Cables to permit heating cables to be installed under floor coverings similar to the permission in 424.99. Heating cables are now permitted under floor coverings provided they are identified by the manufacturer for use with the floor covering to be applied. There are many different types of floor covering used in residential and commercial installations that include but are not limited to ceramic tile, floor tile, linoleum, carpet and carpet squares. It is imperative that the installer read the manufacturers instructions to ensure the heating cable is identified for the floor covering to be applied. Installation over an expansion joint is not permitted unless the cable has an expansion type fitting. Heating cables must be secured to the floor as directed by the manufacturer before application of the floor covering. All installations of heating cable under floor coverings require that the branch circuit be GFCI protected. The entire length of heating cables under floor coverings must have a grounding means surrounding the cable such as copper braid, metal sheath, or other approved means.

New 424.47 requires labeling of panelboard to identify the branch circuits that supply heating cables as presently required in 424.92(D).

Code Language

424.45 Installation of Cables Under Floor Coverings. (A) Identification, **(B)** Expansion Joints, **(C)** Connection to Conductors, **(D)** Anchoring, **(E)** Ground-Fault Circuit-Interrupter Protection, **(F)** Grounding Braid or Sheath.

424.47 Label Provided by Manufacturer. The manufacturers of electric space-heating cables shall provide marking labels that indicate that the space-heating installation incorporates electric space-heating cables and instructions that the labels shall be affixed to the panelboards to identify which branch circuits supply the circuits to those space heating installations. If the electric space-heating cable installations are visible and distinguishable after installation, the labels shall not be required to be provided and affixed to the panelboards.

(See NEC for actual text)

Change Summary

- New 424.45 permits heating cables to be installed under floor coverings.
- Similar to permission in 424.99 for installation of heating panels under floor coverings.
- New 424.47 requires labeling of panelboard similar to 424.92(D).

FRs: 4834, 4823
SR: None

GFCI Protection, Grounding of Heating Panels/Sets

Code Language

424.99 Installation Under Floor Covering

(B) Installation

(5) GFCI Protection. Branch circuits supplying the heating panel or heating panel sets shall have ground-fault circuit-interrupter protection for personnel.

(6) Grounding Braid or Sheath. Excluding nonheating leads, grounding means, such as copper braid, metal sheath, or other approved means, shall be provided with or as an integral part of the heating panel or heating panel set.

(See NEC for actual text)

Change Summary

- A grounding braid or sheath is now required for all heating panels and heating panel sets installed under floor covering.
- GFCI protection is now required for all heating panels and heating panel sets installed under floor covering.
- The combination of a grounding braid or sheath and GFCI increases protection from shock.

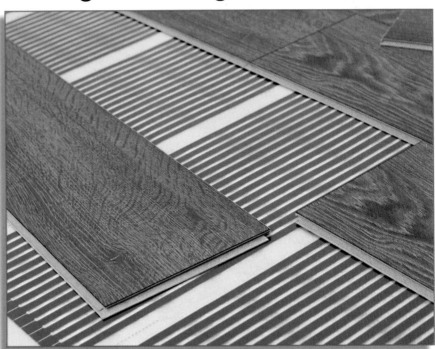

Significance of the Change

A new requirement is added in second level subdivision 424.99(B)(6) for a ground braid or sheath over the active electrical circuit in heating panels and heating panel sets. This "shielding" of the heating panels is required to allow a GFCI protecting the circuit to open in the event of a ground fault.

Existing first level subdivision 424.99(B)(5) is re-titled "GFCI Protection" and is revised to require that all branch circuits supplying heating panels and/or heating panel sets are provided with GFCI protection. The previous requirement in 424.99(B)(5) required "Fault Protection" which could have been but was not required to be a GFCI type device. The previous requirement mandated that the "fault protection," be provided by the manufacturer. GFCI protection is the most common and effective means available to provide protection against the risk of shock. The previous informational note which informed the *Code* user that an integral grounding shield may be required to provide "fault protection" is deleted and relocated as a requirement in 424.99(B)(6).

FR: 4838
SR: 4812

Article 425 Industrial Process Heating Equipment

Code Language

425.1 Scope. This article covers fixed industrial process heating employing electric resistance or electrode heating technology. For the purpose of this article, heating equipment shall include boilers, electrode boilers, duct heaters, strip heaters, immersion heaters, process air heaters, or other approved fixed electric equipment used for industrial process heating. This article shall not apply to heating and room air conditioning for personnel spaces covered by Article 424, fixed heating equipment for pipelines and vessels covered by Article 427, induction and dielectric heating equipment covered by Article 665, and industrial furnaces incorporating silicon carbide, molybdenum, or graphite process heating elements.

(See NEC for actual text)

Significance of the Change

The scope of Article 424 covers only fixed electric equipment used for space heating and does not address industrial process heating. Therefore a new "Article 425 titled Fixed Resistance and Electrode Industrial Process Heating Equipment" has been added to the *NEC* to address industrial installations. The scope of Article 425 includes fixed industrial process heating employing electric resistance or electrode heating technology including; boilers, electrode boilers, duct heaters, strip heaters, immersion heaters, process air heaters, or other approved fixed electric equipment used for industrial process heating. The requirements contained in Article 425 mirror the existing requirements in Article 424.

The scope in 425.1 specifically excludes equipment that is already covered in the *NEC* including; heating and room air conditioning for personnel spaces covered by Article 424, fixed heating equipment for pipelines and vessels covered by Article 427, and induction and dielectric heating equipment covered by Article 665. The scope also excludes industrial furnaces incorporating silicon carbide, molybdenum, or graphite process heating elements. These installations may require the application of NFPA 86, *Standard for Ovens and Furnace*s or NFPA 79 *Electrical Standard for Industrial Machinery*.

Change Summary

- A new Article 425 is added to cover fixed industrial process heating employing electric resistance or electrode heating technology.

- The requirements of Article 425 mirror existing Article 424.

- Article 425 does not apply to heating and room air conditioning for personnel spaces, fixed heating equipment for pipelines/vessels, and induction and dielectric heating equipment and other special applications.

FR: 4841
SRs: 4813, 7509

Single Motor Tap Conductors, Group Installations, 25-Feet

Code Language

430.53(D) Single Motor Taps.

430.53(D)(4) Conductors from the point of the tap from the branch circuit to a listed manual motor controller additionally marked "Suitable for Tap Conductor Protection in Group Installations," or to a branch-circuit protective device, shall be permitted to have an ampacity not less than one-third that of the branch-circuit conductors. The conductors from the controller to the motor shall have an ampacity in accordance with 430.22. The conductors from the point of the tap to the controller(s) shall (1) be suitably protected from physical damage and enclosed either by an enclosed controller or by a raceway and be not more than 7.5 m (25 ft) long or (2) have an ampacity not less than that of the branch-circuit conductors.

(See NEC for actual text)

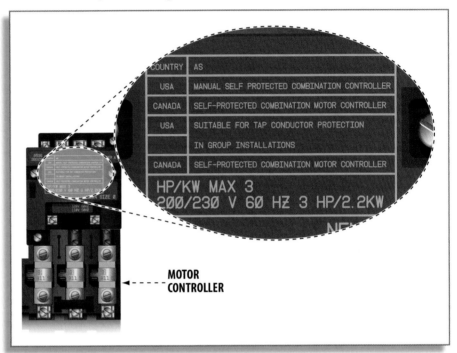

MOTOR CONTROLLER

Change Summary

- Existing 430.53(D) addresses single motor taps for group installations.
- New 430.53(D)(4) permits single motor tap conductors at not more than 25-feet.
- Existing 430.53(D)(3) permits single motor tap conductors at not more than 10-feet.

Significance of the Change

List item 430.53(D)(3) is editorially revised to clarify that the "tap conductors" addressed in this requirement are "from the point of the tap from the branch circuit" not from "branch-circuit short-circuit and ground-fault protective device." The tap conductors may originate at the branch-circuit short-circuit and ground-fault protective device but are not required to originate at that location.

A new list item 430.53(D)(4) is added to permit tap conductors up to 25-feet to mirror the existing 10-foot tap permitted in 430.53(D)(3). This new list item allows 25-foot tap conductors with the same conditions as 430.28. The existing 430.53(D)(3) rule limits the maximum length of reduced ampacity tap conductors to only 10 feet in all locations. This revision is necessary to permit single motor tap conductors up to 25 feet. This requires the conductors from the point of the tap from the branch circuit to terminate in a listed manual motor controller additionally marked "Suitable for Tap Conductor Protection in Group Installations," or to a branch-circuit protective device. The tap conductors are permitted to have an ampacity not less than one-third that of the branch-circuit conductors.

FR: 3014
SR: None

MCC Available Fault Current, Documentation

MCC-ESW18
Available Fault Current
18,654 Amperes
Date of Calculation
5/14/2017

Code Language

430.99 Available Fault Current.
The available short circuit current at the motor control center and the date the short circuit current calculation was performed shall be documented and made available to those authorized to inspect the installation.

(See NEC for actual text)

Significance of the Change

First level subdivision 430.98(A) requires motor control centers to be marked in accordance with 110.21, with the common power bus current rating and the motor control center short circuit current rating. In order to determine compliance with the motor control center short circuit current rating, the electrical inspector needs to know what the level of available short-circuit current is at the motor control center at the time of installation. This has proven difficult because in most cases the information is not available. This new requirement will mandate that the available short circuit current at the motor control center be documented along with the date the short circuit current calculation was performed. This documentation is also required to be made available to those authorized to inspect the installation to confirm compliance with 430.98(A).

The available short circuit current at the motor control center will be determined in the design phase in order for the installer to comply with sections 110.9 Interrupting Rating and 110.10 Circuit Impedance, Short-Circuit Current Ratings, and Other Characteristics. The installer can simply document the amount of available short-circuit current at the motor control center on the drawing along with the date the calculation was made. While a label or marking of available short circuit current is not required on the motor control center, it may be the most feasible method of complying with this new requirement.

Change Summary

- New 430.99 requires that the amount of available short circuit at the MCC and the date the calculation was made is now required to be documented by new Section 430.99.

- This information must be documented and available for the AHJ to ensure compliance with 430.98(A).

- While a label or marking of available short circuit current is not required on the motor control center, it may be the most feasible method of complying with this new requirement.

FR: 3016
SR: None

Circuits Containing Power Conversion Equipment

Code Language

430.130(A) Circuits Containing Power Conversion Equipment.
Where an instantaneous trip circuit breaker or semiconductor fuses are permitted in accordance with the drive manufacturer's instructions for use as the branch-circuit short circuit and ground-fault protective device for listed power conversion equipment, they shall be provided as an integral part of a single listed assembly incorporating both the protective device and power conversion equipment.

(See NEC for actual text)

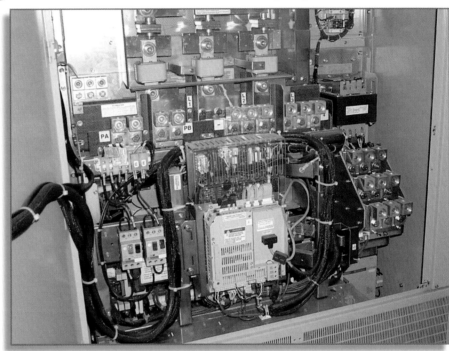

Change Summary

- New 430.130(A)(4) replaces the previous informational note to address the type of protective device for circuits containing power conversion equipment.
- 430.130(A)(4) requires that where instantaneous trip circuit breaker or semiconductor fuses are used, they must be an integral part of a single listed assembly.
- This correlates the *NEC* with the applicable product standard, UL 508C.

FR: 3017
SR: None

Significance of the Change

Section 430.130 was added in the 2014 *NEC* revision cycle to address branch-circuit, short-circuit and ground-fault protection for single motor circuits containing power conversion equipment. This requires the rating and type to be determined by 430.52(C) except where the manufacturer stipulated a lower value. Self-protected combination controllers are only permitted where specifically identified in the manufacturer's instructions for the power conversion equipment or otherwise marked on the equipment. The previous informational note informed the *Code* user that the type of protective device, the rating, and the setting are often marked on or provided with the power conversion equipment.

This revision deletes the informational note and now requires that where an instantaneous trip circuit breaker or semiconductor fuses are used, they must be an integral part of a single listed assembly provided by the manufacturer. The applicable product standard UL 508(C) requires specific markings on the equipment where semiconductor fuses and instantaneous trip circuit breakers are applied. These markings include the fuse manufacturer and fuse model number or breaker manufacturer and breaker model number. The product standard also requires that the drive controller and overcurrent protection device must be integrated within the same overall assembly.

Grounding and Bonding, EGC

Code Language

440.9 Grounding and Bonding.
Where multimotor and combination-load equipment is installed outdoors on a roof, an equipment grounding conductor of the wire type shall be installed in outdoor portions of metallic raceway systems that use non-threaded fittings.

(See NEC for actual text)

Significance of the Change

New Section 440.9 Grounding and Bonding now requires that rooftop (outdoor) installations that utilize metallic raceway systems that use non-threaded fittings (EMT) install an equipment grounding conductor (EGC) of the wire type. The substantiation for this revision is the potential for damage to all raceway systems that are installed on rooftops. The physical damage noted in substantiation for this revision includes the fact that raceways of all types are stepped on and moved by workers that are on the roof for many reasons including but not limited to, snow removal, roof replacement, installation of new equipment and much more. Where the non-threaded connectors and couplings on a metallic raceway system are opened, the ground fault return path on the metal raceway is eliminated. An installation of rigid conduit with threaded fittings is far less likely to have the fault return path on the metal raceway eliminated. Loss of the ground fault return path is a serious concern for all persons that could come in contact with the equipment on the roof. This issue has been seriously debated over the last few *NEC* revision cycles. EMT has proven to be an extremely reliable raceway and ground fault return path but in a rooftop environment, it is subject to physical damage.

Change Summary

- New 440.9 now requires a "wire-type" EGC for outdoor portions of metallic raceway systems that use non-threaded fittings installed on a roof.
- Physical damage caused by activities on a roof combined with the weather can cause non-threaded connectors and couplings to open and eliminating the fault return path on the metal raceway.
- While this is a significant revision in the *NEC*, there will be little impact on industry as the vast majority of EMT installations include a "wire type" EGC without regard to where the EMT is installed.

FR: 3005
SR: None

Short-Circuit Current Rating

Code Language

440.10 Short-Circuit Current Rating.

(A) Installation. Motor controllers of multimotor and combination-load equipment shall not be installed where the available short-circuit current exceeds its short-circuit current rating as marked in accordance with 440.4(B)

(B) Documentation. When motor controllers or industrial control panels of multimotor and combination load equipment are required to be marked with a short circuit current rating, the available short circuit current and the date the short circuit current calculation was performed shall be documented and made available to those authorized to inspect the installation.

(See NEC for actual text)

Change Summary

- New 440.10(A) requires equipment be installed in accordance with the marked ASCC rating.

- New 440.10(B) requires that the available short circuit current at the equipment be documented along with the date the short circuit current calculation was performed.

- While a label or marking of available short circuit current is not required on the motor controller, it may be the most feasible method of complying with this new requirement.

FR: 3006
SR: 3005

Significance of the Change

First level subdivision 440.4(B) requires multimotor and combination load equipment to be marked with the short-circuit current rating of the motor controllers or industrial control panel. In order to determine compliance with the equipment short circuit current rating, the electrical inspector needs to know what the level of available short circuit current is at the equipment at the time of installation. This has proven difficult because in most cases the information is not available. New 440.10(A) requires that motor controllers of multimotor and combination-load equipment be rated for the available short circuit current at the equipment. New 440.10(B) requires that the available short circuit current at the equipment be documented along with the date the short circuit current calculation was performed. This documentation is also required to be made available to those authorized to inspect the installation to confirm compliance with 440.4(B).

This information is readily available during the design of the system. The available short circuit current at the equipment will be determined in the design phase in order for the installer to comply with sections 110.9 Interrupting Rating and 110.10 Circuit Impedance, Short-Circuit Current Ratings, and Other Characteristics. The installer can simply document the amount of available short circuit current at the equipment on the drawing along with the date the calculation was made.

Protection Devices, Room Air Conditioners

Code Language

440.65 Protection Devices. Single-phase cord- and plug-connected room air conditioners shall be provided with one of the following factory-installed devices:

(1) Leakage-current detector-interrupter (LCDI)

(2) Arc-fault circuit interrupter (AFCI)

(3) Heat detecting circuit interrupter (HDCI)

The protection device shall be an integral part of the attachment plug or be located in the power supply cord within 300 mm (12 in.) of the attachment plug.

(See NEC for actual text)

Significance of the Change

Section 440.65 is retitled to "Protective Devices" and editorially revised into list items. This section contains requirements for cord and plug connected room air conditioning units. These requirements are necessary to prevent fires associated with cord and plug connected room air conditioners. In addition to leakage-current detector-interrupters (LCDI) and arc-fault circuit interrupters (AFCI), a new device, the heat detecting circuit interrupter (HDCI) is now permitted. The devices must be an integral part of the attachment plug or be located in the power supply cord within 300 mm (12 in.) of the attachment plug.

The *NEC* includes these requirements to protect against fire because only newer homes have branch circuits protected with AFCI's. In a similar fashion, the *NEC* requires appliances such as hair dryers, flat irons and other appliances to incorporate safety features designed to prevent shock and fire. This new protection device, the heat detecting circuit interrupter or HDCI incorporates all of the protection functions of an LCDI but also includes a thermal detecting function to provide protection against overheating of the air conditioner's compressor. The HDCI is now included in 440.65 because it provides all of the protection functions of an LCDI and additionally provides a thermal detecting function to protect the air conditioner's compressor.

Change Summary

- 440.65 is retitled "Protection Devices."
- The permitted protective devices are an LCDI, an AFCI or an HDCI.
- An HDCI incorporates all of the protection functions of an LCDI but also includes a thermal detecting function to provide protection against overheating of the air conditioner's compressor.

FR: 3021
SR: None

Generator Location, Exhaust

Code Language

445.10 Location. Generators shall be of a type suitable for the locations in which they are installed. They shall also meet the requirements for motors in 430.14.

Informational Note: See NFPA 37, Standard for the Installation and Use of Stationary Combustion Engines and Gas Turbines for information on the location of generator exhaust.

(See NEC for actual text)

Change Summary

- A new informational note is added to 445.10 informing *Code* users to refer to NFPA 37 on the location of generator exhaust.
- There are a number of serious considerations for generator installations; the type of fuel, how the fuel is routed to the generator, fuel storage, and generator exhaust.
- Generators must be installed a minimum distance from buildings/structures and exhaust must be directed away from all openings in walls of buildings/structures.

FR: 7502
SR: None

Significance of the Change

Section 445.10 requires in general that generators be of a type suitable for the locations in which they are installed. This addresses all locations for all types of generators. Where a generator is installed, there are a number of serious considerations for the installer including but not limited to the type of fuel, how the fuel is routed to the generator, fuel storage, and generator exhaust. A new informational note is added to section 445.10 to send the *Code* user to NFPA 37, *Standard for the Installation and Use of Stationary Combustion Engines and Gas Turbines* for information on the location of generators and generator exhaust. It is imperative that installers follow all manufacturer instructions and the minimum requirements of NFPA 37 to keep the generator exhaust away from the building or structure supplied and to prevent a fire. NFPA 37 provides prescriptive requirements for the location of outdoor generators and requires they be located at least five feet from openings in walls and at least five feet from structures having combustible walls.

The Consumer Product Safety Commission provided substantiation that included multiple fatalities and many other very serious incidents that have occurred because a permanently installed outdoor generator was not installed in accordance with NFPA 37 and the exhaust entered buildings through windows or other openings.

Ampacity of Conductors

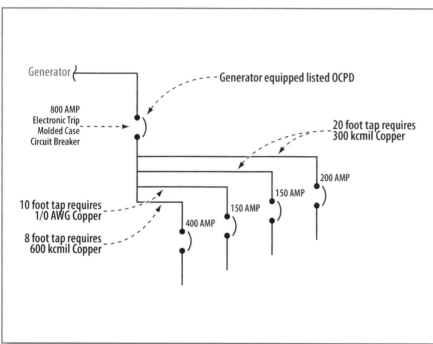

- Generator
- Generator equipped listed OCPD
- 800 AMP Electronic Trip Molded Case Circuit Breaker
- 20 foot tap requires 300 kcmil Copper
- 200 AMP
- 150 AMP
- 150 AMP
- 10 foot tap requires 1/0 AWG Copper
- 400 AMP
- 8 foot tap requires 600 kcmil Copper

Code Language

445.13 Ampacity of Conductors.

(B) Overcurrent Protection Provided. Where the generator set is equipped with a listed overcurrent protective device, or a combination of a current transformer and overcurrent relay, conductors shall be permitted to be tapped from the load side of the protected terminals in accordance with 240.21(B). Tapped conductors shall not be permitted for portable generators rated 15 kW or less where field wiring connection terminals are not accessible.

(See NEC for actual text)

Significance of the Change

A new first level subdivision 445.13(B) is added to clarify the allowable ampacity rating of conductors supplied by a generator. The general rule in 445.13(A) is clarified to require the ampacity of the conductors from the generator "output" terminals to the first distribution "device(s) containing overcurrent protection" be not less than 115% of the nameplate current rating of the generator. This general rule applies only to the portion of the conductor from the "output" terminals (that has no upstream overcurrent protection) to an overcurrent protective device (OCPD.) In many cases, the generator is factory equipped with an OCPD such as a set of fuses or a circuit breaker. The general requirement for conductors rated at 115% applies only to the conductors supplying integral the factory supplied OCPD. 445.13(A) does not apply to the conductors on the load side of the OCPD. New first level subdivision 445.13(B) now clarifies that where overcurrent protection is provided with a listed OCPD, including a combination of a current transformer and overcurrent relay, conductors are permitted to be tapped from the load side of the protected terminals in accordance with 240.21(B).

A generator may supply a single load with a single set of conductors, or it may serve multiple loads with multiple sets of conductors.

Change Summary

- New 445.13(B) clarifies that generator supplied conductors on the load side of an OCPD are not required to be sized at 115% of the nameplate current.

- Generator supplied conductors on the load side of an OCPD may be applied in accordance with 240.21(B).

- The 115% rule applies only to conductors from the generator output terminals to an OCPD.

FR: 3603
SR: 3618

Disconnecting Means and Shutdown of Prime Mover

Code Language

445.18 Disconnecting Means and Shutdown of Prime Mover.
(A) Disconnecting Means.
(B) Shutdown of Prime Mover.
(C) Generators Installed in Parallel.

(See NEC for actual text)

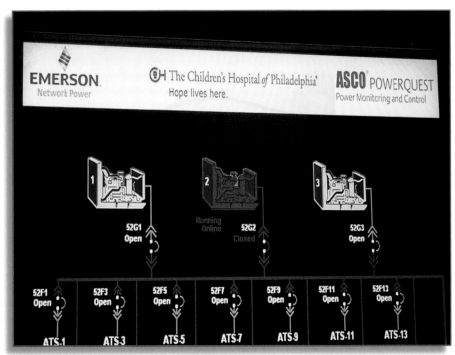

Change Summary

- 445.18 is separated into three first level subdivisions for clarity.
- 445.18(A) requires one or more disconnecting means (110.25) that simultaneously open all ungrounded conductors for all generators other than cord- and plug-connected portable generators.
- 445.18(B) requires a means to shut down the prime mover disabling all prime mover start control circuits, rendering the prime mover incapable of starting.
- 445.18(C) provides clarity for disconnects where generators are installed in parallel.

FR: 3661
SRs: 3619, 3620
SCR: 82

Significance of the Change

Section 445.18 is revised for clarity. New 445.18(A) requires all generators, other than cord- and plug-connected portable generators, to have one or more disconnecting means. Each disconnecting means must simultaneously open all associated ungrounded conductors and be lockable in the open position in accordance with 110.25.

New 445.18(B) requires a means to shut down the prime mover that will disable all prime mover start control circuits to render the prime mover incapable of starting and initiate a shutdown mechanism that requires a mechanical reset. This means to shut down the prime mover is permitted as the disconnecting means required in 445.18(A) where it is lockable in accordance with 110.25. Generators with greater than 15 kW rating have an additional means to shut down the prime mover that is located outside the equipment room. This additional requirement now provides a remote shutdown means in the event of an emergency for larger generators.

New 445.18(C) provides clarity for a generator disconnecting means where a generator is installed in parallel with other generators. The disconnect required in 445.18(A) must be capable of isolating the generator output terminals from the paralleling equipment. The disconnecting means is not required to be located at the generator as it may be located at the paralleling equipment.

Listing of Batteries and Management Equipment

Courtesy of PDE Total Energy Solutions

Code Language

480.3 Equipment. Storage batteries and battery management equipment shall be listed. This requirement shall not apply to lead-acid batteries.

(See NEC for actual text)

Significance of the Change

This new section 480.3 now requires all storage batteries (other than lead-acid type batteries) and battery management equipment to be listed. New advanced battery technologies have changed the energy storage industry. The need for more energy storage in tighter spaces has lead to advances driving more energy into smaller physical packages. The consequences of battery failure modes with these new technologies have increased significantly. Advanced battery technologies can be placed into unsafe operating modes, which can lead to thermal runaway, fires, and explosions. This is particularly applicable to battery chemistries such as lithium-ion, which have flammable electrolytes. A fault event within a single battery can quickly be driven by the chemistry to cascade to an event that consumes the battery. An event within a single battery can also cascade into a large-scale event. This new requirement will mandate rigorous validation of the battery design for safety reasons. This is especially critical for these advanced technologies but not for lead acid type batteries. The listing process will also impact the manufacturing process of advanced batteries. This is critical to the safe operation of the battery itself because small contaminants in the manufacturing process can lead to the formation of dendrites over the life of the battery, which can cause catastrophic consequences.

Change Summary

- New section 480.3 requires all batteries and their associated battery management equipment to be listed.
- The listing requirement excludes lead acid type batteries.
- Catastrophic failures in new battery technology systems mandate rigorous testing for safety.

FR: None

SR: 3629

480.7(D)

Required Labeling

Code Language

480.7 DC Disconnect Methods

(D) Notification. The disconnecting means shall be legibly marked... (See *NEC* text) and shall include the following:

(1) Nominal battery voltage

(2) Maximum available short circuit current derived from the stationary battery system

(3) Date the fault current calculation was performed

(4) The battery disconnecting means shall be marked in accordance with 110.16.

Informational Note No. 1: Battery equipment suppliers can provide ... (See *NEC* text) short-circuit current ...

Informational Note No. 2: The available short circuit current marking(s) addressed in 480.6(D)(2) is related to required short circuit current ratings of equipment. NFPA 70E-2015, provides assistance in determining the severity of potential exposure, planning safe work practices, and selecting personal protective equipment.

(See NEC for actual text)

Change Summary

- New list item (4) references arc flash warning label requirements in 110.16.
- New Informational Note No. 2 explains that the ASCC must be known to determine safe work practices in accordance with NFPA 70E.

FR: 3643

SR: 3630

SCR: 83

Significance of the Change

First level subdivision 480.6(D) is revised to better illustrate that the required field markings for battery systems are necessary for the safety of persons that will install and maintain storage battery systems. 480.6(A) requires a disconnecting means for all ungrounded conductors supplied by a battery system rated at over a nominal value of 50-volts. 480.6(D) contains four list items with required information that must be placed on the label that is required on the disconnect. The information must include (1) the voltage, (2) the maximum available short circuit current, (3) the date the calculation was performed and (4) a new list item that references the required arc flash warning label required in section 110.16.

A new informational Note No. 2 is added to explain that the available short circuit current marking(s) for the battery system disconnect label addressed in 480.6(D)(2), is related to the short circuit current ratings of equipment, the batteries themselves. In order for an installer/maintainer to determine the necessary arc rated personal protective equipment (PPE) when performing justified energized work on a battery system, the available short circuit current (ASCC) must be known. The only way to determine the ASCC of the battery system is to get the information from the battery manufacturer.

480.10 Battery Locations

(A) Ventilation. Provisions appropriate to the battery technology shall be made for sufficient diffusion and ventilation of gases from the battery, if present, to prevent the accumulation of an explosive mixture.

480.11 Vents.

(A) Vented Cells. Each vented cell shall be equipped with a flame arrester.

Chapter 5

Articles 500–590
Special Occupancies

Definitions in 500.2 Relocated

Code Language

Multiple Definitions have been relocated from Section 500.2 to Article 100. The following represents an example of how each relocated will appear in Article 100.

Example:

Combustible Dust [as applied to Hazardous (Classified) Locations]. Dust particles that are 500 microns or smaller (material passing a U.S. No. 35 Standard Sieve as defined…(CMP-14)… (See *NEC* text)

(See NEC for actual text)

Change Summary

- Multiple definitions previously located in 500.2 have been relocated to Article 100.

- Section 2.2.2.1 of the *NEC Style Manual* requires that if a term appears in more than two articles, it shall be included in Article 100.

- The words [as applied to Hazardous (Classified) Locations] have been added in brackets following each relocated defined term.

FRs: 3929, 3904, 3906, 3907, 3912, 3915, 3916, 3913, 3909, 3918
SR: None
SCR: 121

Significance of the Change

Compliance with the *NEC Style Manual* is essential. Many of the defined terms that apply to hazardous (classified) locations appeared in more than just Article 100. To resolve the Style Manual conflict and improve usability, the following 500.2 definitions (in part) are now located in Article 100.

Combustible Dust (as applied to Hazardous (Classified) Locations), Combustible Gas Detection System (as applied to Hazardous (Classified) Locations), Control Drawing (as applied to Hazardous (Classified) Locations), Dust-Ignitionproof (as applied to Hazardous (Classified) Locations), Hermetically Sealed (as applied to Hazardous (Classified) Locations), Purged and Pressurized (as applied to Hazardous (Classified) Locations), Unclassified Locations (as applied to Hazardous (Classified) Locations) Nonincendive Circuit (as applied to Hazardous (Classified) Locations) Nonincendive Component (as applied to Hazardous (Classified) Locations)…(See *NEC* text)

No technical revisions were made to these definitions. Adding the words [as applied to Hazardous (Classified) Locations)] following each relocated term provides a differentiation from the same term that may apply to general wiring methods or equipment, and thus not located within Chapter 5. Another revision in Article 100 is to include in parenthesis the Code-Making Panel having technical responsibility for each of the definitions i.e. (CMP-1).

Ammonia Areas May Be Unclassified

Photo from iStock

Significance of the Change

Section 500.5(A) is applicable to Sections 500.5(B), 500.5(C), and 500.5(D), therefore, the text of 500.5(A) has been retitled as "General." Refrigerant machinery rooms containing ammonia refrigeration systems and are equipped with adequate continuously operating mechanical ventilation or where initiation occurs by a detection system at a concentration, not exceeding150 ppm shall be permitted to be classified as "unclassified" locations. Two methods of protection are recognized in this section, allowing refrigerant machine rooms for ammonia systems to be unclassified. The first method involves continuously operating and adequate mechanical ventilation while the other recognizes ammonia gas detection systems that initiate at levels not to exceed 150 parts per million. Informational note no. 2 to this section has been revised to correct the date and title of **ANSI/ASHRAE 15** *Safety Standard for Refrigeration Systems* and to provide a reference to **ANSI/IIAR 2** *Standard for Safe Design of Closed-Circuit Ammonia Refrigeration Systems.* **ANSI/IIAR 2** provides the criteria that must be met for installing and operating closed-circuit ammonia refrigeration detection systems. These standards are typically mandated by the applicable fire and mechanical codes. A similar revision was incorporated in Section 505.5(A) covering the zone system of hazardous location classification.

Code Language

(A) General. Locations shall be classified…(see *NEC* text)

Refrigerant machinery rooms that contain ammonia refrigeration systems and are equipped with adequate mechanical ventilation that operates continuously or is initiated by a detection system at a concentration not exceeding150 ppm shall be permitted to be classified as "unclassified" locations.

Informational Note No 2: For further information regarding classification and ventilation of areas involving closed circuit ammonia refrigeration systems, see **ANSI/ASHRAE 15-2013,** *Safety Standard for Refrigeration Systems* and **ANSI/IIAR 2-2014** *Standard for Safe Design of Closed-Circuit Ammonia Refrigeration Systems.*

(See NEC for actual text)

Change Summary

- The title of Subdivision (A) has been changed from "Classifications of Locations" to "General."

- Classification of ammonia system refrigerant machinery rooms for ammonia systems has been revised and clarified.

- Adequate continuous mechanical ventilation or initiation by a detection system at concentrations, not exceeding150 ppm shall be permitted to be as unclassified locations.

FR: 3934
SR: 3916
SCR: 2

Factory Seal Marking and Removal of Conduit Bodies

Code Language

c. (See *NEC* text)...and marked "Leads Factory Sealed," or "Factory Sealed" or "Seal Not Required" or equivalent.

(2) The entry...(See *NEC* text)

An enclosure identified for the location, and marked "Leads Factory Sealed," or "Factory Sealed" or "Seal Not Required" or equivalent shall not be considered to serve as a seal for another adjacent enclosure...(See *NEC* text)

Conduit seals... (See *NEC* text)... marking. Only explosionproof unions, couplings, reducers, elbows, and capped elbows that are not larger than the trade size of the conduit shall be permitted between the sealing fitting and the explosionproof enclosure.

(See NEC for actual text)

Change Summary

- This section was revised to clarify requirements relative to factory seals and conduit bodies.
- Conduit bodies was removed from 501.15(A)(2) as allowable explosionproof fittings between the seal and the expolsionproof enclosure.
- The change is consistent with the seal requirements marked on many exposionproof en-closures and reduces conduit volume between the seal and the enclosure.

FR: 3974
SR: 3922

Significance of the Change

This revision provides relief from a field-installed sealing fitting under specific restrictive conditions related to whether or not a factory seal is an integral part of the equipment. The revision provides additional clarification about markings on equipment that allow wiring to be installed without inclusion of a field-installed sealing fitting. Many types of explosionproof equipment are produced in a way that includes sealing any integral arcing contacts prevents ignition of flammable gases or vapors that enter the enclosure. The clarification deals with the marking that indicates factory sealing is integral with the equipment. Equipment identified for the location, and marked "Leads Factory Sealed," or "Factory Sealed" or "Seal Not Required" or equivalent does not require a field-installed seal. Another revision in this section indicates explosionproof conduit bodies are no longer a permitted fitting between a conduit sealing fitting and an explosionproof enclosure. This revision correlates with a similar revision to 501.15(D)(1). Some explosionproof enclosures require a seal located less than 18 in. away and are so marked. It is not intended that this section override any manufacturer's re-strictions. Conduit bodies were removed because they should not be allowed in this application due to the increased volume in the raceway system.

Cable Seals at Explosionproof Enclosures

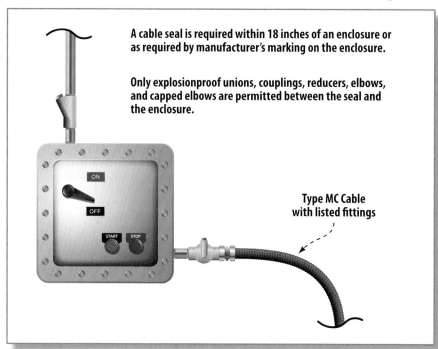

A cable seal is required within 18 inches of an enclosure or as required by manufacturer's marking on the enclosure.

Only explosionproof unions, couplings, reducers, elbows, and capped elbows are permitted between the seal and the enclosure.

Type MC Cable with listed fittings

Code Language

501.15(D)(1) At Terminations.
Cables shall be sealed... (See *NEC* text)...Seals for cables entering enclosures shall be installed within 450 mm (18 in.) of the enclosure or as required by the enclosure marking. Only explosionproof unions, couplings, reducers, elbows, and capped elbows that are not larger than the trade size of the enclosure entry shall be permitted between the sealing fitting and the enclosure.

(See NEC for actual text)

Significance of the Change

Section 501.15(D) addresses cable seals in Class I, Division 1 locations. List item (1) in this section was revised to clarify requirements relative to locations of cable seals at enclosures. Sealing fittings used for cables are required to be listed with one or more specific compounds and must be accessible as provided in 501.15(C). The requirement in (D)(1) has been revised to specify a maximum distance of 18 inches from the enclosure. The revised text also addresses the need for other types of explosionproof fittings that can be safely utilized between a cable seal and an enclosure. As a result, explosionproof unions, couplings, reducers, elbows, and capped elbows that are not larger than the trade size of the enclosure entry shall be permitted between the sealing fitting and the enclosure. This change provides consistency between 501.15(A)(1) and this section.

Some explosionproof enclosures require the seal located less than 18 in. from the enclosure, and are so marked. In these cases the more restrictive sealing fitting location requirements included in the manufacturer's markings take precedent.

Change Summary

- Section 501.15(D)(1) was revised to clarify requirements relative to locations of cable seals at enclosures.
- A cable seal is required within 18 inches of an enclosure or as required by manufacturer's markings on the enclosure.
- Only explosionproof unions, couplings, reducers, elbows, and capped elbows are permitted between the seal and the enclosure.

FR: 3973
SR: None

Shaft Bonding Device in Class I, Division 2 Locations

Code Language

(B) Class I, Division 2. In Class I, Division 2 locations, motors, generators, and other rotating electrical machinery shall comply with (1), (2), or (3). They shall also comply with (4) and (5), if applicable

(1) Be identified for...(See *NEC* text)

(5) A sliding contact shaft bonding device used for the purpose of maintaining the rotor at ground potential shall be permitted where the potential discharge energy is determined to be nonincendive for the application. The shaft bonding device shall be permitted to be installed on the inside or the outside of the motor.

(See NEC for actual text)

Change Summary

- A new list item (5) has been added to Section 501.125(B) and addresses motor shaft bonding achieved through a sliding contact.
- A sliding contact shaft bonding device is permitted where potential discharge is determined to be nonincendive for the applications.
- The shaft bonding device can be internal or external to the motor housing.

Significance of the Change

Section 501.125(B) is revised to provide a more logical layout and improve usability, in addition, to be consistent with the format of 501.125(A). The new list item (5) recognizes a shaft bonding device to be used on inverter-fed motors for the purpose of maintaining the rotor at ground potential to reduce bearing failure due to arcing. Variable frequency drives used for AC and DC motors can induce harmful voltages on the shaft of the motor. Often these voltages can exceed the resistance of shaft bearing lubricants and result in discharge through the motor bearings causing severe pitting and other damage. Excessive bearing noise and eventual failure of the shaft bearing is the result. A shaft-bonding device provides a diversion path to ground for such induced voltages making these motors resilient to such effects. One of the key conditions of this provision is the shaft-bonding device is permitted where the potential discharge energy is determined to be nonincendive for the application. Shaft bonding devices can be installed on the inside or the outside of the motor. A new informational note no. 5 was added to provide guidance on the application of shaft bonding devices.

FR: 3970
SR: 3927

Ammonia Areas May Be Unclassified in the Zone System

Photo from iStock

Significance of the Change

Article 505 provides requirements for classification under the zone system of hazardous (classified) locations. Refrigerant machinery rooms containing ammonia refrigeration systems and are equipped with adequate continuously operating mechanical ventilation or where initiation occurs by a detection system at a concentration, not exceeding150 ppm shall be permitted to be classified as "unclassified" locations. Two methods of protection are recognized in this section for allowing refrigerant machine rooms for ammonia systems to be unclassified. The first method involves continuously operating and adequate mechanical ventilation while the other recognizes ammonia gas detection systems that initiate at levels not to exceed 150 parts per million. The existing informational note to this section has been revised to correct the date and title of **ANSI/ASHRE 15** *Safety Standard for Refrigeration Systems* and to provide a reference to **ANSI/ARIIR 2** *Standard for Safe Design of Closed-Circuit Ammonia Refrigeration Systems.* **ANSI/ARIIR 2** provides the criteria that must be met for installing and operating closed-circuit ammonia refrigeration detection systems. These standards are typically mandated by the applicable fire and mechanical codes. A similar revision was incorporated in Section 505.5(A) covering the zone system of hazardous location classification.

Code Language

505.5(A) Classification of Locations. Locations shall be classified depending...(See *NEC* text)

Refrigerant machinery rooms that contain ammonia refrigeration systems and are equipped with adequate mechanical ventilation that operates continuously or is initiated by a detection system at a concentration not exceeding 150 ppm shall be permitted to be classified as "unclassified" locations.

Informational Note: For further information regarding classification and ventilation of areas involving closed circuit ammonia refrigeration systems, see **ANSI/ASHRAE 15-2013,** *Safety Standard for Refrigeration Systems* and **ANSI/IIAR 2-2014** *Standard for Safe Design of Closed-Circuit Ammonia Refrigeration Systems.*

(See NEC for actual text)

Change Summary

- Article 505 provides requirements for classification under the zone system of hazardous (classified) locations.
- Classification of ammonia system refrigerant machinery rooms for ammonia systems has been revised and clarified.
- Adequate continuous mechanical ventilation or initiation by a detection system at concentrations, not exceeding150 ppm shall be permitted to be as unclassified locations.

FR: 3936
SR: 3915
SCR: 5

Limits for Wiring Methods in Class I, Zone 0 Locations

Code Language

(A) Class I, Zone 0. In Class I, Zone 0 locations, equipment protected by intrinsic safety "ia" and equipment protected by encapsulation "ma" shall be connected using intrinsically safe "ia" circuits with wiring methods in accordance with Article 504.

(See NEC for actual text)

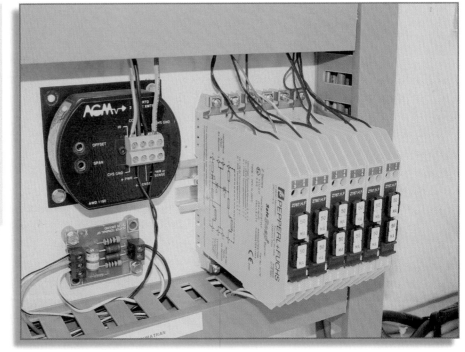

Change Summary

- Section 505.15(A) provides requirements for allowable wiring methods in Class I, Zone 0 locations.
- The previous allowance for all intrinsically safe wiring methods in accordance with Article 504 has been reduced.
- Only intrinsic safety "ia" and equipment protected by encapsulation "ma" are allowed to be connected using intrinsically safe "ia" circuits as provided in Article 504.

Significance of the Change

The previous text permitted any wiring method as provided in Article 504.20 has been revised to be more restrictive. Prior to this revision wiring in Zone 0 areas could have been by any unclassified wiring method in accordance with 504.20. This would have permitted the use of intrinsically safe "ia" and "ib" and encapsulation "ma" and "mb" equipment in Zone 0 classified locations. Intrinsically safe "ib" and encapsulation "mb" equipment are only suitable for use in Class I, Zone 1 or 2 locations. Encapsulation "mb" is only suitable for Class I, Zone 1 and 2 applications. Intrinsically safe systems as described in Article 504 and designated as "ia" are only permitted for equipment in Zone 0 locations, if they are connected to an intrinsically safe "ia" circuit. The same restriction is also included for equipment using the encapsulation "ma" protection technique. The revision clearly limits wiring methods for Zone 0 to intrinsically safe "ia" circuits only for intrinsically safe "ia" equipment and encapsulation "ma" equipment. Previously, it could have been interpreted that either type of intrinsically safe equipment and circuit and either type of encapsulation equipment and circuit were allowed in a Zone 0 environment. The revision clarifies the limitations and improves understanding of permitted protection techniques in Zone 0 areas.

FR: 3986

SR: None

Classification of Areas in Repair Garages

Photo from iStock

Code Language

(C) Repair Garages, Major and Minor. Where vehicles using Class I liquids or heavier-than-air gaseous fuels (such as LPG) are repaired, hazardous area classification guidance is found in Table 511.3(C).

Informational Note: For additional information, see NFPA 30A-2015, Code for Motor Fuel Dispensing Facilities and Repair Garages, Table 8.3.2.

Table 511.3(C) Extent of Classified Locations for Major and Minor Repair Garages with Heavier-Than-Air Fuel.

…(See *NEC* Table 511.3(C))

(See NEC for actual text)

Significance of the Change

In the 2014 *NEC*, Section 511.3(C) provided classification of areas related to major repair garages and 511.3(D) provided classification of areas related to minor repair garages. The terms *minor repair garage* and *major repair garage* are defined in 511.2 for additional clarification. In order to align with NFPA 30A-2015, 511.3(C) is replaced in its entirety with a new 511.3(C) and covers both major and minor repair garages where heavier than air gaseous Class I liquids are transferred or dispensed. The previous requirements in 511.3(C) and (D) have been incorporated into 511.3(C) and associated new Table 511.3(C). Providing the area classification requirements for these facilities in tabular format is a significant improvement in usability and clarity. The new Table 511.3(C) is a replica of the corresponding portion of Table 8.3.2 of NFPA 30A as adjusted in order to comply with the *NEC Style Manual* with regards to internal references that exist within the NFPA 30A table. The new informational note was added to refer back to the original table in NFPA 30A. Former Section 511.3(D) now provides the area classification for major repair garages for vehicles that use lighter-than-air fuel such as hydrogen and natural gas.

Change Summary

- Section 511.3(C) has been revised, and Subdivision (C) has been retitled as "Repair Garages, Major and Minor."

- The previous requirements addressing classification of areas have been reorganized and incorporated into a new Table 511.3(C).

- The new informational note provides a reference to NFPA 30A and Table 8.3.2, the origin of the classification requirements.

FR: 3954
SR: None

Classification of Areas in Repair Garages

Code Language

(D) Repair Garages, Major. Where vehicles using lighter-than-air gaseous fuels (such as hydrogen and natural gas) are repaired or stored, hazardous area classification guidance is found in Table 511.3(D).

Informational Note: For additional information see NFPA 30A -2015, *Code for Motor Fuel Dispensing Facilities and Repair Garages*, Table 8.3.2.

Table 511.3(D) Extent of Classified Locations for Major Repair Garages with Lighter-than-Air Fuel

…(See *NEC* Table 511.3(D))

(See NEC for actual text)

Photo from iStock

Significance of the Change

Section 511.3(D) in the 2014 *NEC* was incorporated into revised Section 511.3(C) and associated Table 511.3(C). In order to align with NFPA 30A-2015, 511.3(D) is replaced in its entirety with a new 511.3(D) covering major repair garages where vehicles using lighter than air gaseous fuels are repaired or stored. The new Table 511.3(D) is a duplicate of the corresponding portion of Table 8.3.2 of NFPA 30A *Code for Motor Fuel Dispensing Facilities and Repair Garages*. In order to comply with the *NEC Style Manual*, existing internal references in NFPA 30A, Table 8.3.2 have been revised or removed. An informational note was added to refer *Code* users back to the original table in NFPA 30A. Notes were added to the table to apply the correct groups for hydrogen applications and differentiate from liquefied petroleum gas. Including the area classifications in tabular form is a significant improvement in usability and enhances consistency between the Article 511 and NFPA 30A where many of the requirements for commercial repair garages and motor fuel dispensing facilities originate.

Change Summary

- Subdivision (D) in 511.3 has been revised and is titled "Repair Garages, Major."

- This subdivision and new associated Table 511.3(D) provide area classification for major repair garages that use lighter-than-air gaseous fuels.

- The new informational note provides a reference to NFPA 30A and Table 8.3.2, the origin of the classification requirements.

FR: 3955
SR: None

Underground Wiring Methods

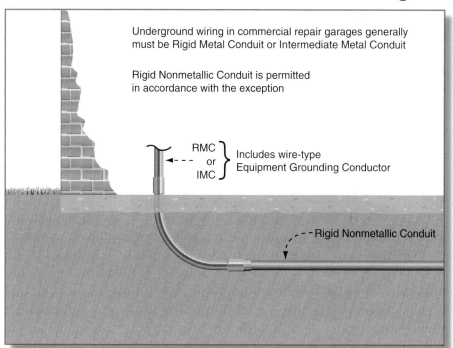

Underground wiring in commercial repair garages generally must be Rigid Metal Conduit or Intermediate Metal Conduit

Rigid Nonmetallic Conduit is permitted in accordance with the exception

RMC
or
IMC
} Includes wire-type Equipment Grounding Conductor

--- Rigid Nonmetallic Conduit

Code Language

511.8 Underground Wiring. Underground wiring shall be installed in threaded rigid metal conduit or intermediate metal conduit.

Exception: Type PVC conduit, Type RTRC conduit, and Type HDPE conduit shall be permitted where buried under not less than 600 mm (2 ft) of cover. Where Type PVC conduit, Type RTRC conduit, or Type HDPE conduit is used, threaded rigid metal conduit or threaded steel intermediate metal conduit shall be used for the last 600 mm (2 ft) of the underground run to emergence or to the point of connection to the aboveground raceway, and an equipment grounding…(See NEC text)

(See NEC for actual text)

Significance of the Change

Section 511.7 provides the requirements for wiring installed above Class I locations in commercial repair garages. Section 511.8 is new and indicates that as a general rule, rigid metal conduit and intermediate metal conduit must be installed for underground wiring in commercial repair garage facilities. The associated exception indicates that nonmetallic raceways, specifically Type PVC conduit, Type RTRC conduit, and Type HDPE conduit can be used where buried under not less than 2 feet of cover under the floor in a commercial garage. From the point of being under less than 2 feet of cover to where the conduit run terminates, the wiring methods set forth in Article 511 apply. This section does include a minimum depth of 2 feet and applies whether there is a concrete or other floor material. The new underground wiring requirements in this section are very similar to those that exist in Sections 515.8(A) and 514.8 and associated exception. The new section clarifies that PVC or RTRC can be used where buried under not less than 2 feet of cover under a commercial garage, and, where used, is not required to be encased in 2 inches of concrete where buried under not less than 2 feet of cover.

Change Summary

- A new Section 511.8 titled "Underground Wiring" and an associated exception have been added to Article 511.

- The driving text requires threaded rigid metal conduit or intermediate metal conduit be installed as underground wiring methods.

- The exception permits nonmetallic wiring methods under restrictive conditions dealing with depth, transitions to metallic conduit methods and installing an equipment grounding conductor.

FR: 3994

SR: None

RELOCATE / *REVISION*

Definitions of Mobile Equipment and Portable Equipment Relocated

Code Language

Mobile Equipment. Equipment with electrical components suitable to be moved only with mechanical aids or is provided with wheels for movement by person(s) or powered devices. (CMP-14)

Portable Equipment. Equipment with electrical components suitable to be moved by a single person without mechanical aids. (CMP-14)

(See NEC for actual text)

Photo from iStock

Change Summary

- The terms *Mobile Equipment* and *Portable Equipment* have been relocated to Article 100.

- The *NEC Style Manual* indicates that if a term appears in more than two articles it should be included in Article 100.

- The parenthetical words "(CMP-14)" have been inserted following each definition indicating Code-Making Panel 14 has technical responsibility of the relocated defined terms.

Significance of the Change

The terms *Mobile Equipment* and *Portable Equipment* have been relocated to Article 100.

Both terms are used in more than two articles of the *NEC* and should be relocated to Article 100 in accordance with the *NEC Style Manual*. Compliance with the *NEC Style Manual* is essential. Many of the defined terms that apply to hazardous (classified) locations appeared in more than just Article 100. These two definitions have been relocated to Article 100 to resolve the Style Manual conflict and improve usability. No technical revisions were made to these definitions. Adding the words "(CMP-14)" following each relocated defined term provides an indication that while Article 100 is the place holder for these definitions, Code-Making Panel 14 has technical responsibility of these defined terms. This revision is consistent with another significant relocation of multiple defined terms from Chapter 5 to Article 100 to improve consistency with *NEC Style Manual* requirements. See the associated revision and relocations in 500.2 and Article 100. No technical revisions were made to either definition, just relocation and insertion of the parenthetical term (CMP-14).

FR: 3926
SR: None
SCR: 121

Classification of LNG, CNG and LPG Use Areas

Photo from iStock

Significance of the Change

To align with NFPA 30A-2015, Section 514.3(B)(2) has been revised and associated Table 514.3(B)(2). The associated Table 514.3(B)(2) is extracted from NFPA 30A Table 12.6.2 located in TIA 15-1. Section 514.3(B)(2) has been revised and expanded to address dispensing of both gaseous type fuels and liquid type fuels. The key new requirements in the revised section include separation distances from the dispensing equipment for each fuel type. Previously this section and table did not provide such information and users had to refer to NFPA 30A for the separation rules. As revised separation distances between LPG and any dispensing device for Class I liquids must generally be at least 10 feet from any dispensing device for Class I liquids. The separation must be at least 1.5 m (5 ft) from any dispensing device for Class I liquids if the LP gas delivery nozzle and the filler valve releases no more than 4 cm3 (0.1 oz.) of liquid upon disconnection and the fixed maximum liquid level gauge remains closed during the fueling operation. The revised table provides a more concise area classification associated with dispensing equipment for LPG, CNG and LNG.

Code Language

(2) Compressed Natural Gas, Liquefied Natural Gas, and Liquefied Petroleum Gas Areas. Table 514.3(B)(2) shall be used to delineate and classify areas where CNG, LNG, compressed or liquefied hydrogen, LP-Gas, or combinations of these, are dispensed as motor vehicle fuels along…(See *NEC* text)

Where CNG or LNG dispensers are installed beneath a canopy or enclosure…(See *NEC* text)

Dispensing devices for LP-Gas shall be located as follows:

(1) At least 3 m (10 ft) from any dispensing device for Class I liquids.

(2) At least 1.5 m (5 ft) from any dispensing device for Class I liquids…(See *NEC* text)

(See NEC for actual text)

Change Summary

- Section 514.3(B)(2) has been revised and associated Table 514.3(B)(2) has been revised.

- The revisions specify distance separations between CNG, LNG and LPG dispensing devices and Class I liquid dispensing devices.

- The revised Table 514.3(B)(2) is now consistent with Table 12.6.2 in NFPA 30A.

FR: 4001
SR: None

Storage Areas for LNG, CNG and LPG

Code Language

(3) Fuel Storage.

(a) Aboveground tanks storing CNG or LNG shall be separated from any adjacent property line that is or can be built upon, any public way, and the nearest important building on the same property. [**30A**:12.3.1]

Informational Note: The relevant distances are given in Section 8.4 of NFPA 52-2013, Vehicular Gaseous Fuel Systems Code.

(b) Aboveground tanks storing hydrogen shall be separated from any adjacent property line that is or can be built upon, any public way, and the nearest important building on the same property. [**30A**:12.3.2]

Table 514.3(B)(2) shall be used to delineate and classify…(See *NEC* text)

(See NEC for actual text)

Change Summary

- A list item (3) in Section 514.3(B) is new and addresses LNG, CNG, and LPG storage tank areas and locations.
- The new requirements provide separation distances from property lines and from other gas storage tanks.
- Table 514.3(B)(2) is referenced from this new list item for establishing classification of areas containing CNG, LNG or LPG storage or dispensing operations.

FR: 4002
SR: None

Photo from iStock

Significance of the Change

A list item (3) in Section 514.3(B) is new and addresses LNG, CNG, and LPG storage tank areas and locations. The new requirements provide rules addressing separation distances from property lines and from other gas storage tanks. This information is not new as it is derived from Sections 12.3.1, 12.3.2, 12.3.3, 12.4 and 12.5 of NFPA 30A the *Code for Motor Fuel Dispensing Facilities and Repair Garages*. However, this information on separation from property lines and public ways is new to the *NEC*. Because this information is directly related to installations of aboveground storage tanks for these gases, CMP-14 determined it was essential to include it in the *NEC*. Two key criteria are necessary when dealing with electrical installations and equipment in hazardous (classified) locations. These are the type of gas or explosive atmosphere, and the area classification associated with that type of gas. This new information was extracted from NFPA 30A and new informational notes have been included that refer to the relevant distances provided in NFPA 2 *Hydrogen Technologies Code* and NFPA 52 *Liquefied Petroleum Gas Code*. This new list item also references Table 514.3(B)(2) which is extracted from NFPA 30A Table 12.6.2 and conveys information about area classification related to dispensing equipment for CNG, LNG, and LPG.

Disconnects for Motor Fuel Dispensing Equipment

Photo from iStock

Significance of the Change

Section 514.11 is revised to reflect the requirements in Section 6.7 of NFPA 30A-2015 and result in consistency between the two *Codes*. NFPA 30A the *Code for Motor Fuel Dispensing Facilities and Repair Garages* contains many requirements that are often extracted and included in the *NEC* as prescriptive installation requirements. This revision removes the long-standing provisions that addressed circuit disconnects feeding motor fuel dispensing equipment. Section 514.13 already addresses requirements for circuit disconnects that are for other than emergency purposes. The circuit disconnect requirements apply to all external voltage sources and require removal of all sources and associated feedback. This made the previous circuit disconnect provisions in 514.11 redundant. Section 210.4(B) includes circuit disconnect requirements for all ungrounded conductors of a circuit, including multi-wire branch circuits. A new exception to (A) relaxes the emergency electrical disconnect requirement for intrinsically safe electrical equipment. As revised, Section 514.11 and 514.13 will clearly distinguish between the requirements for emergency control and shut off provisions, and circuit disconnects that are necessary for personnel involved in maintenance and service work of dispensing equipment.

Code Language

514.11 Circuit Disconnects.

(A) Emergency Electrical Disconnects. Fuel dispensing systems shall be provided...(See *NEC* text)

Exception: Intrinsically safe electrical equipment need not meet this requirement. [**30A**:6.7]

(B) Attended Self-Service Motor Fuel Dispensing Facilities. At attended motor fuel dispensing facilities, the devices or disconnects shall be readily accessible to the attendant. [**30A**:6.7.1]

(C) Unattended Self-Service Motor Fuel Dispensing Facilities. At unattended motor fuel dispensing facilities, the devices or disconnects shall be readily accessible to patrons and at least one additional device or disconnect shall be readily accessible to each group of dispensing devices on an individual island. [**30A**:6.7.2]

(See NEC for actual text)

Change Summary

- Section 514.11 has been revised to align with the requirements contained in NFPA 30A-2015.

- Subdivision (A) now addresses only emergency disconnects for dispensing equipment and no longer addresses circuit disconnects and breaking all conductors of the circuit(s).

- Subdivisions (B) and (C) address locations of disconnects for attended and unattended dispensing facilities, respectively.

FR: 3996
SR: None

Complete Rewrite of Article 516

Code Language

Article 516 Spray Application, Dipping, Coating, and Printing Processes Using Flammable or Combustible Materials

Part I General (See *NEC* text)

516.1 Scope…(See *NEC* text)

516.2 Definitions…(See *NEC* text)

Part II Open Containers…(See *NEC* text)

Part III Spray Application Processes…(See *NEC* text)

Part IV Spray Application Operations in Membrane Enclosures…(See *NEC* text)

Part V Printing, Dipping, and Coating Processes…(See *NEC* text)

(See NEC for actual text)

Change Summary

- Article 516 has been completely rewritten to align more closely with NFPA 33 and 34 including extracted material.

- The rewrite includes organizing the previous requirements into separately titled parts of Article 516.

- The revisions provide a more logical layout enhancing usability and more consistency with *NEC Style Manual* requirements.

Photo from iStock

Significance of the Change

Several revisions to the 2017 *NEC* involve alignment with another NFPA Standard or Code and inclusion of extracted material. Many actions by CMP-14 during the 2017 development cycle reflect such revisions. Article 516 has been completely rewritten and organized into separate parts to provide a logical order and comply with the *NEC Style Manual*. Provisions within the rewritten article that are followed by a reference in brackets have been extracted from NFPA 33-2015, *Standard for Spray Application Using Flammable and Combustible Materials*, or NFPA 34-2015, *Standard for Dipping, Coating, and Printing Processes Using Flammable or Combustible Liquids*. Editorial changes were made to the extracted text to make it consistent with the *NEC* style. New requirements appear to address specific protection from static discharges, including grounding of persons and metal parts of process equipment. Provisions must also be made to dissipate static electric charges from all nonconductive substrates in printing processes. An informational note references NFPA 77-2014, *Recommended Practice on Static Electricity* providing additional guidance on reducing the risk of ignition from electrostatic discharges.

FR: 3956
SR: 3914

Governing Body of Health Care Facilities

Photo from iStock

Code Language

Governing Body. The person or persons who have the overall legal responsibility for the operation of a health care facility. [**99**:3.3.62]

(See NEC for actual text)

Significance of the Change

The governing body provides an essential function of deciding upon many operational functions of a health care facility. As an example, the governing body typically designates the level of care provided in various areas or rooms of the facility in addition to information related to determining wet procedure locations and anesthetizing relative to requirements for essential electrical systems. The term is used in several sections within Article 517 but has never been defined or described in the *NEC*. Inclusion of the term *Governing Body* and definition will provide valuable clarification for design teams, engineering groups, installing contractors and *Code* enforcers. Section 3.3.62 of the 2015 NFPA 99 *Health Care Facilities Code* is the reference of the extracted definition. Including the defined term in Article 517 results in an effective correlation between the two documents and meets the requirements in Section 4.3.2 of the *NEC Style Manual*. As defined, the governing body of the facility, which can be a person or a group of persons, such as a board of directors. A key aspect of the defined term is that such a person or persons is not only responsible for the designation of areas and levels of care, but has the overall legal responsibilities associated with the operation of a health care facility.

Change Summary

- The term *Governing Body* appears in multiple sections within Article 517 of the *NEC*.
- A new definition of the term *Governing Body* has been added to Section 517.2 to meet *NEC Style Manual* requirements.
- The new definition correlates between NFPA 99 *Health Care Code* and NFPA 70 *National Electrical Code*, as it is an extracted definition.

FR: 4255
SR: None

NEW

Invasive Procedure

Code Language

Invasive Procedure. Any procedure that penetrates the protective surfaces of a patient's body (i.e., skin, mucous membrane, cornea) and that is performed with an aseptic field (procedural site). Not included in this category are placement of peripheral intravenous needles or catheters used to administer fluids and/or medications, gastrointestinal endoscopies (i.e., sigmoidoscopies), insertion of urethral catheters, and other similar procedures. [**99**:3.3.81]

(See NEC for actual text)

Change Summary

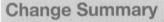

- A new definition of the term *Invasive Procedure* has been added to 517.2.
- The definition describes the type of treatment and procedures that constitute being categorized as "Invasive."
- The revision aligns Article 517 with the term defined and used within NFPA 99 *Health Care Code*.

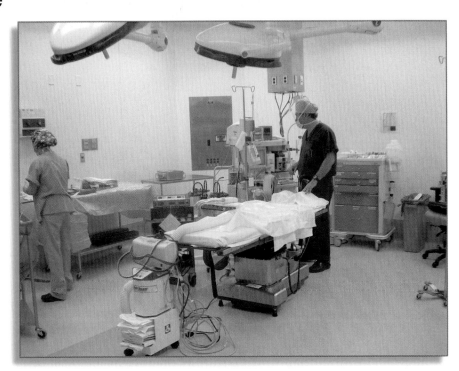

Significance of the Change

A new definition of the term *Invasive Procedure* has been added to Section 517.2. The definition describes the type of treatment and procedures that constitute being categorized as "Invasive."

The defined term *Invasive Procedure* aligns with the same defined term included in NFPA 99-2015 *Health Care Facilities Code*. The term is used in Article 517 but was never clearly defined. As defined it is clear that invasive is a process of care where medical equipment penetrates the protective surfaces of a patient's body, and that is performed with an aseptic field. The definition also clarifies that placement of peripheral intravenous needles or catheters used to administer fluids and/or medications, gastrointestinal endoscopies, insertion of urethral catheters, and other similar procedures are not included in this category. The addition of this new definition correlates information between these documents in accordance with the *NEC Style Manual*, Section 4.3.2 and subsequent sections. Incorporating the new definition in 517.2 aligns Article 517 with the same term defined and used within NFPA 99 *Heath Care Facilities Code*. Rules that use the term invasive procedure will now be clear as defined within Article 517 to promote accuracy in the application of other essential requirements.

FR: 4256
SR: None

Isolation Transformer

Code Language

Isolation Transformer. A transformer of the multiple-winding type, with the primary and secondary windings physically separated, that inductively couples its ungrounded secondary winding(s) to the grounded feeder system that energizes its primary winding(s). [**99**:3.3.84]

(See NEC for actual text)

Significance of the Change

The term *Isolation Transformer* is used in a few locations in Article 517 as related to installation and use of isolated power systems. Isolation transformers are an integral component of isolated power systems such as those addressed in Sections 517.20(B) and 517.160(A)(4). The term *isolation transformer* is included in 517.2 and has been in several previous editions of the *NEC*. The text in this revised definition of the term *Isolation Transformer* aligns the Article 517 of the *NEC* with 2015 NFPA 99 *Health Care Facilities Code*. As revised, it is clear that these transformers have multiple windings, and the windings are physically separated other than through a magnetic couple (induction) from primary to secondary. The definition was also revised to clarify that the primary (supply) circuit for such systems typically supplied by a feeder that is connected to a grounded system, such as a 208Y/120-volt system or a 480Y/277-volt system. The addition of this new definition correlates information between NFPA 70 *National Electrical Code* and NFPA 99 *Health Care Facilities Code* and meets the requirements in Section 4.3.2 of the *NEC Style Manual*.

Change Summary

- The definition of the term *Isolation Transformer* has been revised.
- The revision more clearly describes the isolation achieved by use of isolation transformers and the primary (supply) is typically supplied by a grounded system.
- The revision aligns *NEC* Article 517 with the term defined and used within NFPA 99 *Health Care Code*.

FR: 4240
SR: None

Medical Offices and Dental Offices

Code Language

Medical Office (Dental Office). A building or part thereof in which the following occur:

(1) examinations and minor treatments or procedures are performed under the continuous supervision of a medical or dental professional;

(2) only sedation or local anesthesia is involved, and treatment or procedures do not render the patient incapable of self-preservation under emergency conditions; and

(3) overnight stays for patients or 24-hour operation are not provided. [**99**:3.3.98]

(See NEC for actual text)

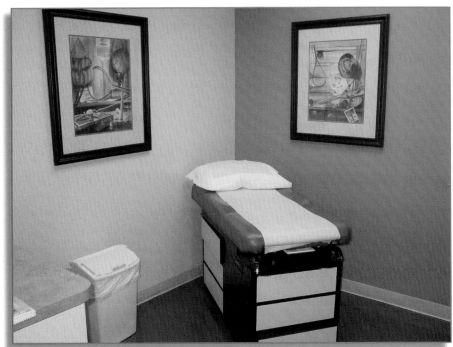

Photo from iStock

Change Summary

- A new definition of the term *Medical Office (Dental Office)* has been added to 517.2.

- The definition describes the type of treatment and procedures administered in such offices and the extent of anesthesia that can be used.

- The revision aligns Article 517 with the term defined and used within NFPA 99 *Health Care Code*.

FR: 4244

SR: None

Significance of the Change

A new definition of the term *Medical Office (Dental Office)* has been added to 517.2. The definition describes the type of treatment and procedures administered in such offices and the extent of anesthesia that can be used. The terms *medical office* and *dental office* are used in 517, yet no definition was ever included in the *NEC* to clarify what constitutes a dental office or other medical office. Inclusion of the defined term will provide clarity for *NEC* users such as engineers, designers, installing contractors and others. This definition is extracted from NFPA 99-2015 *Health Care Facilities Code*. Prior to including this definition some confusion existed for those that use this term for design, installation and the determination of *NEC* requirements specific to medical and dental offices. Along with new category designations in Article 517, this new definition will provide inspectors and installers with more information about these occupancies. As defined, examinations and minor treatments or procedures are performed under the continuous supervision of a medical or dental professional, and only sedation or local anesthesia is involved, and treatment or procedures do not render the patient incapable of self-preservation under emergency conditions. The new definition is an improvement in clarity, usability, and results in an effective correlation between the two *Codes*.

Basic, General, Critical, and Support Spaces

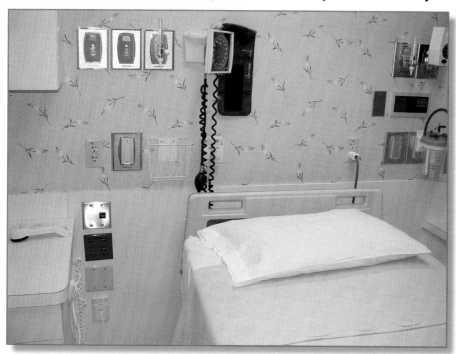

Code Language

Patient Care Space. Space within a health care facility...(See *NEC* text) [**99**:3.3.127]

Basic Care Space (Category 3 Space). Space in which failure... (See *NEC* text) is not likely to cause injury to the patients, staff, or visitors but can cause patient discomfort. [**99**:3.3.127.3]

General Care Space (Category 2 Space). Space in which failure...(See *NEC* text) is likely to cause minor injury to patients, staff, or visitors. [**99**:3.3.127.2]

Critical Care Space (Category 1 Space). Space in which failure...(See *NEC* text) is likely to cause major injury or death to patients, staff, or visitors. [**99**:3.3.127.1]

(See NEC for actual text)

Significance of the Change

The care locations within a health care facility are now defined as "spaces" and are each provided with a specific category that indicates the level of care under that designation. The revisions to these definitions align the NFPA 70 *National Electrical Code* with NFPA 99-2015 *Health Care Facilities Code* while introducing an assigned category for each patient care space designation. These definitions are extracted information from NFPA 99 in order to assure continued coordination between these documents. As revised, the patient care spaces are now categorized as follows:

Basic Care Space (Category 3 Space). [**99**:3.3.127.3]

General Care Space (Category 2 Space). [**99**:3.3.127.2]

Critical Care Space (Category 1 Space). [**99**:3.3.127.1]

Support Space (Category 4 Space). [**99**:3.3.127.4]

Informational Note No. 5 was also revised to match the correct terminology and defined term of wet procedure location rather than area.

Change Summary

- The defined terms under the main definition of "Patient Care Space" have been revised, and descriptive informational notes follow each term.

- The revisions incorporate numerical categories (1 through 4) following each definition, and the bracketed information contains the location of the extract.

- The revision aligns Article 517 with terms defined and used within NFPA 99 *Health Care Facilities Code*.

FR: 4247

SR: 4215

REVISION

Selected Receptacles

Code Language

Selected Receptacles. A minimum number of receptacles selected by the governing body of a facility as necessary to provide essential patient care and facility services during loss of normal power. [**99**:3.3.148]

(See NEC for actual text)

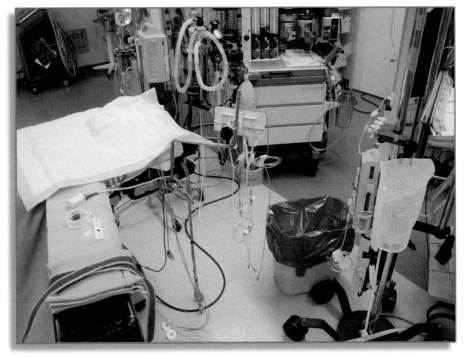

Change Summary

- The term *Selected Receptacles* in 517.2 has been revised and expanded.
- The term *Governing Body* has been added to this definition to clarify the entity responsible for the selection and designation process of receptacles.
- The revised definition correlates between NFPA 99 *Health Care Facilities Code* and NFPA 70 *NEC* as it is an extracted definition.

Significance of the Change

The term *Selected Receptacles* in 517.2 has been revised and expanded. The term *governing body* has been added to this definition. The term *governing body* is used in 517 in several sections. The governing body of a health care facility is defined as the person or persons who have the overall legal responsibility for the operation of a health care facility. Inclusion of the term *governing body* in the definition of selected receptacles will provide clarity for *Code* users as to the entity responsible for making the designation of receptacle use selections. The extraction is from Section 3.3.28 of NFPA 99-2015 *Health Care Facilities Code*. By including the extracted definition of the term *selected receptacles* in 517.2, a closer alignment between NFPA 99 and the *NEC* results. The revision is important as it clarifies who selects certain receptacles for designated and special purposes within health care facilities. NFPA-99 the *Health Care Facilities Code* contains performance requirements within the HEA-ELS portion of the document. These performance requirements are often the origin of prescriptive installation requirements contained in Article 517 of the *National Electrical Code*.

FR: 4251
SR: None

Grounding of Receptacles and Fixed Electrical Equipment

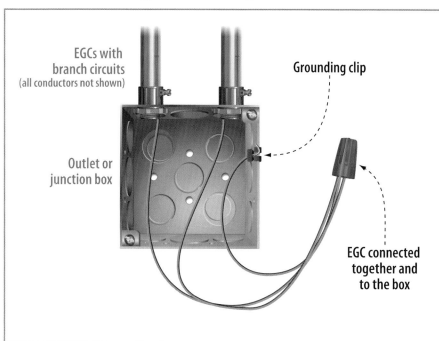

EGCs with branch circuits (all conductors not shown)

Grounding clip

Outlet or junction box

EGC connected together and to the box

Code Language

517.13 Grounding of Receptacles and Fixed Electrical Equipment in Patient Care Spaces.

(B) Insulated Equipment Grounding Conductors and Insulated Equipment Bonding Jumpers.

(1) General. The following shall be directly connected to an insulated... along its entire length by green insulation and...(See *NEC* text)

(1) The grounding terminals of... (See *NEC* text)

(2) Metal outlet boxes, metal...(See *NEC* text)

(3) All non-current-carrying ...(See *NEC* text)

Exception No. 1: For other than... (See NEC text)...Isolated ground receptacles shall be connected in accordance with 517.16.

(See NEC for actual text)

Significance of the Change

Part II of Article 517 covers wiring and protection for patient care spaces in health care facilities. This section provides more restrictive branch circuit equipment grounding conductor requirements than those contained in Article 250. Redundancy in the branch circuit equipment grounding conductor paths is achieved by the requirement for two separate EGC paths, one being the metal raceway or cable armor that qualifies as an EGC according to 250.118, the other being the required insulated copper equipment grounding conductor. This section has been revised to clarify it applies to branch circuit wiring and grounding for circuits supplying patient care "spaces" rather than "areas." Changing the word "area" to the word "space" results in alignment between NFPA 99 *Health Care Facilities Code* and NFPA 70 *National Electrical Code*. List item (1) to 517.13(B) has been revised to more clearly specify the identification by the color green along the entire length of the conductor. Exception No. 1 to 517.13(B)(1)(3) has been revised with a new sentence indicating that isolated ground receptacles must be connected in accordance with 517.16 which clarifies only two equipment grounding conductor paths are required. The minimum sizing requirements for wire-type EGCs must be in accordance with the prescriptive sizing rules in 250.122.

Change Summary

- The word "area" has been changed to "spaces" within Section 517.13(A) and (B).
- The words "green along its entire length and" have been added to 517.13(B)(1).
- Exception No. 1 to 517.13(B)(1)(3) has been revised with a new sentence clarifying that isolated ground receptacles must be connected in accordance with 517.16.

FR: 4261
SR: 4216
SCR:16

Permitted Uses for Isolated Ground Receptacles

Code Language

517.16 Use of Isolated Ground Receptacles.

(A) Inside of a Patient Care Vicinity. An isolated grounding receptacle shall not be installed within a patient care vicinity. [99:6.3.2.2.7.1(B)]

(B) Outside of a Patient Care Vicinity. Isolated ground receptacle(s) installed in patient care spaces outside of a patient care vicinity shall comply with 517.16(B)(1) and (2).

(1) The grounding terminals of isolated ground receptacles installed in branch circuits for patient care spaces...(See *NEC* text)

(2) The insulated grounding conductor required in 517.13(B)(1)...(See *NEC* text)

(See NEC for actual text)

Change Summary

- Section 517.16 is titled Use of Isolated Ground Receptacles and has been expanded into two subdivisions.
- Subdivision (A) provides a clear prohibition of IG receptacles within any patient care vicinity and is extracted from NFPA 99.
- Subdivision (B) provides allowable installations of isolated ground receptacles that are outside of a defined patient care vicinity.

FR: 4260
SRs: 4217, 4228

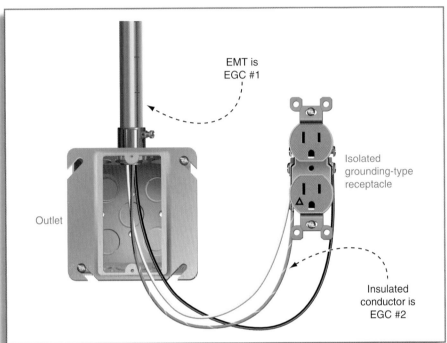

EMT is
EGC #1

Isolated grounding-type receptacle

Outlet

Insulated conductor is EGC #2

Significance of the Change

Section 517.16 has been revised and expanded providing users with clear direction regarding uses for isolated ground receptacles and prohibited locations. In the 2014 *NEC*, the installation of IG receptacles is prohibited within the patient care vicinity. This prohibition aligns the *NEC* with Section 6.3.3.2.7.1 of NFPA 99. This revision provides requirements for branch circuits serving areas where isolated equipment grounding conductor and IG receptacles are specified. Changing this section will reduce confusion that exists regarding the number of equipment grounding conductors that must be installed for isolated grounding receptacles installed outside the patient care vicinity in patient care spaces. IG receptacles installed in these locations require two EGC paths. The color designation of green with one or more yellow stripes will provide a color used as an industry standard for IG grounds. This revision clarifies what is required to satisfy the equipment grounding conductor requirements for branch circuits serving these areas where the isolated equipment grounding conductor and IG receptacles are specified. As revised subdivision (A) provides a clear prohibition of IG receptacles within any patient care vicinity and is extracted from NFPA 99. Subdivision (B) provides allowable isolated ground receptacles that are outside of a patient care vicinity.

Identification of Receptacles in Critical Care Spaces

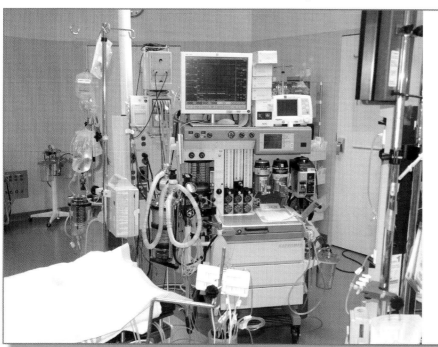

Code Language

517.19 Critical Care (Category 1) Space.

(A) Patient Bed Location Branch Circuits. Each patient bed location... (See *NEC* text)

The electrical receptacles or the cover plates for the electrical receptacles supplied from the life safety and critical branches shall have a distinctive color or marking so as to be readily identifiable. [**99**:6.4.2.2.6.2(C)]

(See NEC for actual text)

Significance of the Change

A critical care space is now identified as a "Category 1" space to align with terminology being used in NFPA 99. The care locations within a health care facility are now defined as "spaces" as compared to "areas" or "locations" and are each provided with a specific category that indicates the level of care under that designation. The revised definition of "patient care space" now provides the different categories (in parenthesis) for each patient care or support space and signifies a level of care anticipated in each. NFPA-99 the *Health Care Facilities Code* contains performance requirements within the HEA-ELS portion of the document. These performance requirements are often the origin of prescriptive installation requirements contained in Article 517 of the *National Electrical Code*. Incorporating the categories 1 through 4 with each patient care or support space aligns the *NEC* with terminology being used in NFPA 99. Another significant revision in this section incorporates an identification requirement for receptacles supplied from the life safety and critical branches of the essential electrical system (EES). The identification must be a distinctive color or marking to render the receptacle readily identifiable as connected to the EES. The identification can be the receptacle itself or the cover plate.

Change Summary

- The title to 517.19 includes "Category 1" and a new last sentence has been added to (A).
- The revision incorporates an identification requirement for receptacles supplied from the life safety and critical branches of the EES.
- The identification must be a distinctive color or marking to render the receptacle readily identifiable as connected to the EES.

FR: 4267
SR: None

Type 1 and Type 2 Essential Electrical Systems

Code Language

517.29 Essential Electrical Systems for Hospitals and Other Health Care Facilities.

(A) Applicability. The requirements of Part III, 517.29 through 517.30, shall apply to critical care (Category 1) and general care (Category 2) hospitals and other health care facilities using Type 1 essential electrical systems where patients are sustained by electrical life-support equipment.

Informational Note No. 1: For performance, maintenance, and testing (See *NEC* text)

Informational Note No. 2: For additional information, on Type 1 and Type 2 essential electrical systems, see NFPA 99-2015, *Health Care Facilities Code*.

(B) Critical care (Category 1) spaces shall be served only by a Type 1 essential electrical system. [99:6.3.2.2.10.1]

(See NEC for actual text)

Change Summary

- A new Section 517.29 has been added in Part III of Article 517.
- This section provides information relative to Types of Essential Electrical Systems (EESs) required for Category 1 and Category 2 care locations.
- Subdivision (B) clarifies that Critical Care (Category 1) spaces shall be served only by a Type 1 Essential Electrical System.

Significance of the Change

NFPA-99 the *Health Care Facilities Code* contains performance requirements within the HEA-ELS portion of the document. These performance requirements are often the origin of prescriptive installation requirements contained in Article 517 of the *National Electrical Code*. A new section 517.29 was created to provide introductory information for the revised requirements in 517.30 thru 517.35. This new section incorporates the NFPA 99 language and extracted material in accordance with Section 4.3.2 of the *NEC Style Manual* and results in correlation between the NFPA 99-2015 with the 2017 *NEC*. This new section provides information relative to Types of Essential Electrical Systems (EESs) required for Category 1 (critical care) and Category 2 (general care) care locations. Subdivision (B) clarifies that Critical Care (Category 1) spaces shall be served only by a Type 1 (Level 1) Essential Electrical System (EES). NFPA 99 *Health Care Facilities Code* provides additional information on Type 1 and Type 2 essential electrical systems.

FR: 4271

SR: None

Sources of Power Expanded

Significance of the Change

The text in 517.35 covering power sources was relocated to 517.30 to provide a logical order and flow of the text and to align with requirements in NFPA 99-2015 *Health Care Facilities Code*. Fuel cells are now included as an alternate source of power for an essential electrical system. This revision provides accurate alignment with NFPA 99 language and extracted material addressing fuel cells to coordinate the two documents required by the *NEC Style Manual* 4.3.2. Subdivision (C) has been significantly revised to improve usability and enforcement. Previously this section was very subjective in requiring "careful consideration" be given to the location of essential electrical system services and sources. This revision removes the subjectivity and makes it mandatory that installations of electrical services be located in a manner to reduce possible interruption of normal electrical services resulting from similar causes as well as possible disruption of normal electrical service due to internal wiring and equipment failures. Continuity of power in the essential electrical system is very important in health care facilities for the safety of patients and other occupants. This revision makes it clear that more than consideration must be applied when implementing the requirements in this section.

Code Language

517.30 Sources of Power.

(A) Two Independent Power Sources. Essential electrical systems shall have a minimum of the following two independent sources of power…(See *NEC* text) [**99**:6.4.1.1.4]

(B) Types of Power Sources.

(1) Generating Units. Where the normal source consists of generating units on the premises, the alternate source shall be either another generating set or an external utility service. [**99**:6.4.1.1.5]

(2) Fuel Cell Systems. Fuel cell systems shall be permitted…(See *NEC* text)

(C) Location of Essential Electrical System Components. Essential electrical system components shall be located to minimize…(See *NEC* text)

(See NEC for actual text)

Change Summary

- Required sources of power have been relocated from Section 517.35 to 517.30 for usability.

- Fuel cells are now included as a source of power for ESS and must be listed for that use.

- Subdivision (C) has been revised to remove the subjective "careful consideration" provisions and include mandatory requirements for location of EES components and services.

FR: 4276

SR: 4225

SCR: 12

517.40

Type 2 EES for Nursing Homes and Limited Care Facilities

Code Language

517.40 Type 2 Essential Electrical Systems for Nursing Homes and Limited Care Facilities.

Informational Note: Nursing homes and other limited care facilities can be classified as critical care (Category 1) or general care (Category 2) patient care space depending on the design and type of care administered in the facility. For small, less complex facilities, only minimal alternate lighting and alarm service may be required. At nursing homes and other limited care facilities where patients are not sustained by electrical life-support equipment or inpatient hospital care the requirements of 517.40 through 517.41 apply. If the level of care is comparable to that provided in a hospital, see the essential electrical system requirements of 517.29 through 517.30.

(See NEC for actual text)

Change Summary

- The words "Type 2" have been added to the title of Section 517.40.
- The revision clarifies the Type of Essential Electrical System that is required for nursing homes and limited care facilities.
- The new informational note assigns categories to the types of care in these facilities and provides the trigger for application of 517.29 through 30.

Photo from iStock

Significance of the Change

NFPA-99 the *Health Care Facilities Code* contains performance requirements within the HEA-ELS portion of the document. These performance requirements are often the origin of prescriptive installation requirements contained in Article 517 of the *National Electrical Code*. Section 517.40 provides requirements for essential electrical systems in nursing homes and limited care facilities. New for this edition of the *NEC* is the Type 2 designation for the essential electrical system in nursing homes and limited care facilities. This system is comprised of the life safety branch and the equipment branch. There is no longer a critical branch addressed in this section, as it is not required for a Type 2 essential electrical system. A level 2 EES is required for facilities where power system failure is less critical to human life and safety. NFPA 99 coordinates with these EES designations and refers to them as either Type 1 (Level 1) or Type 2 (Level 2) essential electrical systems (EES). Because they appear in NFPA 99 as Type 1 and 2, they are included in Article 517 with the same designations. Type 2 EES for nursing homes and limited care facilities now include the life safety branch and the equipment branch. The associated figures have been revised accordingly.

FR: 4268
SR: None

Required Sources of Power

Significance of the Change

NFPA-99 the *Health Care Facilities Code* contains performance requirements within the HEA-ELS portion of the document. These performance requirements are often the origin of prescriptive installation requirements contained in Article 517 of the *National Electrical Code*. Subdivision (C) has been significantly revised to improve usability and enforcement. Previously this section was very subjective in requiring consideration be given to the location of essential electrical system services and sources. This revision removes the subjectivity of this provision and makes it mandatory that installations of electrical services be located in a manner to the reduce possible interruption of normal electrical services resulting from similar causes as well as possible disruption of normal electrical service due to internal wiring and equipment failures. The new last sentence provides clear requirements to maintain separation between feeders of the essential electrical system and the normal system to prevent possible simultaneous interruption if one or the other were to fail. Continuity of power in the essential electrical system is very important in health care facilities for the safety of patients and other occupants. This revision makes it clear that more than consideration must be applied when implementing the requirements in this section.

Code Language

517.41 Required Power Sources.

(A) Two Independent Power Sources...(See *NEC* text)

(B) Types of Power Sources...(See *NEC* text)

(C) Location of Essential Electrical System Components. Essential electrical systems shall be located to minimize interruptions caused by natural forces common to the area (e.g., storms, floods, earthquakes, or hazards created by adjoining structures or activities). Installations of electrical services shall be located to the reduce possible interruption of normal electrical services resulting from similar causes as well as possible disruption of normal electrical service due to internal wiring and equipment failures. Feeders shall be located to give physical separation...(See *NEC* text)

(See NEC for actual text)

Change Summary

- The title of this section and subdivisions (A) and (B) have been revised to align with NFPA 99-2015 *Health Care Facilities Code*.
- Subdivision (C) has been revised by removing the concept of careful consideration being given to the location of installed services.
- Additional text addresses separation between feeders from the normal alternate sources.

FR: 4279

SR: None

Type 2 EES for Nursing Homes and Limited Care Facilities

Code Language

517.42 Essential Electrical Systems.

(A) General. Essential electrical systems for nursing homes and limited care facilities shall be divided into the following two branch circuits, the life safety branch, and the equipment branch. [99:A.6.5.2.2.1.2] The division between the branches shall occur at transfer switches where more than one transfer switch is required.

Informational Note No. 1: Essential electrical systems are comprised of two separate branches capable of supplying a limited amount of lighting and power service, which is considered essential for the protection of life and safety and effective operation...(See *NEC* text)

(See NEC for actual text)

Change Summary

- Type 2 EES for nursing homes and limited care facilities includes the life safety branch and the equipment branch and associated figures have been revised accordingly.
- Separation is required between the equipment and the life safety branches.
- Identification is required for EES receptacles or receptacle plates and if by color, the same color should be used.

Photo from iStock

Significance of the Change

NFPA-99-2015 the *Health Care Facilities Code* contains performance requirements within the HEA-ELS portion of the document. These performance requirements are often the origin of prescriptive installation requirements contained in Article 517 of the *National Electrical Code*. Subdivisions (A) and (B) are extracted and have been updated to align with the NFPA 99-2015 provisions. Type 2 EES for nursing homes and limited care facilities now includes the life safety branch and the equipment branch and associated figures have been revised accordingly. There is no longer a critical branch included in these facilities where only a Type (Level) 2 essential electrical system is installed.

Separation is required between the wiring of the equipment branch and the life safety branches. Informational note figures 517.42(a) and (b) have been revised to illustrate that the life safety branch and equipment branch make up the essential electrical systems in these facilities. Receptacle identification is required for EES receptacles or receptacle plates and if by color, the same color should be used as indicated in the informational note following Subdivision (E).

FR: 4277

SR: None

Type 2 EES Connection to Equipment Branch

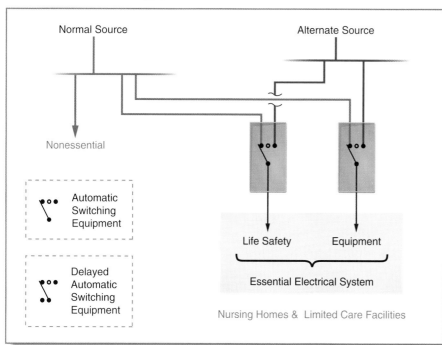

Nursing Homes & Limited Care Facilities

Code Language

517.44 Connection to Equipment Branch. The equipment branch shall be installed and connected to the alternate power source so that the equipment listed in 517.44(A) shall be automatically restored to operation at appropriate time-lag intervals following the restoration of the life safety branch to operation. [**99**:6.5.2.2.3.1(A)]

(A) Delayed Automatic Connections to Equipment Branch...(See *NEC* text)

The equipment branch arrangement shall also provide for the additional connection of equipment listed in 517.44(B) [**99**:6.5.2.2.3.1]

(See NEC for actual text)

Significance of the Change

NFPA-99 the *Health Care Facilities Code* contains performance requirements within the HEA-ELS portion of the document. These performance requirements are often the origin of prescriptive installation requirements contained in Article 517 of the *National Electrical Code*. NFPA 110 *Standard for Emergency and Standby Power Systems* contains defined designations of Level 1 and Level 2 emergency power supply systems (EPSS). Level 1 EPSS is required where the failure of equipment to perform could result in loss of human life or serious injury. A level 2 EPSS is required for facilities where power system failure is less critical to human life and safety. NFPA 99 coordinates with these EPSS designations and refers to them as either Type 1 (Level 1) or Type 2 (Level 2) essential electrical systems (EES). Because they appear in NFPA 99 as Type 1 and 2, they now appear in the *NEC* with the same designations. A Type 2 EES for nursing homes and limited care facilities now includes the life safety branch and the equipment branch and associated figures have been revised accordingly. Separation is required between the equipment and the life safety branches. Receptacle identification is required for EES receptacles or receptacle plates and if by color, the same color should be used.

Change Summary

- Type 2 EES for nursing homes and limited care facilities includes the life safety branch and the equipment branch.
- The word "Critical" has been changed to "Equipment" in this section and figures.
- The loads formerly identified for connection to the critical branch are now identified for connection to the equipment branch of the Type 2 EES.

FR: 4278
SR: 4229

Type 2 EES Connection to Equipment Branch

Code Language

517.45 Essential Electrical Systems for Other Health Care Facilities.

(A) Essential Electrical Distribution. If required by the governing body, the essential electrical distribution system for basic care (Category 3) patient care spaces...(See *NEC* text).

(B) Electrical Life Support Equipment. Where electrical life support equipment is required, the essential electrical distribution system shall be as described in 517.29 through 517.30.

(C) Critical Care (Category 1) Patient Care Spaces. Where critical patient care (Category 1) spaces are present, the essential electrical distribution system shall be as described in 517 through 517.30.

(D) General Care (Category 2) Patient Care Spaces...(See *NEC* text)

(E) Power Systems...(See *NEC* text)

(See NEC for actual text)

Change Summary

- Section 517.45 has been revised to incorporate category levels for patient care spaces.
- Subdivision (A) no longer specifies a generator or battery as the essential electrical system source and references that applicable Part of Article 517 for the required power sources.
- New Subdivision (D) incorporates essential electrical system requirements for general (Category 2) patient care spaces.

FR: 4280
SR: None

Significance of the Change

Subdivision (A) has been revised to indicate that if an essential electrical system is required by the governing body of the facility the EES for basic (Category 3) care spaces, that it be comprised of a system capable of supplying a limited amount of lighting and power for orderly cessation of procedures during the time of the power interruption. The care locations within a health care facility are designated as "spaces" and are provided with a specific category that indicates the level of care under that designation. These revisions align the NFPA 70 *National Electrical Code* with NFPA 99-2015 *Health Care Facilities Code* while introducing an assigned category for each patient care space designation. Subdivision (A) no longer specifies a generator or battery as the essential electrical system source. Subdivisions (B), (C), and (D) now reference the applicable Part of Article 517 for the required essential electrical system power sources. Subdivision (D) is new and incorporates essential electrical system requirements for general (Category 2) patient care spaces. Former Subdivision (D) was re-identified as (E) and has been revised to indicate that if an essential electrical system is required, that the source be acceptable to the governing body of the facility and meet the provisions of NFPA 99.

Ground-Fault Circuit-Interrupter (GFCI) Protection

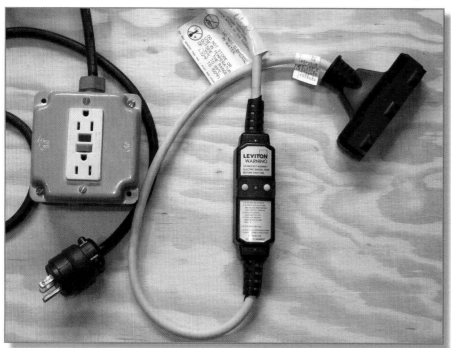

Code Language

525.23 Ground-Fault Circuit-Interrupter (GFCI) Protection.

(D) Receptacles Supplied by Portable Cords. Where GFCI protection is provided through the use of GFCI receptacles, and the branch circuits supplying receptacles utilize flexible cord, the receptacles shall be listed and identified for portable use.

(See NEC for actual text)

Significance of the Change

It is extremely common to see junction boxes with receptacles and cover plates installed on the end of flexible cord. Where this occurs, it is a blatant violation of section 110.3(B), which requires listed or labeled equipment to be installed in accordance with the product listing or labeling. Standard junction boxes and receptacles are not identified for "portable use." There are many configurations of female "cord caps" that are listed for the purpose. There are many venues that employ these types of violations where they make their own cord sets. Examples include meeting venues, convention halls, Article 525 venues and repair of extension cord sets. This revision now specifically requires GFCI receptacles that are identified for "portable use" in Article 525 venues where the branch circuit supplying the receptacle is a flexible cord, and the receptacle provides the GFCI protection. This is a significant improvement in safety.

A standard GFCI receptacle is not identified for portable use and does not provide "open neutral" protection. A GFCI device that is identified for portable use does provide "open neutral" protection. If through "portable use" the neutral connection to a standard type GFCI opens, the brains for the device loses power and the standard GFCI type receptacle will not open due to a ground fault or due to a loss of power to the device. A GFCI receptacle that is listed for "portable use" will provide "open neutral" protection by opening both the ungrounded conductor and the neutral (grounded conductor) if either conductor is opened.

Change Summary

- New 525.23(D) clearly prohibits standard type GFCI receptacles from being installed in boxes on the end of flexible cord.

- Installing standard type GFCI receptacles in boxes on the end of an extension cord is a violation of 110.3(B).

- A GFCI device that is identified for "portable use" provides "open neutral protection" while a standard type GFCI receptacle does not.

FR: 4225
SR: 4208
SCR: 120

Recreational Vehicle Parks Distribution Systems

Code Language

551.72 Distribution System.

(A) Systems. Distribution systems shall provide the voltage and have a capacity for the receptacles provided in the recreational vehicle (RV) site supply equipment as calculated according to 551.73 and shall have an ampacity not less than 30 amperes. Systems permitted include 120 volts, 1-phase; 120/240 volts, 1-phase; and 120/208 volts, 1-phase.

(B) Three-Phase Systems. Feeders from 208Y/120-volt, 3-phase systems shall be permitted to include two ungrounded conductors and shall include one grounded conductor and one equipment grounding conductor. So far as practicable, the loads shall be equally distributed on the 3-phase system.

(C) Receptacles. (Relocated from 551.73(D))

(D) Neutral Conductors. (Relocated from 551.73(D))

Informational Note (Revised and relocated from 551.73(D))

(See NEC for actual text)

Change Summary

- 551.72 is separated into first level subdivisions for clarity.
- Requirements for receptacles and neutral conductors are relocated from 551.73 (D) into 551.72 in two new first level subdivisions.
- RV Parks are permitted to utilize three wire 208/120 volt feeders only.

FR: 5412
SR: 5410
SCR:18

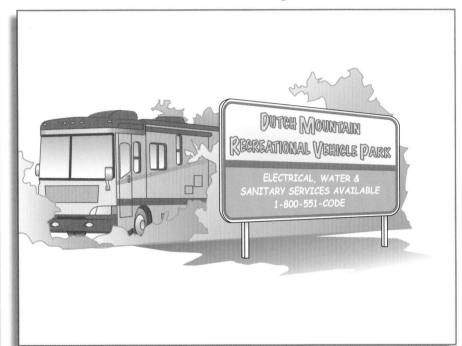

Significance of the Change

The requirements for distribution systems in RV parks are modified for clarity and usability. Requirements for receptacles and neutral conductors are relocated from 551.73 (D) into 551.72 in two new first level subdivisions (C) Receptacles and (D) Neutral Conductors for clarity. Existing 551.73(D) is deleted, and the accompanying informational note is revised and relocated into 551.72(D).

Two new first level subdivisions (A) and (B) are added to provide clarity on permitted systems to supply RV's and a new limitation for single phase feeders only from three phase 208/120 volt systems. New first level subdivision (A) Systems, now requires that the capacity for the receptacles provided be in compliance with section 551.73. New first level subdivision (B) Three Phase Systems now clearly limits feeders from a 208/120 volt, 3-phase system, to include two ungrounded conductors, one grounded conductor and one equipment grounding conductor. This new requirement also mandates that the load on the three-phase 208/120 volt system be balanced equally.

RV Park Grounding Electrodes

Courtesy of Donny Cook

Code Language

551.75 Grounding.

(A) General. All electrical equipment and installations in recreational vehicle parks shall be grounded as required by Article 250.

(B) Grounding Electrode. Power outlets or recreational vehicle site supply equipment, other than those used as service equipment, shall not be required to have a grounding electrode. An auxiliary grounding electrode(s) in accordance with 250.54 shall be permitted to be installed.

(See NEC for actual text)

Significance of the Change

In the 2014 *NEC* revision cycle, the issue of where grounding electrodes were required at power outlet locations in RV parks was discussed at length. A task group was formed to investigate and determine where electrodes were necessary in these locations. At the center of this discussion are applicable sections in Article 250, which require grounding electrodes. As per section 90.3, the requirements in Article 551, may only supplement or modify the requirements in Chapters 1 through 4 including Article 250. There is no question that a grounding electrode conductor is required at service equipment in RV parks. Section 551.75 is revised in two first level subdivisions with (A) General, containing the previous text that requires compliance with all of Article 250. A new first level subdivision (B) now provides requirements for grounding electrodes and exempts power outlets or recreational vehicle site supply equipment, other than those used as service equipment, from requirements to include a grounding electrode. Clarity is also provided with text that permits an auxiliary grounding electrode(s) in accordance with 250.54.

This issue has roots in Article 100 as well. The Article 100 definition "Structure" has been modified and does not apply to electrical equipment.

Change Summary

- RV park electrical distribution systems now require grounding electrodes at service equipment only.
- Substantiation provided suggested that past practice proves no need for electrodes at power outlet locations.
- The Article 100 definition "Structure" has been modified as follows: That which is built or constructed, other than equipment."

FR: 5414
SR: None

Marinas ... and Noncommercial Docking Facilities

Code Language

Article 555 Marinas, Boatyards, and Noncommercial Docking Facilities

555.1 Scope. This article covers... (See *NEC* text) in the areas comprising of fixed or floating piers, wharves, docks, and other areas in marinas, boatyards, boat basins, boathouses, yacht clubs, boat condominiums, docking facilities associated with one-family dwellings, two-family dwellings, multifamily dwellings, and residential condominiums...(See *NEC* text)

(See NEC for actual text)

Photo from iStock

Change Summary

- The title of Article 555 is revised to "Commercial and Noncommercial Docking Facilities" to include dwelling units of all types.

- Scope now includes one-family dwellings, two-family dwellings, and multifamily dwellings.

- This revision recognizes that electrical hazards present in marinas and boat docking facilities are the same without regard to the type or size of the venue in which they are located.

Significance of the Change

The previous *NEC* requirements for marinas and boatyards prescriptively exempted "one-family dwellings, two-family dwellings, and multifamily dwellings" and only a "residential condominium" was included. This revision recognizes that electrical hazards present in marinas and boat docking facilities are the same without regard to the type or size of the venue in which they are located.

The title of Article 555 is revised to include both "Commercial" and "Noncommercial Docking Facilities" removing the dwelling unit exemption. Additionally, the scope in Section 555.1 is expanded to prescriptively include "one-family dwellings, two-family dwellings, and multifamily dwellings." It is well understood that where there is water, the potential for shock increases significantly. A review of the requirements in Article 555 reveals that the same prescriptive requirements to protect persons from shock hazards are also necessary for residential boat docks associated with single-family and multifamily dwelling occupancies. The electrical hazards are the same. Current flow through the body does not change due to the type or size of the venue in which a person is located.

FRs: 5435, 5438
SR: 5412

Ground Fault Protection

Code Language

555.3 Ground-Fault Protection.
The overcurrent protective devices that supply the marina, boatyards, and commercial and noncommercial docking facilities shall have ground-fault protection not exceeding 30 mA.

(See NEC for actual text)

Significance of the Change

This revision significantly enhances electrical safety for all installations involving Marinas and Boatyards. The previous requirement for ground-fault protection (GFP) in Section 555.3 mandated that the "main" over-current protective device (OCPD) feeding the marina provide GFP not exceeding 100 mA. An alternative was permitted to allow the individual branch circuits to provide the GFP not exceeding 100 mA. This revision deletes the requirement to protect the "main" OCPD and now requires all OCPD's to provide GFP not exceeding 30 mA. The previous requirement for GFP at 100 mA was intended to provide a level of protection without permitting what some called "nuisance tripping." Requiring each branch circuit to provide GFP at not more than 30 mA significantly improves protection from shock hazards. This revision does not get to the 4 to 6 mA range provided by a GFCI device because at that level, in this environment, there could be continuous tripping that may result in the owner removing the device resulting in no level of protection. If a 30 mA device is tripping on a branch circuit in a marina/boatyard, there is a significant problem that must be addressed.

The substantiation for this revision is based upon a new report (Assessment of Hazardous Voltage/Current in Marinas, Boatyards, and Floating Buildings) commissioned by The Fire Protection Research Foundation.

Change Summary

- All OCPD's supplying marinas etc. must now provide GFP protection not exceeding 30 mA.
- GFP of each individual branch or feeder circuit is no longer permitted as "a suitable alternative," it is required.
- Revisions are based on the findings in the NFPA Fire Protection Research Foundation report "Assessment of Hazardous Voltage/Current in Marinas, Boatyards, and Floating Buildings."

FR: 5436
SR: 5413

Signage to Warn of Potential Shock Hazards

Code Language

555.24 Signage. Permanent safety signs shall be installed to give notice of electrical shock hazard risks to persons using or swimming near a boat dock or marina and shall comply with all of the following:

1. The signage shall comply with 110.21(B)(1) and be of sufficient durability to withstand the environment.

2. The signs shall be clearly visible from all approaches to a marina or boatyard facility.

3. The signs shall state "WARNING - POTENTIAL SHOCK HAZARD - ELECTRICAL CURRENTS MAY BE PRESENT IN THE WATER."

(See NEC for actual text)

Change Summary

• New section 555.24 requires signage to warn of potential shock hazards in water.

• The signage must comply with 110.21(B)(1) and be of sufficient durability to withstand the environment.

• The signs must be applied on electrical equipment and clearly visible from all approaches to a marina or boatyard facility.

Significance of the Change

The NFPA Fire Research Foundation together with the American Boat and Yacht Council (ABYC) Foundation issued a report titled "Assessment of Hazardous Voltage/Current in Marinas, Boatyards, and Floating Buildings" on November 5, 2014. This report investigated and made suggestions for electrical equipment installed and used in the vicinity of marinas, boatyards, and floating buildings. The ABYC recommends that no recreational swimming at any time take place in a marina environment and that an effective plan against electrical safety drowning (ESD) must include a no swimming policy and "NO SWIMMING" signs posted throughout the facility.

This new section 555.24 now requires that the installer/maintainer install signage to discourage swimming. Leakage current is a reality in a marina environment and keeping persons out of the water will ensure they are not exposed to current flow and potential ESD. The signage must be installed in accordance with 110.21(B)(1) and be of sufficient durability to withstand the environment. This requirement is a bit different in that it is required to be applied and be clearly visible from all approaches to a marina or boatyard facility. Prescriptive text is provided for the signage.

FR: None
SR: 5413

Type SE Cable, Height Restrictions, Underground in Raceway

Significance of the Change

Type SE (and SER) cable is commonly used for temporary power installations during construction activity. The general requirements for Type SE cable previously prohibited use with restrictions on height and use in a raceway installed underground. General height restrictions are located in 338.10(B)(4)(a). This is now modified in 590.4(B)(1) for feeders and 590.4(C)(1) for branch circuits where Type SE cable is used for temporary power in the same manner as Type NM cable.

Additionally, the general rule in 338.12(A)(2) prohibits Type SE cable from being installed underground with or without a raceway. This is now modified in 590.4(B)(2) for feeders and 590.4(C)(2) for branch circuits allowing Type SE cable to be installed in a raceway in an underground installation for temporary power.

This is a very practical revision that recognizes a common practice that has not seen cable failures or other issues. Active construction sites do not lend themselves well to overhead installation of feeders and branch circuits outside of a building or structure under construction. There are many scenarios that require feeders and branch circuits to be run to and from buildings, structures, and job-site trailers. Installing overhead conductors in some cases is infeasible due to the movement of materials by cranes, and lull type forklifts, etc.

Code Language

590.4 General.

(B) Feeders. (See *NEC* text)...the following wiring methods shall be permitted:

(1) Type NM, Type NMC, and Type SE cables shall be permitted to be used in any dwelling, building, or structure without any height limitation or limitation by building construction type and without concealment within walls, floors, or ceilings.

(2) Type SE cable shall be permitted to be installed in a raceway in an underground installation.

Exception: (No change)

(C) Branch Circuits. (Same revisions as seen above)

(See NEC for actual text)

Change Summary

- 590.4(B) and (C) are separated into parent text and list items for clarity.

- Type SE cable is now clearly permitted to be used for temporary power without any height limitation or limitation by building construction type and without concealment within walls, floors, or ceilings.

- Type SE is now permitted to be installed in a raceway in an underground installation for temporary power.

FR: 615
SR: None

Temporary Splices Permitted Without Junction Box

Code Language

590.4 General

(G) Splices. A box, conduit body, or other enclosure, with a cover installed, shall be required for all splices except where:

(1) The circuit conductors being spliced are all from nonmetallic multiconductor cord or cable assemblies, provided that the equipment grounding continuity is maintained with or without the box.

(2) The circuit conductors being spliced are all from metal sheathed cable assemblies terminated in listed fittings that mechanically secure the cable sheath to maintain effective electrical continuity.

(See NEC for actual text)

Change Summary

- 590.4(G) is separated into parent text which includes a box cover and list items for clarity.
- 590.4(G)(1) permits nonmetallic multiconductor cord or cable assembly splice, with the EGC spliced, to be installed without a box or enclosure.
- 590.4(G)(2) permits metal sheathed cable assemblies to be spliced where terminated in listed fittings that mechanically secure the cable sheath to maintain effective electrical continuity without a box or enclosure.

FR: 616
SR: 606

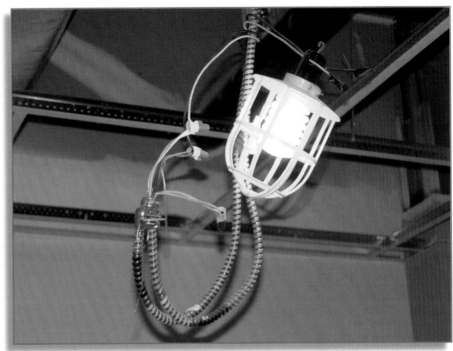

Significance of the Change

This revision provides significant clarity with respect to permitted methods of splicing temporary wiring. The general rule in the parent text requires a box, conduit body, or other enclosure, with a cover installed, for all splices. The previous general requirement did not specifically require a box/enclosure cover. Two exceptions to the general rule are provided in positive text.

The first permits nonmetallic jacketed multiconductor cord or cable assemblies to be spliced without a box and cover provided that the equipment grounding continuity is maintained with or without the box. Note that the requirement is not limited to a single type of flexible cord/cable or cable assembly, the rule is based on nonmetallic jacketed cable with the EGC continuity maintained.

The second and most significant revision is that metal sheathed cable assemblies may be spliced without a box or enclosure provided they are terminated in listed fittings that mechanically secure the cable sheath to maintain effective electrical continuity. As written in 2014, this requirement permits "a terminal fitting" to be used in lieu of a box. The present reference to "terminal fitting" creates confusion since it is not clear at all. While the intent is a terminal fitting such as a duplex connector, OSHA does not recognize such an installation as being compliant.

GFCI Protection, Temporary Wiring

Significance of the Change

This revision corrects a serious error that inadvertently allowed for temporary wiring without GFCI protected receptacle outlets. The error was recognized by the committee as extremely significant and a tentative interim amendment (TIA Number 1133) was issued to correct the mistake in the 2014 *NEC*. The requirements of 590.6(A)(1) were modified to permit listed cord sets or devices incorporating listed GFCI protection for personnel identified for portable use in addition to the general GFCI requirements of 590.6(A)(1). The substantiation for this change was based on the fact that listed cord sets or devices incorporating listed GFCI protection for personnel identified for portable use were added in 590.6(A)(2) but not (A)(1). There is a significant difference between the two as follows:

590.6(A)(1) requires GFCI protected receptacle outlets where temporary wiring is installed.

590.6(A)(2) requires GFCI protected receptacle outlets where existing, permanent receptacle outlets are used. In this case, where one would use an existing receptacle outlet, listed cord sets or devices incorporating listed GFCI protection for personnel identified for portable use is an excellent option.

Code Language

590.6 Ground-Fault Protection for Personnel.

(A) Receptacle Outlets.

(1) Receptacle Outlets Not Part of Permanent Wiring. All 125-volt, single-phase, 15-, 20-, and 30-ampere receptacle outlets that are not a part of the permanent wiring of the building or structure and that are in use by personnel shall have ground-fault circuit-interrupter protection for personnel. In addition to this required ground-fault circuit-interrupter protection for personnel, listed cord sets or devices incorporating listed ground-fault circuit-interrupter protection for personnel identified for portable use shall be permitted.

(See NEC for actual text)

Change Summary

- In the 2014 *NEC* 590.6(A)(1) was revised to allow an option of a listed portable GFCI.
- The Committee did not intend to allow the use of a listed portable GFCI as an option.
- Listed cord sets or devices incorporating listed GFCI protection for personnel identified for portable use are now *permitted in addition* to the GFCI protection required in 590.6(A)(1).

FR: 618
SR: None

590.6(B)

Article 590 Temporary Installations

Part None

REVISION

Special Purpose GFCI (SPGFCI)

Code Language

590.6 Ground Fault Protection for Personnel.

(B) Use of Other Outlets. For temporary wiring installations, receptacles, other than those covered by 590.6(A)(1) through (A)(3) used to supply temporary power to equipment used by personnel during construction, remodeling, maintenance, repair, or demolition of buildings, structures, or equipment, or similar activities, shall have protection in accordance with (B)(1), (B)(2), or the assured equipment grounding conductor program in accordance with (B)(3).

(1) GFCI Protection. Ground-fault circuit-interrupter protection for personnel.

(2) SPGFCI Protection. Special purpose ground-fault circuit-interrupter protection for personnel.

(3) Assured Equipment Grounding Conductor Program... (See *NEC* text)

(See NEC for actual text)

Change Summary

- 590.6(B) is expanded to permit a special purpose GFCI (SPGFCI), Classes C, D, and E.
- A Class A GFCI trips at 6 mA or higher and do not trip when the current to ground is less than 4 mA.
- Classes C, D, and E ground-fault circuit interrupters trip when the current to ground is 20 mA or higher and do not trip when the current to ground is less than 15 mA.

FR: None
SR: 608

Significance of the Change

The provisions of 590.6(A)(1) and (A)(2) address GFCI protection for personnel for receptacle outlets at 125-volts, single phase, 15, 20 ad 30-amps. 590.6(A)(3) addresses GFCI protection for personnel on portable generators 15 kW or smaller that have receptacle outlets at 125/250-volts, single phase, 15, 20 ad 30-amps. GFCI protection of other temporary receptacle outlets is addressed in 590.6(B). This revision adds a new 590.6(B)(2) that permits the use of a special purpose GFCI (SPGFCI) in addition to Class A GFCI protection and the assured equipment grounding conductor program (AEGCP). These SPGFCI's allow for more leakage current than a standard Class A device which will trip at 6 mA or greater but not below 4 mA. SPGFCI's come in classes C, D, and E and trip when the current to ground is 20 mA or higher but do not trip when the current to ground is less than 15 mA.

NECA Guide to Temporary Power

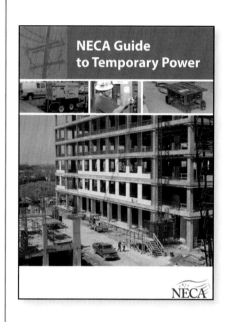
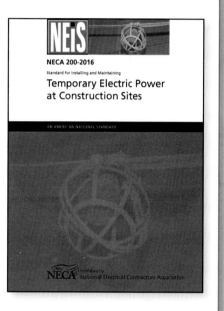

This guide was developed by NECA to assist the industry in understanding and applying all applicable requirements for installing temporary power systems and the use of temporary power. The *NECA Guide to Temporary Power* publication provides essential resources for electrical contractors to help them get it right when it comes to temporary power responsibilities. This new guide is organized in an easy-to-read format and includes links to valuable resources that assist in attaining compliance and safety of temporary power systems. The guide contains essentials such as how to effectively plan the installation, how to prefabricate where practical, and how to implement safe work practices when handling temporary wiring, designs, OSHA compliance, and more. Along with the extensive resources, this product provides access to all Letters of Interpretation from OSHA relative to temporary installations. This new guide is a must for all electrical contractors that have to design, install, maintain, and remove temporary power systems.

- Temporary wiring is often treated as an afterthought—after all, "it's only temporary."
- Temporary wiring must meet the requirements of the *NEC*, applicable OSHA requirements and be installed and maintained by qualified persons.

Chapter 6

Articles 600–695
Special Equipment

Photovoltaic (PV) Powered Signs

Code Language

600.2 Photovoltaic (PV) Powered Sign. A complete sign powered by solar energy consisting of all components and subassemblies for installation either as an off-grid stand-alone, on-grid interactive, or non-grid interactive system.

600.34 Photovoltaic (PV) Powered Sign.

(A) Equipment, (B) Wiring, (C) Flexible Cords and Cables, (D) Grounding, (E) Disconnecting Means &

(F) Battery Compartments

(See NEC for actual text)

Change Summary

• PV powered signs are now defined in 600.2.

• A complete sign powered by solar energy consisting of all components and subassemblies for installation either as an off-grid stand-alone, on-grid interactive, or non-grid interactive system.

• New Section 600.34 now provides installation requirements for PV powered signs.

FRs: 5133, 5145
SR: 5122

Significance of the Change

A new definition is added to Section 600.2 for Photoelectric (PV) Powered Signs. This new definition is necessary to coordinate new requirements for PV powered signs added in new Section 600.34. PV signs are required by UL 48 (the applicable UL Standard) to be installed in accordance with the *NEC*. This new definition in 600.2 and new installation requirements in 600.34 are meant to coordinate between Articles 600, 690 and UL 48.

The new installation requirements in 600.34 are separated into six first level subdivisions. The parent text requires all field wiring of components and subassemblies for an off-grid stand-alone, on-grid interactive, or non-grid interactive PV installation to be installed in accordance with Article 690, as applicable, and the PV powered sign installation instructions. 600.34(A) requires equipment listed and labeled for PV application. 600.34(B) requires wiring external to the sign and between the PV panel and sign to be listed for PV application, routed closely, short as possible and protected from damage. 600.34(C) requires cords and cables comply with Article 400 to be extra hard usage, rated for outdoor use, and water and sunlight resistant. 690.34(D) requires grounding in accordance with Part V or Article 690 and 600.7. 690.34(E) requires disconnects to comply with Part III of Article 690 and 600.6. 600.34(F) requires that battery compartments must require a tool to open them.

Signs with a Retrofitted Illumination System

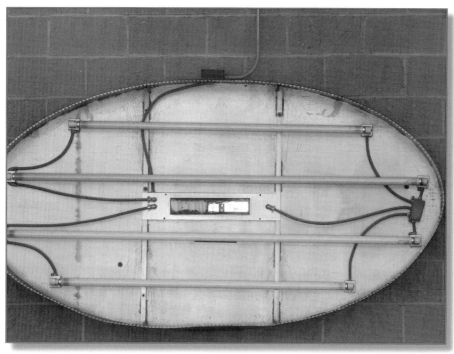

Significance of the Change

A new first level subdivision 690.4(B) is added to require marking of signs that have been retrofitted with new illumination systems. It is typical for existing signs with fluorescent type lighting to be retrofitted with LED lamps to enhance/increase light output and reduce the power consumed. This marking is necessary for the electrical inspector to determine compliance. The retrofit must be performed in accordance with the installation instructions which need to be provided as part of the kits listing. All persons performing maintenance on the retrofitted sign must be informed of the retrofit for safety reasons and for replacement of parts, lamps, etc. Any service performed, and parts replaced must be in accordance with the retrofit and not the original sign configuration.

A significant safety concern exists where signs are equipped with tubular light-emitting diode lamps powered by the existing (fluorescent) sign sockets. If an installer/maintainer attempts to install a regular (fluorescent) lamp with the illumination system energized, the lamp is likely to explode. This warning label must comply with the requirements of 110.21(B), be visible during relamping, alert service personnel that the sign has been modified and must clearly warn not to install fluorescent lamps.

Code Language

600.4 Markings.

(B) Signs with a Retrofitted Illumination System.

(1) The retrofitted sign shall be marked that the illumination system has been replaced.

(2) The marking shall include the kit providers and installer's name, logo, or unique identifier.

(3) Signs equipped with tubular light-emitting diode lamps powered by the existing sign sockets shall include a label alerting the service personnel that the sign has been modified. The label shall meet the requirements of 110.21(B). The label shall also include a warning not to install fluorescent lamps and shall also be visible during relamping.

(See NEC for actual text)

Change Summary

- New 600.4(B) provides marking requirements for retrofitted illumination systems in signs.
- The warning must inform those who service or maintain the sign of the retrofit.
- A warning label must be applied where tubular light-emitting diode lamps are now powered by the existing sign sockets. The warning is not to install fluorescent lamps, and this warning must be visible during relamping.

FR: 5135
SR: 5120

600.6

Disconnects, for Signs and Outline Lighting

Code Language

600.6 Disconnects... (See *NEC* text)

Informational Note: The location of the disconnect is intended to allow service or maintenance personnel complete and local control of the disconnecting means.

(A)(1) At Point of Entry to a Sign. ... (See *NEC* text)

(A)(2) Within Sight of the Sign. ... (See *NEC* text)

(A)(3) Within Sight of the Controller. ... (See *NEC* text)

(See NEC for actual text)

Change Summary

- A new informational note in 600.6 explains the intent of disconnect requirements.
- A new exception No. 2 in 600.6(A)(1) permits an internal panelboard and requires warning labels.
- Warning label requirements are also added in existing 600.6(A)(2) and a new exception in 600.6(A)(3).

FR: 5137
SRs: 5126, 5127
SCR 46

Significance of the Change

Section 600.6 contains disconnect requirements for signs and outline lighting. A new informational note is added to clarify that the intent of these disconnect requirements is to "allow service or maintenance personnel complete and local control of the disconnecting means." This information is extremely valuable where the AHJ and installer must determine an alternative method due to site conditions. The existing exception to 600.6(A)(1) (now Exception No. 1) relieves the need for a disconnecting means where a branch circuit or feeder passes through a sign in a listed Chapter 3 raceway is expanded to include metal-jacketed cable identified for the location. A new exception No. 2 is added to permit a feeder to enter a sign without a disconnect where it supplies an internal panelboard. Larger signs with multiple branch circuits often include a panelboard in the sign to facilitate servicing and control of sign loads at the sign. A field applied permanent warning label, in compliance with 110.21(B), visible during servicing, must be applied where the feeder enters the sign as follows: "Danger. This raceway contains energized conductors." The label must identify the source location, and it must be lockable in the open position in accordance with 110.25. An exception is added to 600.6(A)(3) requiring a warning label where the disconnecting means is not within sight of the sign controller.

Listing Requirements for Manufactured Wiring Systems

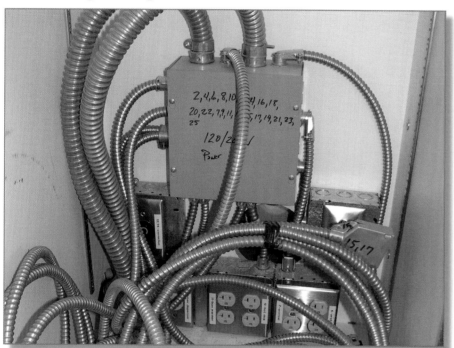

Code Language

604.6 Listing Requirements. Manufactured wiring systems and associated components shall be listed.

Informational Note: ANSI/UL 183, *Standard for Manufacturing Wiring Systems*, is a safety standard for manufactured wiring systems.

(See NEC for actual text)

Significance of the Change

Existing Section 604.6 for construction requirements is relocated to 604.100 to correlate with the numbering system found in Chapter 3 for wiring methods and materials for correlation and clarity. A new Section 604.6 now requires manufactured wiring systems and associated components to be listed.

As per the scope of this article in Section 604.1, manufactured wiring systems must be "field installed." In Section 604.2 a Manufactured Wiring System is defined as a system containing component parts that are assembled in the process of manufacture and cannot be inspected at the building site without damage or destruction to the assembly and used for the connection of luminaires, utilization equipment, continuous plug-in type busways, and other devices These systems according to the article scope must be field installed.

Change Summary

- Manufactured wiring systems as per 604.1 must be "field installed."
- A new Section 604.6 now requires manufactured wiring systems and associated components to be listed.
- The requirement is not for parts to be listed, it must be a "listed system."

FR: 5449
SR: None

620.16

Article 620 Elevators, Dumbwaiters, Escalators, Moving Walks, Platform Lifts, and Stairway Chairlifts

Part II Conductors

NEW

Elevator Control Panel Short Circuit Current Ratings

Code Language

620.16 Short-Circuit Current Rating

(A) Marking. Where an elevator control panel is installed, it shall be marked with its short-circuit current rating, based on one of the following:

1. Short-circuit current rating of a listed assembly
2. Short-circuit current rating established utilizing an approved method

Informational Note: UL 508A-2013, Supplement SB, is an example of an approved method.

(B) Installation. The elevator control panel shall not be installed where the available short-circuit current exceeds its short-circuit current rating, as marked in accordance with 620.16(A).

(See NEC for actual text)

Change Summary

- A new Section 620.16 addresses requirements for short-circuit current ratings of elevator control panels.
- Elevator control panels are now required to be marked with a short-circuit current rating.
- Elevator control panels shall not be installed where the available short-circuit current exceeds its short-circuit current rating.

Significance of the Change

A new Section 620.16 is added to provide requirements for elevator control panel short circuit current rating and the installation of the elevator control panels with respect to the available short circuit current at which they are installed. 620.16(A) now requires that all elevator control panels be marked with their short-circuit current rating, based on either the short-circuit current rating of a listed assembly or the short-circuit current rating established utilizing an approved method. In most cases the individual controllers within the elevator control panel are marked with a short-circuit current rating. However, in most cases those values are not marked on the elevator control panel. Additionally, the short-circuit current rating of the elevator control panel must be based upon all of the equipment located in the elevator control panel, not just the individual controllers.

This marking will provide both the contractor and the AHJ to verify that the upstream overcurrent protection for the elevator control panel is compliant. Elevator control panels are now prohibited to be installed where the available short-circuit current exceeds its short-circuit current rating in 620.16(B).

FR: 3331
SR: 3330

Separate Branch Circuits for Lighting and Receptacles

Code Language

620.23 Branch Circuits for Machine Room or Control Room/Machinery Space or Control Space Lighting and Receptacle(s).

(A) Separate Branch Circuit Circuits. The branch circuit(s) supplying the lighting for machine rooms, control rooms, machinery spaces, or control spaces shall be separate from the branch circuit(s) supplying the receptacle(s) in those places. These circuits shall supply no other loads.

Required lighting shall not be connected to the load side of a ground-fault circuit interrupter.

620.24 Branch Circuit for Hoistway Pit Lighting and Receptacles.

(See NEC for actual text)

Significance of the Change

Requirements for branch circuits supplying lighting and receptacles in a machine room or control room/machinery space or control space are located in Section 620.23, and branch circuit requirements for lighting and receptacles in hoistways and elevator pits are located in Section 620.24.

The previous text in both 620.23(A) and 620.24(A) required a separate branch circuit for lighting and receptacles but due to a significant lack of clarity, they inferred that both the lighting and receptacle loads could be on the same circuit. This represents a very serious hazard. Performing maintenance activity in a machine room, control room, machinery space, control space, hoistway or elevator pit can be hazardous. Where work involves tools powered at 125-volts, and a fault occurs causing an upstream overcurrent device to open, the worker is now in the dark if the receptacles and lighting are on the same circuit. This creates a significant safety hazard. This revision now provides clarity by requiring that the receptacles and lighting be on different branch circuits and those circuits shall not supply other loads. The text in 620.23(A) provides significant clarity while the changes in 620.24 clearly require the receptacles and lighting be on different branch circuits but do not specifically rule out other loads.

Change Summary

- Lighting and receptacle loads in equipment spaces must be on separate branch circuits.
- These branch circuits cannot supply other loads.
- Significant safety concerns are created where lighting and receptacle loads are supplied from the same branch circuit in equipment spaces.

FRs: 3386, 3387
SRs: 3331, 3332
SCR: 72

ASCC and Surge Protection

Code Language

620.51 Disconnecting Means.

(D) Identification and Signs.

(2) Available Short-Circuit Current Field Marking. Where an elevator control panel is used, it shall be legibly marked in the field with the maximum available short-circuit current at its line terminals. The field marking(s) shall include the date the short-circuit current calculation was performed and be of sufficient durability to withstand the environment involved.

When modifications ... (See *NEC* text)

(E) Surge Protection. Where any of the disconnecting means in 620.51 has been designated as supplying an emergency system load, surge protection shall be provided.

(See NEC for actual text)

Change Summary

- 620.51(D) is separated into second level subdivisions to address field marking of ASCC and surge protection.

- Where an elevator control panel contains the disconnecting means, it must be field marked with the ASCC at its line terminals.

- Where the disconnecting means supplies an emergency system load, surge protection must be provided.

Significance of the Change

In many areas, elevator control panels are installed where the available short-circuit current is quite high. This revision in new 620.51(D)(2) now requires that where an elevator control panel is used as a disconnecting means, it shall be legibly marked in the field with the maximum available short-circuit current at its line terminals. This required field marking correlates with new Section 620.16 but goes further by requiring the date the short-circuit current calculation was performed and mandates the label be of sufficient durability to withstand the environment involved. The second paragraph in 620.51(D)(2) requires that where the electrical system is modified in a manner that impacts the ASCC at the elevator control panel, the new or revised maximum level of ASCC must be verified or recalculated as necessary to ensure continued compliance. The new value of ASCC must be applied to the required field marking. The study, "Data Assessment for Electrical Surge Protective Devices" commissioned by the Fire Protection Research Foundation, provides results of a 2013 and 2014 survey of facility managers concerning surge damage. It shows that 24% had damage to elevators or escalators due to voltage surges. New 620.51(E) requires surge protection for circuits supplying emergency loads.

FRs: 3393, 3395

SR: 3334

Wireless Power Transfer

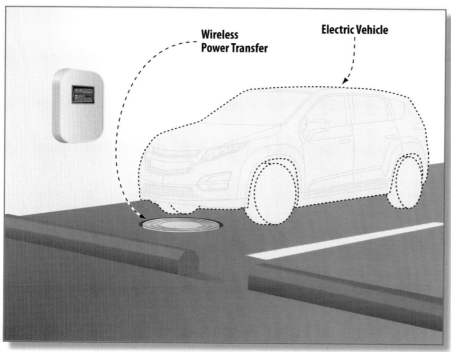

Wireless Power Transfer

Electric Vehicle

Code Language

625.1 Scope. This article covers... (See *NEC* text)... conductive, inductive, or wireless power transfer (contactless inductive charging) means, and the installation of equipment and devices related to electric vehicle charging.

625.16 Means of Coupling. The means of coupling to the electric vehicle shall be conductive, inductive, or wireless power transfer. Attachment plugs, electric vehicle connectors, ... (See *NEC* text) listed or labeled for the purpose.

(See NEC for actual text)

Significance of the Change

The scope of Article 625 is revised to include "wireless power transfer (contactless inductive charging)." This revision is necessary to address this new wireless charging technology as several vehicle manufacturers are planning to start offering wireless charging for their electric vehicles in 2016. Informational Note No. 2 is modified adding the word "conductive" in two places to clarify that these standards are not applicable to wireless power transfer. A new standard to address wireless charging of vehicles is in progress but was not completed in time to be recognized in this *NEC* revision. UL 2750, *Wireless Charging Equipment for Electric Vehicles* will address product standards for wireless power transfer.

Section 625.16 contains requirements for "means of coupling" the electric vehicle to a power source and is modified to include "wireless power transfer."

New definitions are added in 625,2 and a new Part IV to provide prescriptive requirements for wireless power transfer to charge electric vehicles. This new technology is sought after by consumers for convenience, ease of use, avoidance of having to plug-in and unplug, and, since it is automatic, consumers simply park the vehicle, and it will charge on its own.

Change Summary

- The scope of Article 625 is modified to include "wireless power transfer (contactless inductive charging)."

- Section 625.16 is modified to recognize "wireless power transfer" as a permitted means of coupling the electric vehicle to a power source for charging.

- Informational Note No. 2 is modified to clarify that UL 2594-2013 and UL 2202-2009 are safety standards for conductive electric vehicle charging equipment. A new standard UL 2750 is being developed to address *Wireless Charging Equipment for Electric Vehicles.*

FRs: 3359, 3368
SR: None
SCRs: 73, 74

New Definitions in Article 625

Code Language

625.2 Definitions.

Charger Power Converter

Fastened in Place

Fixed in Place

Output Cable to the Primary Pad

Portable (as applied to EVSE)

Primary Pad

Wireless Power Transfer (WPT)

Wireless Power Transfer Equipment (WPTE)

(See NEC for actual text)

Change Summary

- Eight new definitions are added to Article 625 to support new requirements for electric vehicle charging.
- Multiple new definitions are added to address wireless power transfer.
- These definitions mirror terminology used in SAE J2954, a standard that covers wireless charging of electric and plug-in hybrid vehicles.

FRs: 3361, 3360, 3411, 3410, 3412, 3413

SRs: 3339, 3340

Significance of the Change

The expansion in scope of Article 625 to include wireless power transfer (contactless inductive charging), along with revisions in 625.5, 625.16, and new Part IV for addressing wireless power transfer equipment must be accompanied by definitions where necessary. This is an evolving technology and definitions are added that mirror terminology used in SAE J2954, a standard that covers wireless charging of electric and plug-in hybrid vehicles. Application of these new requirements demands that we define new terms for clarity and usability. Eight new definitions are added as follows: **Charger Power Converter, Fastened in Place, Fixed in Place, Output Cable to the Primary Pad, Portable (as applied to EVSE), Primary Pad, Wireless Power Transfer (WPT), and Wireless Power Transfer Equipment (WPTE).**

Technology for wireless charging of electric vehicles is rapidly moving forward, requiring the following definitions: **Wireless Power Transfer (WPT),** The transfer of electrical energy from a power source to an electrical load via electric and magnetic fields or waves by a contactless inductive means between a primary and a secondary device. **Wireless Power Transfer Equipment (WPTE),** Equipment consisting of a charger power converter and a primary pad. The two devices are either separate units or contained within one enclosure.

Part IV Wireless Power Transfer Equipment

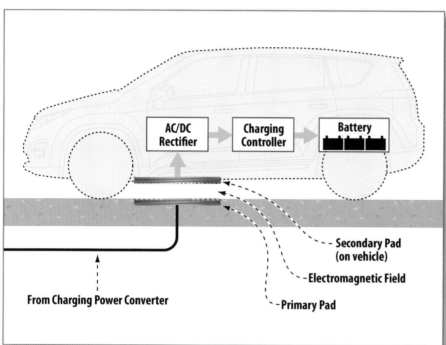

AC/DC Rectifier

Charging Controller

Battery

From Charging Power Converter

Secondary Pad (on vehicle)

Electromagnetic Field

Primary Pad

Code Language

625.5 Listed. EVSE or WPTE shall be listed.

Part IV. Wireless Power Transfer Equipment

625.101 Grounding. The primary pad base plate shall be of a non-ferrous metal and shall be grounded unless the listed WPTE employs a double-insulation system. The base plate shall be sized to match the size of the primary pad enclosure.

625.102 Construction.

(A) Type, **(B)** Installation, **(C)** Primary Pad, **(D)** Protection of the Output Cable, **(E)** Other Wiring Systems

(See NEC for actual text)

Significance of the Change

This revision adds a new Part IV to Article 625 providing prescriptive requirements for wireless power transfer equipment. It is significant to note that the listing requirements for all electrical vehicle charging equipment, including wireless power transfer, are revised this cycle. Section 625.5 now requires all electric vehicle supply equipment (EVSE) and wireless power transfer equipment (WPTE) to be listed.

625.101 requires primary pad base plates to be grounded and made of a non-ferrous metal unless it is a double-insulation system. Base plates must be sized to match the size of the primary pad enclosure.

625.102(A) provides requirements for permitted types of charger power converters. 625.102(B) lists permitted installation methods for types of charger power converters including; pedestal, wall or pole, building or structure and in a raised concrete pad. 625.102(C) addresses permitted installation of the primary pad including on the surface, embedded in the surface of the floor with its top flush with the surface, or embedded in the surface of the floor with its top below the surface. 625.102(E) recognizes that this technology is evolving and permits other wiring systems and fittings specifically listed for use on the WPTE.

Change Summary

- 625.5 now requires all EVSE and WPTE to be listed.
- New Part IV provides prescriptive installation requirements for wireless power transfer equipment.
- Included are requirements for grounding, types of WPTE, installation, primary pad requirements, protection of output cables and other listed wiring systems.

FR: 3378

SR: 3348

SCR: 75

625.40 & 625.47

Article 625 Electric Vehicle Charging System

Part III Installation

NEW

EV Branch Circuits, Multiple Feeder or Branch Circuits

Code Language

625.40 Electric Vehicle Branch Circuit. Each outlet installed for the purpose of charging electric vehicles shall be supplied by an individual branch circuit. Each circuit shall have no other outlets.

625.47 Multiple Feeder or Branch Circuits. Where equipment is identified for the application, more than one feeder or branch circuit shall be permitted to supply equipment.

(See NEC for actual text)

Change Summary

- Requirements for individual branch circuits having no other outlets for charging EV's is relocated from 210.17 to new Section 625.40.
- New Section 625.47 permits more than one feeder or branch circuit to supply equipment where the equipment is identified for the application.

FRs: 3371, 3375
SR: 3347

Significance of the Change

Electric vehicle branch circuit requirements are logically relocated from 210.17 to a new 625.40. Existing Section 625.40 for overcurrent protection is relocated to 625.41. Each outlet (receptacle outlet or hard wired equipment) that is installed to charge electric vehicles must be supplied by an individual branch circuit. Each individual branch circuit may serve only the outlet supplied for charging EV's. This requirement is more appropriately located in Article 625. A new dwelling unit does not require individual branch circuits and outlets in a garage for charging EV's, it is optional for dwelling units or other structures that will supply an EV. This relocation also separates EV requirements from general receptacle requirements in garage spaces.

New Section 625.47 now permits more than one feeder or branch circuit to supply equipment where the equipment is identified for the application. This revision recognizes that there is electric vehicle supply equipment that is listed and identified to be fed by more than one branch circuit or feeder. There is confusion with respect to the requirements of Section 225.30 for number of supplies to structures as well as the defined term *structure*. Where EV charging equipment stands alone in a parking lot, for example, it is often considered as a "structure", and installers/inspectors apply the rules of Section 225.30 limiting the equipment to a single supply. "See revisions to 225.30 and Article 100 Structure."

Alternative Wiring and Surge Protection

Code Language

645.4 Special Requirements for Information Technology Equipment Room. The alternative wiring methods to and Parts I and III of Article 725 for signaling wiring, and Parts I and V of Article 770 for optical fiber cabling, shall be permitted where all of the following conditions are met: (list items (1) through (6))

645.18 Surge Protection for Critical Operations Data Systems. Surge protection shall be provided for critical operations data systems.

(See NEC for actual text)

Significance of the Change

In the 2014 *NEC* revision cycle, Section 645.4 was revised to permit alternate power wiring methods in lieu of those in Article 708 for Critical Operations Power Systems (COPS). This revision removes that permission to correlate with Article 708. The *NEC* does not mandate where a COPS is required, these systems are classed by municipal, state, federal, or other codes where facilities or parts of facilities require continuous operation for the reasons of public safety, emergency management, national security, or business continuity. Article 645 cannot supersede the requirements of Article 708.

Critical operations data systems (CODS) are now required to be provided with surge protection by new section 645.18. A CODS is defined as an information technology equipment system that requires continuous operation for reasons of public safety, emergency management, national security, or business continuity.

These revisions strengthen the survivability of a CODS by ensuring that the hardened wiring methods of Article 708 are employed along with surge protection of the CODS.

Change Summary

- 645.4 is revised to delete references to Article 708 for Critical Operations Power Systems.
- The alternative wiring methods permitted in Article 645 may amend only Chapter 3, and Articles 725 and 770.
- Critical operations data systems are now required to be provided with surge protection.

FRs: 3353, 3356

SR: 3311

645.5(E)

Article 645 Information Technology Equipment

Part None

Supply Circuits and Interconnecting Cables

Code Language

645.5 Supply Circuits and Interconnecting Cables.

(E) Under Raised Floors. (See *NEC* text)... power cables, communication cables, connecting cables, interconnecting cables, cord-and-plug connections, and receptacles (See *NEC* text)... shall be permitted under a raised floor...(See *NEC* text)...

(1) Installation Requirements for Branch Circuit Supply Conductors Under a Raised Floor.

(2) Installation Requirements for Electrical Supply Cords, Data Cables, Interconnecting Cables, and Grounding Conductors Under a Raised Floor.

(3) Installation Requirements for Optical Fiber Cables Under a Raised Floor.

(See NEC for actual text)

Change Summary

- 645.5(E) is revised for clarity and usability with three new second level subdivisions specifying installation requirements under raised floors.
- Branch circuit requirements are addressed in 645.5(E)(1).
- Requirements for electrical supply cords, data cables, interconnecting cables, grounding conductors, and optical fiber cables under raised floors are addressed in 645.5(E)(2) and (3).

FR: 3354
SR: 3312

Significance of the Change

First level subdivision 645.5(E) is revised to provide significant clarity and usability. New parent text includes general requirements from the previous list items for approved construction of raised floors, accessibility of raised floors and openings in them. Power cables, communication cables, connecting cables, interconnecting cables, cord-and-plug connections, and receptacles associated with information technology equipment are then permitted under a raised floor in compliance with 645.5(E)(1) through (3).

645.5(E)(1) includes requirements for permitted branch circuits with general requirements that all branch circuits be installed in accordance with 300.11. In addition to the wiring methods permitted in 300.22(C), there are 17 wiring methods listed for clarity. New to the list of permitted wiring methods is 645.5(E)(1)(17) Type TC power and control tray cable. 645.5(E)(2) includes requirements for electrical supply cords, data cables, interconnecting cables, and grounding conductors. These requirements are revised to reference 725.135(C) for permitted cable types along with permitted additional cable types. The previous Table 645.5(E)(6) is deleted as it is no longer required. 645.5(E)(3) provides permitted types of optical fiber cable permitted to be installed under raised floors in accordance with 770.113(C).

Disconnecting Means, CODS, Cables, and Personnel

Significance of the Change

645.10 contains requirements for disconnecting means. 645.10(B) provides required conditions, which relieve the need for remote disconnecting for critical operations data systems (CODS).

In the 2014 *NEC* list item, 645.10(B)(5) contained section references for permitted cable, other than branch circuits installed under raised floors in CODS. 645.10(B)(2) is revised to require that cables installed under a raised floor, other than branch-circuit wiring, and power cords must be installed in compliance with 645.5(E)(2) or (E)(3), or in compliance with a new Table 645.10(B)(5) .

The new Table is titled, 645.10(B)(5) Cables Installed Under Raised Floors, improving clarity and usability. This new table also includes a reference for branch circuit wiring in revised 645.5(E)(1).

The 2014 *NEC* requirement in 645.10(B)(2) is revised to clarify that qualified personnel must be continuously available to *advise* emergency responders and to *instruct* them of disconnecting methods. The previous requirement mandated that qualified persons must be onsite to "meet" emergency responders. Substantiation provided for this change pointed out that presence of qualified personnel at thousands of facilities is not necessary. The necessary information is location and operation of the approved disconnecting means. This use can be directed from off-site as effectively as from on-site.

Code Language

645.10 Disconnecting Means.

(B) Critical Operations Data Systems. Remote disconnecting controls shall not be required for critical operations data systems when all of the following conditions are met:

(2) Qualified personnel are continuously available to advise emergency responders and to instruct them of disconnecting methods.

(5) Cables installed under a raised floor, other than branch-circuit wiring, and power cords are installed in compliance with 645.5(E)(2) or (E)(3), or in compliance with Table 645.10(B)(5).

Table 645.10(B)(5) Cables Installed Under Raised Floors

(See NEC for actual text)

Change Summary

- 645.10(B)(2) is revised to clarify that qualified personnel are continuously available to advise emergency responders and to instruct them of disconnecting methods.

- The previous requirement mandated that qualified persons must be onsite to "meet" emergency responders.

- 645.10(B) is revised for clarity into a table format to quickly reference requirements for cables under raised floors in critical operations data systems.

FR: 3355

SR: 3315

Field Marking of Short-Circuit Current Values, Surge Protection

Code Language

670.5 Short-Circuit Current Rating.

(1) Industrial machinery shall not be installed where the available short-circuit current exceeds its short-circuit current rating as marked in accordance with 670.3(A)(4).

(2) Industrial machinery shall be legibly marked in the field with the maximum available short-circuit current. The field marking(s) shall include the date the short-circuit calculation was performed and be of sufficient durability to withstand the environment involved.

670.6 Surge Protection. Industrial machinery with safety interlock circuits shall have surge protection installed.

(See NEC for actual text)

Change Summary

- Industrial machinery is now required to be marked in the field with the maximum available short-circuit current.

- The field applied marking must include the date the short-circuit calculation was performed and be of sufficient durability to withstand the environment involved.

- Surge protection is now required for industrial machinery with safety interlock circuits.

Significance of the Change

In the 2014 *NEC,* Section 670.5 required that industrial machinery not be installed where the available fault current exceeded the short-circuit current rating marked on the equipment as required by 670.3(A)(4). It is extremely difficult for the electrical inspector to verify compliance with respect to available short circuit current ratings unless there is a field applied label that documents the maximum short circuit current available at the industrial machinery at the time of installation.

This revision in Section 670.5 now requires that industrial machinery be marked in the field with the maximum available short-circuit current. The field applied marking must include the date the short-circuit calculation was performed and be of sufficient durability to withstand the environment involved.

A new Section 670.6 is added to require that where industrial machinery is installed with safety interlock circuits, surge protection must be provided. Safety interlocking systems are installed to protect persons from injury and possible death while working on or around industrial machinery. The requirement for surge protection will enhance protection of the machinery safety interlocking systems, protecting them from damage caused by a surge.

FRs: 3336, 3357
SR: 3336

Electrically Powered Pool Lifts

Code Language

680.2 Electrically Powered Pool Lift. An electrically powered lift that provides accessibility to and from a pool or spa for people with disabilities.

Part VIII Electrically Powered Pool Lifts

680.80 General. ...(See *NEC* text)

680.81 Equipment Approval. ...(See *NEC* text)

680.82 Protection. ...(See *NEC* text)

680.83 Bonding. ...(See *NEC* text)

680.84 Switching Devices. ...(See *NEC* text)

680.85 Nameplate Marking.

(See NEC for actual text)

Significance of the Change

A new Part VIII and a definition are added to the *NEC* to provide installation requirements for "electrically powered pool lifts. These lifts are mandated by local and federal requirements to provide a means to allow persons with disabilities to access and egress pools and spas. Prior to this *NEC* revision cycle, there were no *NEC* installation requirements for the installation of these lifts, requiring the installer and AHJ to make field judgment calls on the safety of the installation. In most cases this would require a field evaluation of the lift to ensure safe operation.

Part VIII contains six sections for the installation of pool lifts. 680.80 limits the rules for electrically powered pool lifts to the requirements of Part VIII. 680.81 requires they be listed and identified for swimming pool and spa use. There are three exceptions to listing; battery operated lifts below the low-voltage contact limit, solar operated or charged 24-volts or less and a source not exceeding the low-voltage contact limit and supplied by listed transformers or power supplies that comply with 680.23(A)(2). 680.82 requires GFCI protection. 680.83 requires bonding in accordance with 680.26(B)(5) and (B)(7). 680.84 requires switching devices comply with 680.22(C). 680.85 requires nameplate marking with name and model and rating in volts and amperes, or in volts and watts, frequencies, battery types and voltages.

Change Summary

- An electrically powered pool lift is now defined in 680.2 as a lift that provides accessibility to and from a pool or spa for people with disabilities.
- New Article 680 Part VIII provides requirements for electrically powered pool lifts.
- Only the requirements in Part VIII of Article 680 apply to pool lifts.

FRs: 4860, 4859
SR: 4830

Approval of Equipment, Listed

Code Language

680.4 Approval of Equipment. All electrical equipment installed in the water, walls, or decks of pools, fountains, and similar installations shall comply with the provisions of this article. Equipment and products shall be listed.

(See NEC for actual text)

Change Summary

- 680.4 is revised to require that all electrical equipment and products be listed.
- Use of only listed equipment and products ensures that all have been evaluated for the use.
- 110.3(B) mandates that all listed products be installed in accordance with any instructions in the listing or labeling.

Significance of the Change

Section 680.4 is titled Approval of Equipment and requires that "all electrical equipment installed in the water, walls, or decks of pools, fountains, and similar installations shall comply with the provisions of this article." This text infers the defined term *approved* in Article 100 as follows: "Approved. Acceptable to the Authority having jurisdiction." This means that the AHJ gets the final word on how an installation complies with Article 680.

This revision adds a new last sentence that requires all of the electrical equipment installed in the water, walls, or decks of pools, fountains, and similar installations as well as all of the electrical equipment that supplies the pool be listed. The *NEC* does not have a blanket requirement that all electrical equipment and products be listed. The general rule is that the installation be approved which means acceptable to the AHJ. Where the *NEC* mandates listed products or equipment, there is a specific requirement.

This revision will enhance the safety of pools and other equipment by ensuring that all products have been evaluated for safe use by a third party. Section 110.3(B) requires that all listed products be installed in accordance with any instructions in the listing or labeling.

FR: 4851
SR: None

Grounding and Bonding Terminals

Courtesy of Thomas and Betts

Code Language

680.7 Grounding and Bonding Terminals. Grounding and bonding terminals shall be identified for use in wet and corrosive environments. Field-installed grounding and bonding connections in a damp, wet, or corrosive environment shall be composed of copper, copper alloy, or stainless steel. They shall be listed for direct burial use.

(See NEC for actual text)

Significance of the Change

A new Section 680.7 provides requirements for all grounding and bonding terminals applied and required in Article 680. Pools, fountains, spas, hot tubs and similar installations by nature create severe environmental conditions for the electrical equipment and products applied. These environments are wet and in almost all locations corrosive due to the use of chlorine and other chemicals used to treat the water. Grounding and bonding connections are critical to the safety of all persons in the vicinity of the pools, fountains, spas, hot tubs, and similar installations conditions.

This new requirement now mandates that all grounding and bonding terminals be identified for use in wet and corrosive environments. Together with the listing requirement for all electrical equipment and products in 680.4 this means that all grounding and bonding terminals be listed and identified for use in wet and corrosive environments. The grounding and bonding terminals that are field-installed in a damp, wet, or corrosive environment must be made of copper, copper alloy, or stainless steel. All field-installed grounding and bonding terminals must be listed for direct burial use.

Change Summary

- New Section 680.7 provides requirements for all grounding and bonding terminals.
- All must be identified for use in wet and corrosive environments and listed for direct burial use.
- Where field-installed in a damp, wet, or corrosive environment, all must be composed of copper, copper alloy, or stainless steel.

FR: 4852
SR: None

Location of Underground Pool Wiring

Code Language

680.11 Underground Wiring Location. Underground wiring shall be permitted where installed in rigid metal conduit, intermediate metal conduit, rigid polyvinyl chloride conduit, reinforced thermosetting resin conduit, or Type MC cable, suitable for the conditions subject to that location. Underground wiring shall not be permitted under the pool unless this wiring is necessary to supply pool equipment permitted by this article. Minimum cover depths shall be as given in Table 300.5

(See NEC for actual text)

Change Summary

- Section 680.10 for location of underground wiring is relocated to 680.11.
- The prohibition of wiring within five feet of the pool is removed, all permitted wiring methods are listed.
- Table 680.10 for minimum cover depths is deleted, all underground wiring cover depths must be in accordance with Table 300.5.

Significance of the Change

Section 680.10 is relocated to 680.11 to make room for a new Section 680.7 for grounding and bonding terminals. This revision provides clarity by removing the five-foot prohibition of underground wiring for wiring not necessary to supply pool equipment. The previous text contained this prohibition but then permitted other wiring to be installed in the prohibited zone provided it was in a complete raceway system. All underground wiring must now be installed in rigid metal conduit, intermediate metal conduit, rigid polyvinyl chloride conduit, reinforced thermosetting resin conduit, or Type MC cable, suitable for the conditions subject to that location without regard to the distance from the inside wall of the pool.

Cover depths were a source of confusion in the previous edition. Did the burial depths in Table 680.10 apply only within five feet of the pool wall or for the entire length of the circuit? Table 680.10 for minimum cover depths is deleted. All underground wiring must now comply with Table 300.5 for cover depths.

FR: 4853
SR: None

Equipment Rooms and Pits, Corrosive Environments

Courtesy of Mark Ode

Code Language

680.12 Equipment Rooms and Pits. Electrical equipment shall not be installed in rooms or pits that do not have drainage that prevents water accumulation during normal operation or filter maintenance. Equipment shall be suitable for the environment in accordance with 300.6.

Informational Note: Chemicals such as chlorine cause severe corrosive and deteriorating effects on electrical connections, equipment, and enclosures when stored and kept in the same vicinity. Adequate ventilation of indoor spaces such as equipment and storage rooms is addressed by ANSI/APSP-11, *Standard for Water Quality in Public Pools and Spas*, and can reduce the likelihood of the accumulation of corrosive vapors.

(See NEC for actual text)

Significance of the Change

A new last sentence and an informational note have been added to 680.12 to address corrosive environments. Article 680 has been significantly revised this cycle to address corrosive environments and the effect they have on electrical equipment and products. Pool, spa, fountain and other equipment are commonly placed in an equipment room or pit. It is common to see chlorine and other chemicals stored in these areas as they are used for the pool, spa, etc. This storage immediately adjacent to electrical equipment and products can quickly damage and corrode the electrical equipment and often fail due to this exposure.

A new last sentence now requires all equipment be suitable for the environment in accordance with 300.6. While the requirements of 300.6 have always applied for pool installations, this reference will prompt both the installer and AHJ to comply with all of the requirements. A new informational note explains that chemicals such as chlorine cause severe corrosive and deteriorating effects on electrical connections, equipment, and enclosures, when stored and kept in the same vicinity as the pool/spa electrical equipment and that adequate ventilation of these indoor spaces such as equipment and storage rooms, can reduce the likelihood of the accumulation of corrosive vapors.

Change Summary

- A new last sentence is added to Section 680.12 to require equipment suitability with Section 300.6.

- Storage of chemicals such as chlorine cause severe corrosive and deteriorating effects on electrical connections, equipment, and enclosures when stored and kept in the same vicinity.

- A new informational note addresses ventilation of equipment rooms to address the corrosive environment.

FR: 4854
SR: None

NEW

Corrosive Environments

Code Language

680.14 Corrosive Environment.

(A) General. Areas where pool sanitation chemicals are stored as well as areas with circulation pumps, automatic chlorinators, filters, open areas under decks adjacent to or abutting the pool structure and similar locations, shall be considered to be a corrosive environment. The air in such areas shall be considered to be laden with acid, chlorine, and bromine vapors... (See *NEC* text)

(B) Wiring Methods. Wiring methods in the areas described in 680.14(A) shall be listed, and identified for use in such areas. Rigid metal conduit, intermediate metal conduit, rigid polyvinyl chloride conduit, and reinforced thermosetting resin conduit shall be considered to be resistant to the corrosive environment specified in 680.14(A).

(See NEC for actual text)

Change Summary

- New 680.14 provides the *Code* user with the ability to identify a "corrosive environment."
- Permitted wiring methods for corrosive environments are provided.
- 680.14 is now referenced in 680.21(A)(1), 680.23(F)(1) and 680.25(A) for permitted wiring methods.

FRs: 4854, 4855, 4862, 4863

SRs: 4817, 4818, 4828, 4829

SCR: 43

Significance of the Change

A new section 680.14 is added to correlate requirements for corrosive environments throughout Article 680 for clarity and usability. New section 680.14 does two things, first in 680.14(A) it provides the *Code* user with what constitutes a "corrosive environment" and in 680.14(B) permitted wiring methods for "corrosive environments" are provided. There were multiple other changes that accompany this new section. This new requirement is now referenced in sections 680.21(A)(1), 680.23(F)(1) and 680.25(A) to address wiring methods in a single location in 680.14. This new requirement considers areas where pool sanitation chemicals are stored as well as areas with circulation pumps, automatic chlorinators, filters, open areas under decks adjacent to or abutting the pool structure, and similar locations as a corrosive environment. In 680.14(B) all wiring methods in "corrosive environments" are required to be listed and identified for use in "corrosive environments." Rigid metal conduit, intermediate metal conduit, rigid polyvinyl chloride conduit, and reinforced thermosetting resin conduit are listed in 680.14(B) and are considered to be resistant to the corrosive environment.

Sections 680.21(A)(1), 680.23(F)(1) and 680.25(A) all deal with permitted wiring methods and now reference 680.14 for permitted wiring methods in "corrosive environments."

680.22(B)(7) & 680.28
Article 680 Swimming Pools, Fountains, and Similar Installations
Part II Permanently Installed Pools

NEW | *REVISION*

Gas-Fired Luminaires...

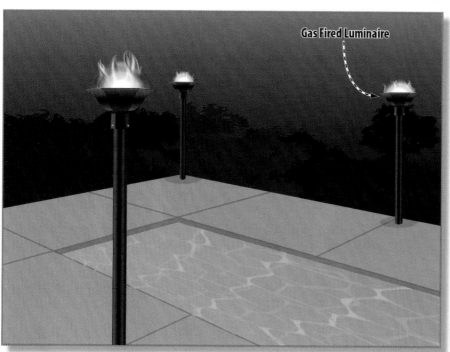

Gas Fired Luminaire

Code Language

680.22 Lighting, Receptacles, and Equipment.

(B) Luminaires, Lighting Outlets, and Ceiling-Suspended (Paddle) Fans.

(7) Low-Voltage Gas-Fired Luminaires, Decorative Fireplaces, Fire Pits, and Similar Equipment.

680.28 Gas-Fired Water Heater. Circuits serving gas-fired swimming pool and spa water heaters operating at voltages above the low-voltage contact limit shall be provided with ground-fault circuit-interrupter protection for personnel.

(See NEC for actual text)

Significance of the Change

A new second level subdivision 680.22(B)(7) now permits listed low-voltage gas-fired luminaires, decorative fireplaces, fire pits, and similar equipment. This is more of a clarification than a new permissive requirement. An electronically ignited gas-fired decorative luminaire that otherwise meets applicable *NEC* requirement in 680.22(B)(6) for low-voltage luminaires is permitted. Part of the problem this revision addresses is that many installers and AHJ's did not understand that a gas-fired luminaire actually existed and that these devices were not by definition a luminaire. Gas-fired luminaires, decorative fireplaces, fire pits, and similar equipment that use low-voltage ignitors that do not require grounding, and are supplied by listed transformers or power supplies that comply with 680.23(A)(2) with outputs that do not exceed the low-voltage contact limit are permitted to be located less than five feet from the inside walls of the pool.

New section 680.28 now provides electrical requirements for gas-fired water heaters and now mandates GFCI protection if the water heater operates at voltages above the low-voltage contact limit. Many gas-fired water heaters require a line voltage connection and no GFCI requirements existed in past editions of the *NEC*. These water heaters are typically located with other pool and spa equipment that require GFCI protection.

Change Summary

- A new 680.22(B)(7) now specifically recognizes gas fired luminaires and similar equipment.
- Gas fired water heaters operating at voltages above the low-voltage contact limit are required to be GFCI protected.

FRs: 4857, 4869
SR: 4819

Article 690 Scope and PV System Component Figures

Code Language

690.1 Scope. This article applies to solar PV systems, other than those covered by Article 691... (See *NEC* text) *[See Figure 690.1(a) and Figure 690.1(b).]* The systems covered by this article may be interactive with other electrical power production sources or stand-alone or both, and may or may not be connected to energy storage systems such as batteries. These PV systems may have ac or dc output for utilization.

Informational Note: Article 691 covers the installation of large-scale PV electric supply stations.

Figure 690.1(a) Identification of PV Power Source Components.

Figure 690.1(b) Identification of PV System Components in Common Configurations.

(See NEC for actual text)

Change Summary

- The scope of Article 690 is revised to recognize new Article 691 (Large scale PV), starting at 5000 kW.
- Figure 690.1(a) is revised to include dc-to-dc converters and more.
- Figure 690.1(b) is significantly revised including the addition of PV disconnect locations.

FR: 949
SR: 928

Significance of the Change

The scope of Article 690 is revised to recognize that new Article 691 (Large scale PV) applies to systems with a generating capacity of no less than 5000 kW, and not under exclusive utility control. Article 691 now clarifies the difference between smaller ground-mount and building-mounted PV systems and those systems that are built for large-scale utility power production. The new Article 691 sets forth the various criteria for a plant to be called a large-scale PV electric supply station and establishes criteria for how the design and installation is documented for the AHJ.

Diagram 690.1(a) is helpful to show the individual components in a PV power source. The terms *solar cells*, *modules*, *panels*, and *arrays* are used in Article 690 both in the definitions and in the Article. Dc-to-converters were added to show that they may be part of a PV power source. This *Code* cycle contains new requirements for dc-to-dc converters. Now there are numerous uses of the term, plus a new term, *PV system dc circuit*.

Figure 690.1(b) shows how common configurations of PV systems are organized and is significantly revised including PV disconnect locations. This figure now addresses Interactive systems, AC module systems, DC coupled multimode systems, AC coupled multimode systems, and Stand-alone systems.

Figure 690.1(B)

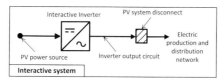

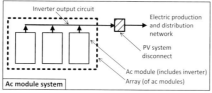

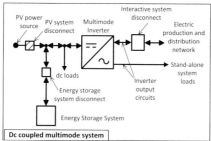

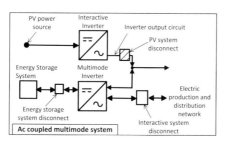

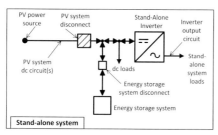

Notes:

(1) These diagrams are intended to be a means of identification for PV system components, circuits and connections.

(2) The PV system disconnect in these diagrams separates the PV system from all other systems.

(3) Not all disconnecting means required by Article 690, Part III, are shown.

(4) System grounding and equipment grounding are not shown. See article 690, Part V

(5) Custom designs occur in each configuration, and some components are optional.

Figure 690.1(b) Identification of PV System Components in Common Configurations.

Reprinted with permission from NFPA 70–2017, *National Electrical Code*®, Copyright © 2016, National Fire Protection Association, Quincy, MA 02169. This reprinted material is not the complete and official position of the NFPA on the referenced subject, which is represented only by the standard in its entirety.

Definitions

Code Language

DC-to-DC Converter Output Circuit. Circuit conductors between the dc-to-dc converter source circuit(s) and the inverter or dc utilization equipment.

DC-to-DC Converter Source Circuit. Circuits between dc-to-dc converters and from dc-to-dc converters to the common connection point(s) of the dc system.

Photovoltaic System DC Circuit. Any dc conductor supplied by a PV power source, including PV source circuits, PV output circuits, dc-to-dc converter source circuits or dc-to-dc converter output circuits.

(See NEC for actual text)

Change Summary

• The definition of the term *Array* is revised to clarify that it is a dc or *ac* power producing unit.

• Two new definitions are added to define "dc-to-dc Converter Output Circuit" and "dc-to-dc Converter Source Circuit."

• A new definition is added to refer to multiple source circuits, "Photovoltaic System DC Circuit."

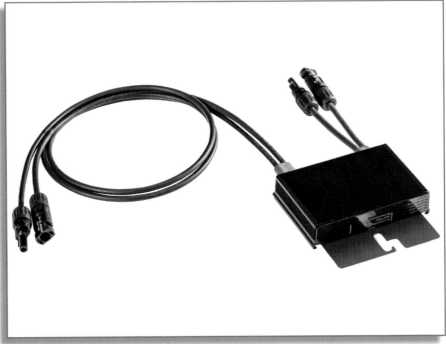

Courtesy of Bill Brooks

Significance of the Change

Most existing PV arrays have a dc output. However, it is becoming very common to see PV arrays that have an ac output. The defined term *Array* is modified to clearly cover both ac and dc power producing units to clarify that an assembly of modules or panels with an ac output is, in fact, an array. Additionally, the *NEC* did not address common types of circuits in PV systems related to dc-to-dc converters. This is now addressed with two new definitions which are added to define "dc-to-dc Converter Output Circuit" and "dc-to-dc Converter Source Circuit." The 2017 *NEC* comprehensively covers these circuits in PV systems through these new definitions.

There are many requirements within Article 690 that apply to all dc circuits in a PV system including PV source circuits, PV output circuits, dc-to-dc converter source circuits, or dc-to-dc converter output circuits. Listing all of these terms in each requirement would be cumbersome and not user-friendly. A new term *Photovoltaic System DC Circuit* is defined to capture all of these dc sources for clarity. This will allow for the use of a single term in all of the associated requirements to refer to all dc sources.

FRs: 950, 952
SR: None

Definitions

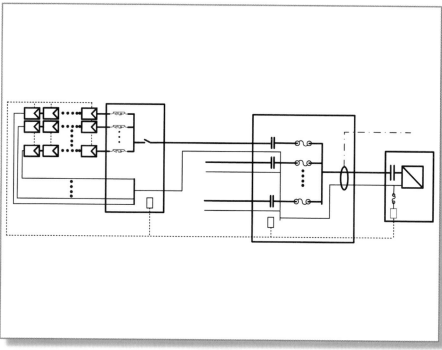

Courtesy of Bill Brooks

Code Language

Generating Capacity. The sum of parallel-connected inverter maximum continuous output power at 40°C in kilowatts.

Interactive Inverter Output Circuit. The conductors between the interactive inverter and the service equipment or another electrical power production and distribution network.

Inverter Input Circuit and Inverter Output Circuit (Revised)

Functional Grounded PV System. A PV system that has an electrical reference to ground that is not solidly grounded.

Informational Note: ...(See *NEC* text)

(See NEC for actual text)

Significance of the Change

The term *generating capacity* is defined to clarify the use of this term within Article 690 as it refers to larger PV systems that are engineered, allowing for engineering calculations of voltage and current that are not allowed for smaller, simpler PV systems.

A definition of "Interactive inverter output circuit" is added to clarify that these conductors are not "PV feeders." This will help to eliminate confusion with the application of requirements in other Articles of the *NEC*. This new definition is very similar to the defined term *Utility-Interactive Inverter Output Circuit* in Article 705.

The defined terms *inverter input circuit* and *inverter output* are simplified to remove inaccurate terminology and to be more general for future PV system configurations.

A new definition of "Functional Grounded PV System" is added to provide clarity with the use of grounded systems and conductors throughout 690 and the use of the term *solidly grounded*. This new definition clears up confusion over the use of the terms *grounded systems* and *conductors* throughout 690 and the use of the term *solidly grounded*. Most PV systems are not solidly grounded, but yet the installation requirements are written as if they were solidly grounded. This creates significant confusion. The following informational note is included to warn installer/maintainers that conductors that they expect to be at ground potential could actually be lethal.

An informational note is included to warn installer/maintainers that conductors that they expect to be at ground potential could actually be lethal.

Change Summary

- A new definition of "Generating Capacity" is added for clarity.
- "Interactive Inverter Output Circuit" is added in a similar manner as seen in Article 705.
- A new definition of "Functional Grounded PV System" is added to provide clarity with the use of grounded systems and conductors throughout 690 and the use of the term *solidly grounded*.

FRs: 1002, 953, 960, 954
SRs: 930, 932

690.4(D)

Multiple PV Systems

Code Language

690.4 General Requirements.

(D) Multiple PV Systems. Multiple PV systems shall be permitted to be installed in or on a single building or structure. Where the PV systems are remotely located from each other, a directory in accordance with 705.10 shall be provided at each PV system disconnecting means.

(See NEC for actual text)

Change Summary

- The title of 690.4(D) is revised from Multiple Inverters to Multiple PV Systems.
- 690.4(D) is revised to permit multiple PV systems, not just multiple inverters.
- Where multiple PV systems are located remotely, the required signage is clarified to be located at the PV system disconnecting means.

Significance of the Change

The previous *NEC* requirement in 690.4(D) permitted multiple PV inverters to be installed in or on a building or structure. This requirement is modified to more accurately describe the intended requirement. Individual PV systems often have multiple inverters, and that is permitted. This requirement now recognizes that there may be multiple PV systems on buildings or structures, and those systems may be remote from one another. The requirements for a directory in accordance with 705.10, where PV systems are located remotely, are clarified and apply only at the PV system disconnecting means for each system.

This revision provides significant clarity. It is common for many inverters to make up a single PV system. The signage related to the PV system (705.10) is located at the PV system disconnecting means as required in Section 690.13. Directories are required for different PV systems, not at each inverter as the 2014 *NEC* and prior suggests. This eliminates confusion in the field and provides necessary clarity by recognizing that multiple PV systems are permitted and may be on the same structure.

FR: 963
SR: 934

Maximum Voltage of PV System DC Circuits

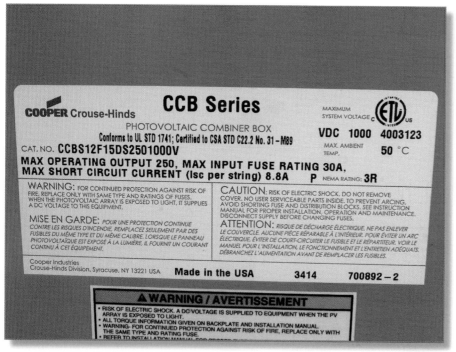

Code Language

690.7 Maximum Voltage. The maximum voltage of PV system dc circuits shall be the highest voltage between any two circuit conductors or any conductor and ground. PV system dc circuits on or in one- and two-family dwellings shall be permitted to have a maximum voltage of 600 volts or less. PV system dc circuits on or in other types of buildings shall be permitted to have a maximum voltage of 1000 volts or less. Where not located on or in buildings, listed dc PV equipment, rated at a maximum voltage of 1500 volts or less, shall not be required to comply with Parts II and III of Article 490.

(See NEC for actual text)

Significance of the Change

New parent text is added to section 690.7, Maximum Voltage, to clarify maximum allowed dc voltages for PV systems. This separates PV systems by dc voltage in three separate scenarios (1) where installed on or in dwelling units, maximum voltage of 600 volts or less, (2) where installed on or in other types of buildings, maximum voltage of 1000 volts or less and (3) where not located on or in buildings, listed dc PV equipment, rated at a maximum voltage of 1500 volts or less.

A new last sentence relieves listed dc PV equipment, rated at 1500 volts or less, from the requirements of Parts II and III of Article 490. The 1500-volt limitation in the last sentence addresses equipment that is listed to but may not be compliant with all the requirements of Article 490. Article 490 covers equipment up to much higher voltages. Since there is not a demarcation at 1500-volts dc, the requirements of 490, relating to higher voltage equipment would be imposed on listed PV equipment rated at 1500-volts dc.

This revision reveals the significance of the movement within the *NEC* to raise voltage thresholds. This revision simply raises the threshold voltage and permits listed equipment to be applied within its rating up to 1500-volts dc.

There is very little equipment available between 1000-volts and 4000-volts ac. PV has a significant amount of hardware listed for 1500-volts dc that is listed for operation at rated voltage.

Change Summary

- Section 690.7 is significantly revised and is condensed from six first level subdivisions to three.

- PV system dc circuits on or in one- and two-family dwellings 600 volts or less, other types of buildings of 1000 volts or less.

- Where not located on or in buildings, listed dc PV equipment, 1500 volts or less, is not required to comply with Parts II and III of Article 490.

FR: 1020

SR: None

SCR: 62

690.7(A), (B), & (C)

Calculating Maximum DC PV Voltages

Code Language

690.7 Maximum Voltage.

(A) Photovoltaic Source and Output Circuits. In a dc PV source circuit or output circuit, the maximum PV system voltage for that circuit shall be calculated in accordance with one of the following methods: ...(See *NEC* text)

(B) DC-to-DC Converter Source and Output Circuits. In a dc-to-dc converter source and output circuit, the maximum voltage shall be calculated in accordance with 690.7(B)(1) or (B)(2)... (See *NEC* text)

(C) Bipolar Source and Output Circuits. For 2-wire dc circuits connected to bipolar PV arrays, the maximum voltage shall be... (See *NEC* text)

(See NEC for actual text)

Change Summary

- 690.7 is significantly revised into parent text and three first level subdivisions.

- 690.7(A) provides three methods to calculate maximum voltage for PV source and output circuits.

- 690.7(B) provides two methods to calculate maximum voltage for dc-to-dc converter source and output circuits, and 690.7(C) addresses maximum voltage for bipolar source and output circuits.

FR: 1020
SR: 938
SCR: 63, 64

Significance of the Change

This revision simplifies 690.7 into three first level subdivisions to calculate maximum voltage. 690.7(A) provides three methods to calculate maximum voltage for PV source and output circuits. They are (1) Instructions in listing or labeling of the module, (2) Crystalline and multicrystalline modules and (3) PV systems of 100 kW or larger. Method (2) Crystalline and multicrystalline modules include the use of the voltage correction factors now located in Table 690.7(A). Method (3) permits engineering supervision for PV systems with a generating capacity of 100 kW or greater with a documented and stamped PV system design, using an industry standard method and provided by a licensed professional electrical engineer. One such standard industry method is the Sandia Array Performance Model.

Dc-to-dc converters have become far more common in PV systems over the past few years, and the 2014 *NEC* had very little installation information on this equipment. 690.7(B) separates requirements for calculating maximum voltage for dc-to-dc converter source and output circuits into two second-level subdivisions: 690.7(B)(1) Single DC-to-DC Converter, and 690.7(B)(2) Two or More Series Connected DC-to-DC Converters.

New 690.7(C) provides methods for calculating maximum voltage for bipolar source and output circuits.

Calculation of Maximum Circuit Current

Courtesy of Eaton Corporation

Code Language

690.8 Circuit Sizing and Current.

(A) Calculation of Maximum Circuit Current.

(1) Photovoltaic Source Circuit Currents. The maximum current shall be calculated by one of the following methods:

(1) The sum of parallel-connected PV module–rated short-circuit currents multiplied by 125 percent

(2) For PV systems …(See *NEC* text) 100 kW or greater, a documented and stamped PV system design, using an industry standard method, and provided by a licensed professional electrical engineer, shall be permitted. …(See *NEC* text) The current value used by this method shall not be less than 70 percent of the value calculated using 690.8(A)(1)(1).

Informational Note: …(See *NEC* text)

(See NEC for actual text)

Significance of the Change

The 2014 requirement for calculating PV source circuit currents was simply the sum of parallel-connected PV module–rated short-circuit currents multiplied by 125 percent. This resulted in extremely conservative current calculations at all times in all systems. This revision recognizes a second option for calculating PV source circuit current that is limited to larger PV systems above 100 kW. Where PV systems have a generating capacity of 100 kW or greater, a documented and stamped PV system design, using an industry standard method, and provided by a licensed professional electrical engineer, is now permitted.

The calculated maximum current value is to be based on the highest 3-hour current average resulting from the simulated local irradiance on the PV array accounting for elevation and orientation. Where a licensed professional electrical engineer performs this type of calculation, the current values arrived at must not be less than 70 percent of the value calculated using the more conservative method in 690.8(A)(1)(1). An engineer qualified to design PV systems is capable of making the necessary calculations or running the necessary simulations to develop accurate maximum circuit currents of PV source circuits based on the specifics of an installation location. The informational note recognizes an industry standard that may be applied: Sandia National Laboratories, reference SAND 2004-3535, *Photovoltaic Array Performance Model*.

Change Summary

- 690.8(A)(1) is revised to permit engineered calculations for PV systems with a generating capacity of 100 kW or greater.
- Other systems must still have maximum current values at rated short-circuit currents multiplied by 125 percent.
- This allows larger systems to be calculated by a licensed professional electrical engineer.

FR: 966
SR: None
SCR: 65

Ampacity, Adjustable Electronic OCPD

Code Language

690.8 Circuit Sizing and Current.

(B) Conductor Ampacity. PV system currents shall be considered to be continuous. Circuit conductors shall be sized to carry …(See *NEC* text) or where protected by a listed adjustable electronic overcurrent protective device in accordance with 690.9(B)(3), not less than the current in 690.8(B)(3).

(1) Before Application of Adjustment and Correction Factors.

(2) After Application of Adjustment and Correction Factors.

The maximum currents calculated in 690.8(A) after the application of adjustment and correction factors.

(3) Adjustable Electronic Overcurrent Protective Device. The rating or setting of an adjustable electronic overcurrent protective device installed in accordance with 240.6

(See NEC for actual text)

Change Summary

- 690.8(B) is revised to permit current calculations based on an adjustable electronic overcurrent protective device.
- 690.8(B) requires an adjustable electronic overcurrent protective device to be listed.
- Second level subdivision titles are added to 690.8(B)(1) and (B)(2) for clarity.

FR: None
SR: 940
SCR: 66

Courtesy of Eaton Corporation

Significance of the Change

690.8(B) provides requirements for conductor ampacity. New second level subdivisions are added to the existing requirements for sizing conductor ampacity before and after application of adjustment and correction factors. A new 690.8(B)(3) now permits conductor ampacity to be sized based upon the rating or setting of an adjustable electronic overcurrent protective device installed in accordance with 240.6.

The revision recognizes that adjustable electronic overcurrent protective devices are well-suited to PV circuits in that they can react accurately to overload and fault conditions and adequately protect PV output circuit conductors in a PV array. It is important to note that an adjustable electronic overcurrent protective device applied in this manner is required to be listed by the parent text in 690.8(B).

Adjustable electronic overcurrent devices can be installed in accordance with 240.6 for load circuits, and the conductor ampacity can match the setting of the overcurrent device provided 240.6 is followed.

Overcurrent Protection

Courtesy of Bill Brooks

Code Language

690.9 Overcurrent Protection.

(A) Circuits and Equipment. PV system dc circuit and inverter output conductors and equipment shall be protected against overcurrent. Overcurrent protective devices shall not be required for circuits with sufficient ampacity for the highest available current…(See *NEC* text)

(C) Photovoltaic Source and Output Circuits. A single overcurrent protective device, where required, shall be permitted to protect the PV modules and conductors of each source circuit or the conductors of each output circuit. Where single overcurrent protection devices are used to protect PV source or output circuits, all overcurrent devices shall be placed in the same polarity for all circuits within a PV system…(See *NEC* text)

(See NEC for actual text)

Significance of the Change

The previous text in 690.9 had several redundancies due to the reorganization that occurred in the 2014 *NEC* revision cycle. This revision removes these redundancies and deletes previous 690.9(C) and 690.9(E).

690.9(A) is revised for clarity to state that PV circuits must be protected from overcurrent. However, many PV circuits are current limited and are sized sufficiently to handle full available short circuit current and thus do not need overcurrent protective devices. The new second sentence in 690.9(A) clarifies that OCPD's are not for circuits with sufficient ampacity for the highest available current.

690.9(C) is revised and edited for clarity. It clarifies that all PV systems are permitted to be protected by a single overcurrent device. This revision mandates that this overcurrent device must be in the same polarity throughout the system. A new informational note (seen below) is added to clarify that the requirement for a single OCPD provides the necessary protection.

Informational Note: Due to improved ground-fault protection required in PV systems by 690.41(B), a single overcurrent protective device in either the positive or negative conductors of a PV system in combination with this ground-fault protection provides adequate overcurrent protection.

Change Summary

- Section 690.9 is editorially revised to remove redundant requirements.

- 690.9(A) now clarifies that where circuits have sufficient ampacity for the highest available current, no overcurrent protection is required.

- 690.9(C) now permits a single OCPD, and where used they must be placed in the same polarity.

FR: 972

SR: 941

SCR: 100

Arc-Fault Circuit Protection (Direct Current)

Code Language

690.11 Arc-Fault Circuit Protection (Direct Current). ...(See *NEC* text)... The system shall detect and interrupt arcing faults resulting from a failure in the intended continuity of a conductor, connection, module, or other system component in the PV system dc circuits...(See *NEC* text)

Informational Note: ...(See *NEC* text)

Exception: For PV systems not installed on or in buildings, PV output circuits and dc-to-dc converter output circuits that are direct buried, installed in metallic raceways, or installed in enclosed metallic cable trays are permitted without arc-fault circuit protection. Detached structures whose sole purpose is to house PVv system equipment shall not be considered buildings according to this exception.

(See *NEC* for actual text)

Courtesy of Bill Brooks

Change Summary

- 690.11 is revised for clarity.
- A new exception exempts the requirements for arc-fault circuit interrupter or other system components under specified conditions.
- PV systems not installed on or in buildings, PV output circuits and dc-to-dc converter output circuits that are direct buried, installed in metallic raceways, or installed in enclosed metallic cable trays are exempted.

Significance of the Change

Section 690.11 is revised for clarity removing requirements that are addressed in the product standard. A new exception is added to exempt PV systems not installed on or in buildings, PV output circuits and dc-to-dc converter output circuits that are direct buried, installed in metallic raceways, or installed in enclosed metallic cable trays. The exception also clarifies that detached structures whose sole purpose is to house PV system equipment are not considered buildings according to this exception. PV Output Circuits in ground mount systems that are direct buried, or installed in raceways, have not been identified to be the source of ignition events. PV Output Circuits in larger PV systems are typically installed in raceways, directly buried, or otherwise protected from damage, posing a significantly lesser risk of an arc related ignition event.

FR: 971
SR: 945

Rapid Shutdown of PV Systems on Buildings

Code Language

690.12 Rapid Shutdown of PV Systems on Buildings. PV system circuits installed on or in buildings shall include a rapid shutdown function to reduce shock hazard for emergency responders in accordance with 690.12(A) through (D).

Exception: Ground mounted PV system circuits that enter buildings, of which the sole purpose is to house PV system equipment, shall not be required to comply with 690.12.

(A) Controlled Conductors.

(B) Controlled Limits.

    (1) Outside the Array Boundary.

    (2) Inside the Array Boundary.

(C) Initiation Device.

(D) Equipment.

(See NEC for actual text)

Significance of the Change

The requirements for rapid shutdown of PV system circuits installed on or in buildings in section 690.12 is significantly revised with parent text that clarifies this requirement is intended to reduce shock hazards for emergency responders. An exception is added for ground mounted PV system circuits that enter buildings, of which the sole purpose is to house PV system equipment. 690.12(A) clarifies that all PV circuits supplied by the PV system must be protected.

690.12(B) Controlled Limits, establishes an array boundary which is one foot in all directions. PV circuits are inside the array boundary, or they are outside. 690.12(B)(1) requires PV circuits outside the array boundary be limited to 30 volts in 30 seconds. 690.12(B)(2) provides three methods for rapid shutdown inside the array boundary with a delayed implementation date of January 1, 2019 as follows: (1) a listed or field labeled assembly "rapid shutdown PV array", (2) limited to 80 volts in 30 seconds, (3) PV arrays with no exposed wiring methods, no exposed conductive parts, and installed more than 8 feet from exposed grounded conductive parts or ground are not required to comply with 690.12(B)(2).

690.12(B)(2) recognizes that as long as there is light on the array, voltage is present. It is difficult to achieve this protection with products presently available. The delayed implementation date will give the industry and technology time to get it done.

Change Summary

- 690.12 is significantly revised and separated into parent text and four first level subdivisions.
- An "array boundary" is established with requirements for circuits "outside" and "inside" the array boundary.
- Three rapid shutdown methods are provided for circuits inside the array boundary with an effective date of January 1, 2019.

FR: 1008

SR: 1002

SCR: 102

Photovoltaic System Disconnecting Means

Code Language

690.13 Photovoltaic System Disconnecting Means. Means shall be provided to disconnect the PV system from all wiring systems including power systems, energy storage systems, and utilization equipment and its associated premises wiring.

(A) Location. The PV system disconnecting means shall be installed at a readily accessible location.

Informational Note: PV systems installed in accordance with 690.12 address the concerns related to energized conductors entering a building.

(See NEC for actual text)

Change Summary

- 690.13 is revised to clarify that the PV system disconnecting means is the interface with other conductors of other systems.
- The location of the disconnecting means is now required to be readily accessible only.
- The requirements for rapid shutdown address the conductors entering a building or structure.

FR: 1014
SRs: 946, 947, 948
SCR: 103

Significance of the Change

Section 690.13 is revised for clarity and to illustrate that the PV system disconnecting means is the interface with other conductors of other systems. The diagrams in 690.1 are key to understanding 690.13. The PV system disconnect exists to create a defined separation point between a PV system and all other types of electrical systems including building distribution wiring, energy storage systems, wind power systems, and the electric utility conductors. Upstream of this disconnect (toward the PV array), there is nothing but PV system wiring and equipment. Downstream of this disconnect can be any combination of electrical systems and equipment. This defined separation point allows for a clear understanding of where the PV system starts and stops relative to other systems.

690.13(A) now clarifies that the PV system disconnecting means shall be installed at a readily accessible location. It is no longer based on the nearest point of entrance. A new informational note informs the *Code* user that PV systems installed in accordance with 690.12 address the concerns related to energized conductors entering a building. 690.13(B) now requires disconnects be permanently marked "PV SYSTEM DISCONNECT" and indicate an open or closed position. Where line and load terminals may be energized a warning label must be applied. 690.12(D) limits each PV system to six disconnects. New 690.12(F) provides requirements for the types of disconnects permitted.

Disconnection of Photovoltaic Equipment

Code Language

690.15 Disconnection of Photovoltaic Equipment. Isolating devices shall be provided to isolate PV modules, ac PV modules, fuses, dc-to-dc converters inverters, and charge controllers from all conductors that are not solidly grounded. An equipment disconnecting means or a PV system disconnecting means shall be permitted in place of an isolating device. ... (See *NEC* text)

> Informational Note: The purpose of these isolating devices are for the safe and convenient replacement or service of specific PV system equipment without exposure to energized conductors.

(See NEC for actual text)

Significance of the Change

690.15 is revised to clarify equipment isolation and disconnection for maintenance purposes. New parent text clarifies that *isolating devices* must be provided to isolate PV modules, ac PV modules, fuses, dc-to-dc converters inverters, and charge controllers from all conductors that are not solidly grounded. An equipment disconnecting means or a PV system disconnecting is permitted in place of an isolating device. An equipment disconnecting means is required for isolation where the maximum circuit current is greater than 30 amps for the output circuit of a dc combiner or the input circuit of a charge controller or inverter. The 30 amp requirement for an equipment disconnect recognizes that larger current dc circuits cannot be safely disconnected under load with for example exposed plug connectors, so load-break rated equipment is required to disconnect circuits larger than 30-amps on the output of dc combiners or the input of inverters or charge controllers. Much of the equipment in PV systems are very low current and can effectively utilize exposed plug connectors to electrically connect the equipment. 690.15(B) requires equipment disconnects to have a sufficient interrupting rating but not isolation. 690.15(C) lists four permitted types of isolating devices. 690.15(D) lists four permitted types of equipment disconnecting means and requires warnings be applied where the line and load terminals may be energized in the open position.

Change Summary

- 690.15 is revised to require isolating devices shall be provided to isolate PV equipment.
- 690.15 also requires equipment disconnects for equipment that requires load-break capabilities.
- 690.15(C) and (D) provide permitted types of isolating devices and equipment disconnecting means.

FR: 1013
SR: 950
SCRs: 104, 105

Wiring Methods Permitted

Code Language

690.31 Methods Permitted.

(A) Wiring Systems. ...(See *NEC* text) shall be guarded or installed in Type MC cable or in a raceway. For ambient temperatures exceeding 30°C (86°F), conductor ampacities shall be corrected in accordance with Table 690.31(A).

Table 690.31(A) Correction Factors

(B)(1) Identification. ...(See *NEC* text) Only solidly grounded... (See *NEC* text) shall be marked in accordance with 200.6.

(C)(1) General. ...(See *NEC* text)

(D) Multiconductor Cable. ...(See *NEC* text)

(See NEC for actual text)

Change Summary

- 690.31(A) now recognizes the use of Type MC cable where only raceways were previously permitted.

- Only solidly grounded PV system circuit conductors must be marked in accordance with 200.6.

- Multiconductor cable is no longer limited to Type TC-ER or USE-2, all jacketed multiconductor cable assemblies listed and identified for the application are permitted.

FRs: 974, 975, 976, 977, 998, 990, 978, 979

SRs: 953, 954, 955, 956, 957, 959, 961, 962, 963

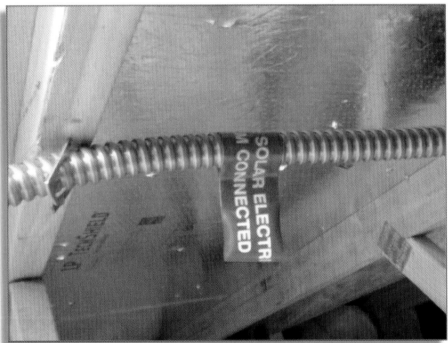

Courtesy of Bill Brooks

Significance of the Change

Type MC cable has been specifically allowed in past *Code* editions as a wiring method in 690.31 for dc conductors inside buildings. 690.31(A) now permits Type MC cable and raceways in readily accessible locations. The correction factor table that was previously located in 690.31(E) for flexible cords and cables is relocated into 690.31(A) as it applies to all wiring methods. 690.31(B)(1) is revised to clarify that only solidly grounded PV system circuit conductors, in accordance with 690.41(A)(5), are required to be marked in accordance with 200.6. For many years, designers and installers have considered grounded conductors in PV circuits as solidly grounded conductors. The 2017 *NEC* now clarifies that these are not to be considered solidly grounded even though they may be functionally grounded as part of a ground-fault detection system. Since grounded conductors in most PV systems are easily energized when a ground-fault occurs, it is misleading to use 200.6 to identify these conductors. The last sentence of 690.31(C)(1) is added to clarify that single conductor PV wire should be installed with methods similar to USE-2 and NM cable. 690.31(D) no longer refers to only Type TC-ER and USE-2 cable as permitted multiconductor cables. All jacketed multiconductor cable assemblies listed and identified for the application are permitted in outdoor locations.

PV System Grounding Configurations and GFP

Courtesy of Bill Brooks

Code Language

690.41 System Grounding

(A) PV System Grounding Configurations. One or more of the following system grounding configurations shall be employed:

(1) 2-wire PV arrays with one functional grounded conductor.

(2) Bipolar PV arrays according to 690.7(C) with a functional ground reference (center tap).

(3) PV arrays not isolated from the grounded inverter output circuit.

(4) Ungrounded PV arrays.

(5) Solidly grounded PV arrays as permitted in 690.41(B) Exception.

(6) PV systems that use other methods that accomplish equivalent system protection... (See *NEC* text).

(B) Ground-Fvault Protection.

Exception: PV arrays ...(See NEC text) not on or in buildings ...(See NEC text) permitted without ground-fault protection where solidly grounded.

(See NEC for actual text)

Significance of the Change

PV system grounding requirements in 690.41 are revised for clarity with a list of six permitted grounding configurations. This is the basis for the fundamental change of terminology to describe how PV systems are grounded in accordance with the *NEC*. A functional grounded PV system is now defined in Article 690 and describes most PV systems installed over the past 15 years.

Most PV systems installed in the United States over that period are functionally grounded, not solidly grounded. The informational note that accompanies the definition provides extremely valuable information. A functional grounded PV system is often connected to ground through a fuse, circuit breaker, resistance device, non-isolated grounded ac circuit, or electronic means that is part of a listed ground-fault protection system. The permitted grounding configurations include reference grounded, solidly grounded and other methods.

New 690.41(B) Ground-Fault Protection replaces section 690.5 and 690.35(C) and simplifies the *NEC* requirements. Ground fault detection is a critical part of the safety of a PV array since the standard that governs PV ground-fault equipment is now well established. The *NEC* no longer describes how to achieve ground fault protection, it is addressed in the applicable product standard.

Change Summary

- System grounding requirements in 690.41 now list six permitted grounding configurations.
- A functional grounded PV system has an electrical reference to ground that is not solidly grounded.
- Ground fault protection requirements are revised and relocated from 690.5 and 690.35(C) to 690.41(B).

FR: 991
SR: 966

Grounding Electrode Systems

Change Summary

- Requirements for grounding electrode system for PV systems have been significantly clarified.
- Only the requirements that are unique to PV systems are included in Article 690.
- Functional grounded systems are connected to the grounding electrode system through the equipment grounding conductor.

FR: 995

SR: 969

SCR: 106

Courtesy of Bill Brooks

Significance of the Change

This revision deletes all the subdivisions that referred to dc and ac system grounding electrode requirements and simplifies 690.47 to only cover the unique aspects of PV systems as it relates to connecting the equipment grounding conductor (EGC) to the grounding electrode system (GES).

The requirements for GES's are located in Part III of Article 250 and there is no logical reason to repeat those in 690.47. Few PV systems installed today are solidly grounded, the GES at the building serves as the ground reference for both the system and the EGC. The EGC is typically used by the ground fault detector in a functionally grounded system as the ground reference.

Revised 690.47(A) requires a GES for all buildings or structures supporting a PV array installed in accordance with Part III of Article 250. Clarity is provided by permitting PV systems that are not solidly grounded to use the EGC for the output of the PV system which is connected to associated distribution equipment, to be the connection to ground for ground-fault protection and equipment grounding of the PV array. Solidly grounded PV systems must be connected to a grounding electrode system by means of a grounding electrode conductor sized in accordance with 250.166.

690.47(B) provides requirements for additional auxiliary electrodes for array grounding.

Marking Requirements, Buildings with Rapid Shutdown

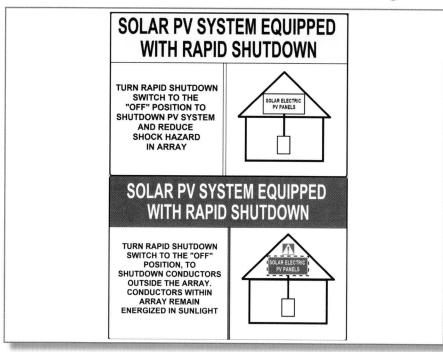

Courtesy of Bill Brooks

Code Language

690.56 Identification of Power Sources. (C) Buildings with Rapid Shutdown. (1) Rapid Shutdown Type.

1. For PV systems that shut down the array and conductors leaving the array:

SOLAR PV SYSTEM IS EQUIPPED WITH RAPID SHUTDOWN.

TURN RAPID SHUTDOWN SWITCH TO THE "OFF"... (See *NEC* text)

2. For PV systems that only shut down conductors leaving the array:

SOLAR PV SYSTEM IS EQUIPPED WITH RAPID SHUTDOWN

TURN RAPID SHUTDOWN SWITCH TO THE "OFF"... (See *NEC* text)

(See NEC for actual text)

Significance of the Change

690.56 provides specific requirements for markings to identify PV power sources. Previous text in 690.56(C) required a plaque or directory that simply stated that the PV system was equipped with rapid shutdown. No additional information was provided for emergency responders. This revision will provide the emergency responders with significantly more information to allow them to activate rapid shutdown.

The revised text is now separated into three, second level subdivisions. 690.56(C)(1) requires a rapid shutdown label be located on or no more than 3 feet from the service disconnecting means to which the PV systems are connected and must indicate the location of all identified rapid shutdown switches if not at the same location. There are two types of rapid shutdown labels, 690.56(C)(1)(a) for shutdown of the PV system and 690.56(C)(1)(b) for shutdown of only the conductors outside the array. Prescriptive label format of each type of rapid shutdown label is provided in two new figures 690.56(C)(1)(a) and (C)(1)(b).

690.56(C)(2) provides requirements for buildings with more than one rapid shutdown type.

690.56(C)(3) requires a label for all rapid shutdown switches which must be located on or no more than 3 feet from the switch.

Change Summary

- Marking requirements for rapid shutdown are significantly revised to warn emergency responders of hazards presented by a PV system and associated conductors.

- Two types of markings now address the type of rapid shutdown of the PV system and conductors in 690.12.

- Two new figures are provided for prescriptive detail of required markings.

FR: 989
SR: None
SCR: 107

Large-Scale Photovoltaic (PV) Electric Power Production Facility

Code Language

691.1 Scope. This article covers the installation of large-scale PV electric power production facilities with a generating capacity of no less than 5000 kW, and not under exclusive utility control.

Informational Note No. 1: Facilities covered by this article have specific design and safety features unique to large-scale PV facilities and are operated for the sole purpose of providing electric supply to a system operated by a regulated utility for the transfer of electric energy.

Informational Note No. 2: Section 90.2(B)(5) includes information about utility-owned properties not covered under this *Code*. For additional information on electric power production facilities, see ANSI/IEEE C2-2012, *National Electrical Safety Code*.

(See NEC for actual text)

Change Summary

- Large scale PV electric power production facilities are cover by new Article 691.

- The number of large-scale PV systems is relatively small, but they generate more power than the combined output of all residential and commercial PV.

- Only qualified personnel are permitted to maintain and operate these systems.

FRs: Multiple
SRs: Multiple

Significance of the Change

New Article 691, Large-Scale Photovoltaic (PV), Electric Power Production Facility, covers the installation of large-scale PV electric power production facilities with a generating capacity of no less than 5000 kW, and not under exclusive utility control. While the number of these "Large Scale PV Systems" is relatively small, the volume of electricity generated by these systems is greater than the combined output of all residential and commercial PV. Informational Note No.1 in 690.1 Scope explains that facilities covered by this article have specific design and safety features unique to large-scale PV facilities and are operated for the sole purpose of providing electric supply to a system operated by a regulated utility for the transfer of electric energy. These systems are in many cases not owned by the electric utility and fall under the scope of the *NEC*.

691.4 requires that large-scale PV electric power production facilities be accessible only to authorized personnel. All circuits and equipment must be maintained and operated only by qualified personnel. The transfer connection between the PV electric power production facilities and the utility transmission or distribution must be through medium- or high-voltage switch gear, substation, switch yard, or similar methods whose sole purpose is to safely and effectively interconnect the two systems and large-scale PV electric power production facilities are not permitted to be installed on buildings.

Power Source(s) for Electric Motor-Driven Fire Pumps

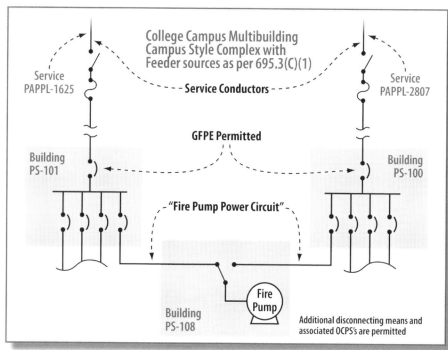

Code Language

695.3 Power Source(s) for Electric Motor-Driven Fire Pumps. Electric motor-driven fire pumps shall have a reliable source of power.

Informational Note: See Sections 9.3.2 and A.9.3.2 from NFPA 20 -2013, Standard for the Installation of Stationary Pumps for Fire Protection, for guidance on the determination of power source reliability.

(See NEC for actual text)

Significance of the Change

The determination of the "reliability" of a service connection supplying an electric fire pump is required in 695.3. The requirement for "reliability" is extracted into the *NEC* from NFPA 20-2013 in 9.3.2. NFPA 20 has purview over the performance of fire pumps. The explanatory material in NFPA 20 Annex A, specifically A.9.3.2 provides significant guidelines for the determination of reliability.

In NFPA 20 Annex A, A9.3.2, the characteristics of a "reliable power source" are as follows:

(1) No shutdowns (loss of power) in the year prior to plan submittal...

(2) No routine power losses...

(3) Overhead conductors outside the protected facility do not supply the normal source of power. ...

(4) Disconnects for the normal source must be installed in accordance with the *NEC*, which derives those requirements from NFPA 20.

Change Summary

- A new informational note in 695.3 provides the *Code* user with useful guidance for determination of reliability.

- NFPA 20 has purview over fire pump performance and the "reliability" of the power source.

- Shutdowns, routine loss of power, and overhead service conductors may consider the source as unreliable.

FR: 3651

SR: None

Multibuilding Campus-Style Complexes

Code Language

695.3 Power Source(s) for Electric Motor-Driven Fire Pumps

(C) Multibuilding Campus-Style Complexes. If the sources in 695.3(A) are not practicable...(See *NEC* text) multibuilding campus-style complex, feeder sources shall be permitted...(See *NEC* text) in accordance with either (C)(1) and (C)(3) or (C)(2) and (C)(3).

(1) Feeder Sources. ...(See *NEC* text) The connection(s), overcurrent protective device(s), and disconnecting means for such feeders shall meet the requirements of 695.4(B)(1)(b).

(2) Feeder and Alternate Source. ...(See *NEC* text) The connection(s), overcurrent protective device(s), and disconnecting means for such feeders shall meet the requirements of 695.4(B)(1)(b).

(See NEC for actual text)

Change Summary

• 695.3(C)(1) and (2) are revised for clarity, not all of 695.4(B)(1) applies to disconnects for feeders under 695.3(C) which applies only to multibuilding campus-style complexes.

• 695.4(B)(1)(b) permits additional disconnecting means and OCPD(s) for feeders installed per 695.3(C).

• Feeder sources are recognized in 695.3(C) in accordance with (C)(1) and (C)(3) or (C)(2) and (C)(3).

FR: 3652

SR: None

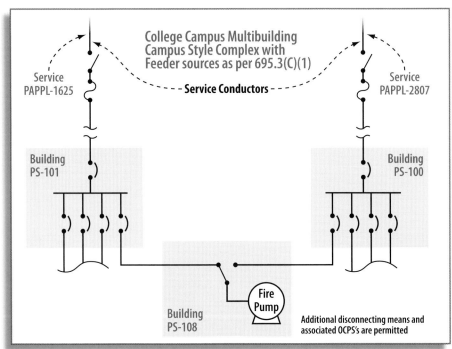

Significance of the Change

This revision clarifies that feeder sources, permitted in 695.3(C), are permitted to have additional disconnecting means and OCPDs. Previous *Code* text applied all of 695.4(B)(1) which inferred that a single disconnect was required.

NFPA 20, the *Standard for the Installation of Stationary Pumps for Fire Protection,* has purview over the performance of an electric fire pump, and minimum electrical installation requirements are extracted from this standard into the *NEC. NEC* section 695.3(C) applies where the individual sources outlined in 695.3(A) are not practicable, and the installation is part of a multibuilding campus-style complex. 695.3(C) permits feeder sources if approved by the authority having jurisdiction. There are two options provided for the installation of feeders in 695.3(C)(1) and (C)(2). 695.3(C)(1) permits two or more feeders to be considered as more than one power source provided these feeders are connected to, or derived from, separate utility services. This ensures that the loss of a single service does not remove the power supply to the fire pump. 695.3(C)(2) permits a feeder as a normal source of power if an alternate source of power (such as a standby generator) independent from the feeder is provided.

695.3(C)(3) requires all feeder overcurrent protective devices to be selectively coordinated with any other supply-side overcurrent protective device(s).

Disconnecting Means and OCPD(s), (695.3(C))

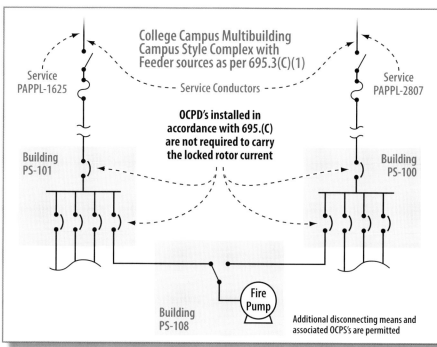

College Campus Multibuilding Campus Style Complex with Feeder sources as per 695.3(C)(1)

— Service Conductors ———

Service PAPPL-1625

Service PAPPL-2807

OCPD's installed in accordance with 695.(C) are not required to carry the locked rotor current

Building PS-101

Building PS-100

Building PS-108

Fire Pump

Additional disconnecting means and associated OCPS's are permitted

Code Language

695.4(B) Connection Through Disconnecting Means and Overcurrent Device.

(2) Overcurrent Device Selection.

(1) Overcurrent protective device(s) shall be rated to carry indefinitely the sum of the locked-rotor current...(See *NEC* text) The requirement to carry the locked-rotor currents indefinitely shall not apply to feeder overcurrent protective devices installed in accordance with 695.3(C). [**20**:9.2.3.4]

(3) Disconnecting Means.

Exception to 695.4(B)(3)(a): For a multibuilding campus-style complex(s) installed under the provisions of 695.3(C), only the requirements in 695.4(B)(3)(a)(2) shall apply for normal power source disconnects

(See NEC for actual text)

Significance of the Change

Permitted power sources for fire pumps installed in multibuilding campus style complexes as permitted in 695.3(C) includes (1) two or more feeder sources or, (2) a feeder and an alternate source. This revision provides significant clarity for the required overcurrent protection and disconnecting means for these feeder sources. The general rule in 695.4(B)(2) requires all overcurrent protective devices to be rated to carry indefinitely the sum of the locked-rotor current of the largest fire pump motor and the pressure maintenance pump motor(s) and the full-load current of all of the other pump motors and associated fire pump accessory equipment. A new last sentence is added to 695.4(B)(2)(a)(1) that clarifies the feeder overcurrent protective devices permitted in 695.3(C) are not required to carry locked rotor currents.

The general rule in 695.4(B)(3(a) requires disconnects to be (1) identified as suitable for service equipment, (2) lockable in the closed position, (3) not located in the same equipment (switchboard etc.) that supplies other loads and (4) be remotely located to prevent inadvertent operation. A new exception is added to 695.4(B)(3)(a) to clarify that normal power source disconnects for multibuilding campus-style complex(s) installed under the provisions of 695.3(C) need only meet the requirements for "lockable in the closed position" in 695.4(B)(3)(a)(2).

Change Summary

- Feeder overcurrent protective devices installed in accordance with 695.3(C) are not required to carry the locked-rotor currents indefinitely.

- Only the requirements in 695.4(B)(3)(a)(2) (lockable in the closed position) apply to the disconnecting means for feeder sources on multibuilding campus-style complex(s) installed.

FR: 3653

SR: 3622

Fire Pump Power and Control Wiring Methods

Code Language

695.6 Power Wiring.

(D) Pump Wiring. All wiring from the controllers to the pump motors shall be in rigid metal conduit, intermediate metal conduit, electrical metallic tubing, liquidtight flexible metal conduit, or liquidtight flexible nonmetallic conduit, listed Type MC cable with an impervious covering, or Type MI cable. Electrical connections at motor terminal boxes shall be made with a listed means of connection. Twist-on, insulation-piercing–type, and soldered wire connectors shall not be permitted to be used for this purpose.

695.14 Control Wiring

(E) Electric Fire Pump Control Wiring Methods.

(See NEC for actual text)

Change Summary

- The use of types of liquidtight flexible nonmetallic conduit is now permitted for fire pump power and control wiring.
- Electrical metallic tubing (EMT) is now permitted for fire pump control wiring.

Significance of the Change

Permitted wiring methods for fire pump power wiring in 695.6(D) and fire pump control wiring in 695.14(E) are revised. In addition to other wiring methods, the previous requirements permitted only liquidtight flexible nonmetallic conduit, type LFNC B. The limitation to type LFNC B is deleted. There are three types of liquidtight flexible nonmetallic conduit described in 356.2, and all are required to be Listed to UL1660 Liquidtight Flexible Nonmetallic Conduit. All three types of LFNC are required to meet the same physical performance testing, such as cold temperature impact, vertical flame, tension, deformation, etc., per UL1660. Since all three types have the same physical characteristics all are suitable for fire pump power and control wiring.

Electrical metallic tubing (EMT) is added to the permitted wiring methods for fire pump control wiring in 695.14(E). EMT is also permitted for fire pump power wiring in 695.6(D).

FRs: 3655, 3656
SR: 3625

Ground Fault Protection of Equipment

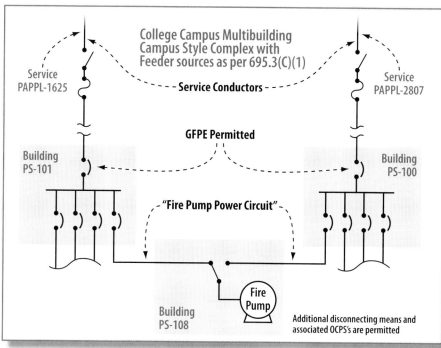

College Campus Multibuilding Campus Style Complex with Feeder sources as per 695.3(C)(1)

- - Service Conductors - - -

Service PAPPL-1625

Service PAPPL-2807

GFPE Permitted

Building PS-101

Building PS-100

"Fire Pump Power Circuit"

Building PS-108

Fire Pump

Additional disconnecting means and associated OCPS's are permitted

Code Language

695.6 Power Wiring.

(G) Ground-Fault Protection of Equipment. Ground-fault protection of equipment shall not be installed in any fire pump power circuit. [20:9.1.8.1]

(See NEC for actual text)

Significance of the Change

Significant clarity has been provided this *NEC* revision cycle with respect to the installation of fire pump power sources in multibuilding campus style complexes covered in 695.3(C). NFPA 20 has purview over the performance of electric fire pumps. NFPA 20, section 9.1.8.1 prohibits ground fault interruption from being installed in any fire pump control or power circuit. As written in the 2014 *NEC*, 695.6(G) prohibited ground-fault protection of equipment for fire pumps, not just the "fire pump power circuit." This prohibited ground-fault protection of equipment that may be required upstream of a permitted feeder source in 695.3(C)(1) and (C)(2). The revised text in 695.6(G) more accurately reflects the performance requirement as seen in section 9.1.8.1 and prohibits ground-fault protection of equipment in the "fire pump power circuit."

Multibuilding campus style complexes utilize feeder sources that in many cases will have ground-fault protection of equipment installed upstream due to requirements in 230.95 and/or 215.10.

NFPA 20 also prohibits arc fault interruption in any fire pump control or power circuit. See NFPA 20 9.1.8.2.

Change Summary

- Clarification is provided for the use of ground-fault protection of equipment and fire pumps.
- Ground-fault protection of equipment is not permitted in any fire pump *power circuit*.
- A feeder source permitted by 695.3(C) may have ground-fault protection of equipment installed at some point upstream.

FR: None
SR: 3624

695.14(F) & 700.10(D)(3)

Article 695 Fire Pumps
Part None

Article 700 Emergency Systems
Part II Circuit Wiring

REVISION

Generator Control Wiring Methods

Code Language

695.14 Control Wiring.

(F) Generator Control Wiring Methods. Control conductors... (See *NEC* text) The integrity of the generator control wiring shall be continuously monitored. Loss of integrity of the remote start circuit(s) shall initiate visual and audible annunciation of generator malfunction at the generator local and remote annunciator(s) and start the generator(s)... (See *NEC* text)

700.10 Wiring, Emergency System.

(D) Fire Protection.

(3) Generator Control Wiring.

(See NEC for actual text)

Change Summary

- Generator control wiring is now required to be continuously monitored.
- Loss of integrity of the generator control conductors is now required to initiate visual and audible annunciation and start the generator(s).

Courtesy of Cummins Power Generation

Significance of the Change

This revision mandates that the integrity of the generator control wiring for fire pump installations (695.14(F) and for emergency systems (700.10(D)(3)) be continuously monitored. A new requirement also mandates that if there is a loss of integrity of the remote start circuit(s), there must be a visual and audible annunciation of generator malfunction at the generator local and remote annunciator(s). The loss of integrity must also start the generator(s).

This revision will ensure that the integrity of control conductors that monitor the status of normal power and start the generator upon loss of normal power is maintained. This includes monitoring batteries or other source of power that will be required to start the generator upon loss of normal power. The visual and audible annunciation of generator malfunction at the generator local and remote annunciator(s) will immediately inform building occupants that a problem has occurred. The loss of integrity of the control conductors will also start the generators. This is necessary due to the fact that emergency power may be needed when the integrity of the control conductors is compromised. A running generator will also inform persons that an issue has occurred.

FRs: 3657, 3614
SRs: 3626, 3611

Surge Protection, Fire Pump Controller

Code Language

695.15 Surge Protection. A listed surge protection device shall be installed in or on the fire pump controller.

(See NEC for actual text)

Significance of the Change

This new section 695.15 requiring a listed surge protection device (SPD) to be installed in or on the fire pump controller is necessary because fire pumps serve a very critical purpose. As seen in the NFPA Research Foundation report there are a significant number of fire pump installations that suffer damage that could have been prevented by an SPD. Mandating surge protection will help to ensure that there is no damage or loss of the fire pump controller after a surge or lightning strike on the local network supplying normal power to the fire pump. The study, "Data Assessment for Electrical Surge Protective Devices" commissioned by the Fire Protection Research Foundation, 1 Batterymarch Park, Quincy, MA 02169-7471, provides results of a 2013 and 2014 survey of facility managers concerning surge damage. It shows that 12% had damage to fire pumps or related equipment due to voltage surges. Much of this damage could have been prevented with properly sized surge protective devices.

The location and type of surge protection device is a design issue and remains with the designer and/or installer. In many cases, the fire pump controller may be equipped with a surge protective device. These devices are already required to be listed by 285.5.

Change Summary

- New section 695.15 requires a listed surge protection device to be installed in or on the fire pump controller.
- An NFPA survey of facility managers concerning surge damage shows that 12% had damage to fire pumps or related equipment due to voltage surges.
- Surge protection devices must be installed in accordance with Article 285.

FR: 3658
SR: None

Chapter 7

Articles 700–770
Special Conditions

Directly Controlled Luminaires

Change Summary

- A new definition is added to 700.2 for directly controlled luminaires.
- A new 700.24 was added in the 2014 *NEC* revision cycle permitting directly controlled luminaires as emergency lighting.
- These fixtures will be driven to full illumination upon loss of normal power.

Significance of the Change

A new 700.24 was added in the 2014 *NEC* revision cycle permitting directly controlled luminaires to be used to supply emergency lighting. However, the term *directly controlled luminaire* was not defined which led to individual interpretation as to what constituted control. The term is now defined in 700.2 as an emergency luminaire that has a control input for an integral dimming or switching function that drives the luminaire to full illumination upon loss of normal power. The *NEC* requirements in Article 700 for directly controlled luminaires are driven by the use of new LED lighting technology being used for emergency lighting. LED lighting systems are being employed in most commercial venues because of their energy savings and the fact that they are easily controlled and fully capable of being dimmed and switched from a remote location. The control input may be a cat 5 cable run to each luminaire that provides the "control input" for an integral dimming or switching function. This control input is also capable of driving the luminaire to full illumination upon loss of normal power.

Section 700.24 requires that where emergency illumination is provided by one or more "directly controlled luminaires" that respond to an external control input (may be cat 5 to each fixture) to bypass normal control upon loss of normal power, such luminaires, and external bypass controls must be individually listed for use in emergency systems.

FR: 3606
SR: 3601

700.3 Maintenance

Courtesy of Burlington Electrical Testing

Code Language

700.3 Tests and Maintenance.

(C) Maintenance. Emergency system equipment shall be maintained in accordance with manufacturer instructions and industry standards.

(See NEC for actual text)

Significance of the Change

Section 700.3 provides requirements for tests and maintenance which are critical to ensuring that the emergency and legally required standby systems will operate when needed. 700.3(C) and 701.3(C) previously addressed only maintenance of battery systems. This requirement is significantly revised by changing the first level subdivision title to "maintenance" and requiring that all "emergency system equipment be maintained in accordance with manufacturer's instructions and industry standards." Maintenance is now required for batteries, battery systems, and all other emergency system equipment. This includes but is not limited to generators, transfer switches, circuit breakers and other equipment that are required to have maintenance performed. Electrical equipment used in emergency and legally required standby systems that require maintenance, are outlined by the equipment manufacturer(s) and applicable industry standards including NFPA 70B.

This revision is now logically in step with the existing testing requirements in both 700.3(C) and 701.3(C). Requiring periodic tests and testing under load without maintenance, may set the system up for failure.

The previous requirement focused only on batteries and battery systems that may be needed to start a standby generator or provide lighting as part of unit equipment.

Change Summary

- 700.3(C) and 701.3(C) are revised to require maintenance on all emergency and legally required system equipment.

- Electrical equipment in these systems must be maintained in accordance with manufacturer's instructions and NFPA 70B.

FRs: 3608, 3623

SR: None

Temporary Source...for Maintenance or Repair...

Code Language

700.3(F) Tests and Maintenance.

(F) Temporary Source of Power for Maintenance or Repair of the Alternate Source of Power. If the emergency system relies on a single alternate source of power that will be disabled for maintenance or repair, the emergency system shall include permanent switching means to connect a portable or temporary alternate source of power, which shall be available for the duration of the maintenance or repair. The permanent switching means to connect a portable, or temporary alternate source of power shall comply with the following:

(List items 1 through 5)

It shall be permissible to utilize manual switching to switch from the permanent source of power to the portable or temporary alternate source of power and to utilize the switching means for connection of a load bank.

Exception: ... (See NEC text) (four list items)

(See NEC for actual text)

Change Summary

- New 700.3(F) requires a permanent switching means to connect a portable or temporary alternate source of power during maintenance or repair.

- The exception provides significant relief, and a new informational note provides the *Code* user with an example single line drawing.

FR: 3616

SR: 3602

SCR: 84

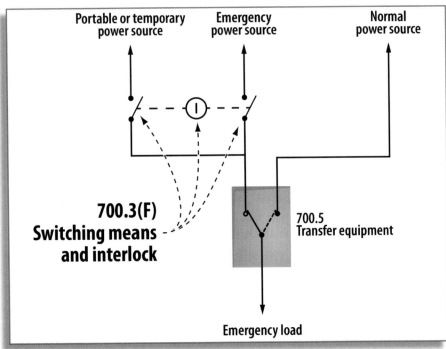

Significance of the Change

A new first level subdivision 700.3(F) is added to require, under prescribed conditions, *a permanent switching means to connect a portable or temporary alternate source of power*, that must be available for the duration of any maintenance or repair that takes the generator out of service. Previous text in 700.4(B) required a portable or temporary alternate source to be available whenever the emergency generator is out of service for major maintenance or repair. This requirement was improperly located in 700.4(B) limiting its application, and the term *major maintenance or repair* is not defined and is subject to wide-ranging interpretation.

New 700.3(F)(1) requires the connection to the portable/temporary means not require modification of permanent wiring, (2) transfer must be in accordance with 700.12, (3) the connection point must be marked with phase rotation and bonding requirements, (4) interlocking to prevent interconnection is required, and (5) the switching point must include a contact point to annunciate at a location remote from the generator to indicate that the permanent emergency source is disconnected. Manual switching is permitted, and this switching means may be used for connection of a load bank. A new informational note and diagram are included for clarity.

The exception relieves this requirement where one of four sets of conditions exist.

Transfer Switch Short-Circuit Current Rating

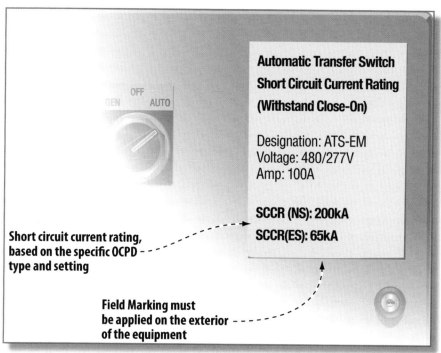

Automatic Transfer Switch
Short Circuit Current Rating
(Withstand Close-On)

Designation: ATS-EM
Voltage: 480/277V
Amp: 100A

SCCR (NS): 200kA

SCCR(ES): 65kA

Short circuit current rating, based on the specific OCPD type and setting

Field Marking must be applied on the exterior of the equipment

Code Language

700.5 Transfer Equipment

(E) Documentation. The short-circuit current rating of the transfer equipment, based on the specific overcurrent protective device type and settings protecting the transfer equipment, shall be field marked on the exterior of the transfer equipment.

(See NEC for actual text)

Significance of the Change

This revision impacts transfer equipment applied in emergency systems in 700.5(E), legally required standby systems in 701.5(D), optional standby systems in 702.5, and critical operation power systems in 708.24(E). Applicable product standards (UL 1008) require that transfer equipment be marked with the short-circuit withstand/closing or short-time current rating (short-circuit current rating). Transfer switches are usually marked by the manufacturer with several different options resulting in many short-circuit current rating values. These short-circuit current rating values are marked on the inside of the transfer equipment and will vary based upon the type of OCPD, the ampere rating, and settings where circuit breakers are applied. An electrical inspector or an installer/maintainer looking at the installation of the transfer switch will not know what the short circuit current rating is without, first determining the ASCC, opening the transfer equipment to find all of the potential short circuit values based upon specific types of overcurrent protection and then determining the type of upstream overcurrent protection and the settings if applicable.

This new requirement mandates that the short-circuit current rating of the transfer equipment, based on the specific overcurrent protective device type and settings protecting the transfer equipment, be field marked on the *exterior of the transfer equipment.*

Change Summary

- Transfer equipment is required by product standards to be provided with the short-circuit withstand/closing or short-time current rating (short-circuit current rating).

- There are many short-circuit current rating values for equipment based upon the specific type of OCPD used.

- Field marking of the short-circuit current rating of the transfer equipment, based on the specific overcurrent protective device type and settings protecting the transfer equipment is now required.

FRs: 7518, 7519, 7520, 7521

SR: None

700.6(D) & 701.6(D)

Article 700 Emergency Systems

Part I General

Ground Fault Sensor Location

Code Language

700.6 Signals

(D) Ground Fault. ... (See *NEC* text) The sensor for the ground-fault signal devices shall be located at, or ahead of, the main system disconnecting means for the emergency source, and the maximum setting of the signal devices shall be for a ground-fault current of 1200 amperes... (See *NEC* text)

For systems with multiple emergency sources connected to a paralleling bus, the ground-fault sensor shall be permitted to be at an alternative location.

(See NEC for actual text)

Change Summary

- Clarification is provided for the permitted location of ground-fault sensors where sources are connected to a paralleling bus.
- This revision recognizes alternative location for ground-fault sensors where multiple generators may supply common bus.

FR: 3638
SR: 3608

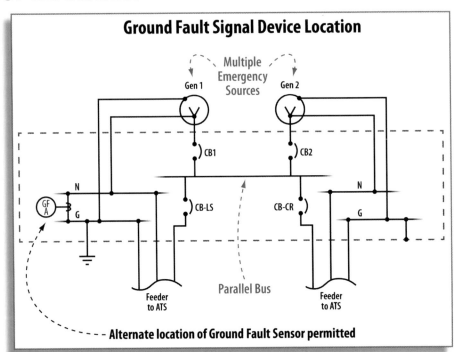

Ground Fault Signal Device Location

Alternate location of Ground Fault Sensor permitted

Significance of the Change

The general requirement 700.6(D) requires ground-fault signal devices to be located at, or ahead of, the main system disconnecting means for the emergency source. This creates problems where multiple standby generators are connected in parallel and acting as the emergency source. This revision now permits systems with multiple sources connected to a paralleling bus to be located at other than the main disconnecting means for the individual generators connected in parallel. This is necessary because where generators are installed in parallel the neutral bonding will occur in the paralleling switchgear, and the ground-fault sensing means cannot be located at or ahead of the generator disconnecting means. For multiple emergency sources, ground-fault sensing may be determined by zero sequence sensing, differential relaying of the paralleling bus in conjunction with residual ground-fault sensing device of the feeders or other equivalent means. This recognizes the common bus as the source allowing the required ground-fault protection to be located on feeders connected to the bus, rather than the standby generators. This allows ground fault protection to discriminate between more critical and less critical loads where the requirement would be to open the device instead of signaling, such as an optional standby system.

A similar revision occurred in 701.6(D) for legally required standby systems.

Identification of Emergency System Wiring

Code Language

700.10 Wiring, Emergency System.

(A) Identification. Emergency circuits shall be permanently marked so they will be readily identified as a component of an emergency circuit or system by the following methods:

(1) All boxes and enclosures (including transfer switches, generators, and power panels) for emergency circuits shall be permanently marked as a component of an emergency circuit or system.

(2) Where boxes or enclosures are not encountered, exposed cable or raceway systems shall be permanently marked to be identified as a component of an emergency circuit or system, at intervals not to exceed 7.6 m (25 ft.)

Receptacles supplied from the emergency system shall have a distinctive color or marking on the receptacle cover plates or the receptacles.

(See NEC for actual text)

Significance of the Change

700.10(A) requires identification of the emergency wiring system and previous text mandated that only "boxes and enclosures (including transfer switches, generators, and power panels)" for emergency circuits be permanently marked so they will be readily identified as a component of an emergency circuit or system. This revision logically expands this requirement to exposed cable or raceway systems where boxes or enclosures are not encountered. This will include but not be limited to the installation of emergency luminaires which may be installed with exposed cable or raceway systems that terminate directly in the luminaire without a junction box or enclosure. Where this occurs the exposed cable or raceway must be permanently marked at intervals that do not exceed 25 ft. This will now allow the AHJ and installer/maintainer to quickly identify such emergency circuits.

A new last sentence is added to require marking of receptacles supplied from an emergency system. This is necessary for the end user to identify emergency supplied devices for connection to equipment needed where there is a loss of normal power.

Change Summary

- Where boxes or enclosures are not encountered, exposed cable or raceway systems must be marked to be identified as a component of an emergency circuit or system at intervals not to exceed 25 ft.
- Receptacles supplied from the emergency system must have a distinctive color or marking on the receptacle cover plates or the receptacles themselves.

SR: 3603
FR: 3612
SCR: 85

Emergency System Wiring, OCPDs

Code Language

700.10 Wiring, Emergency System.

(B) Wiring.

(5) Wiring from an emergency source to supply emergency and other (non-emergency) loads in accordance with 700.10(B)(5)a., b., c., and d., as follows:

b. The common bus of separate sections of the switchgear, separate sections of the switchboard, or the individual enclosures shall be either of the following:

(1) Supplied by single or multiple feeders without overcurrent protection at the source

(2) Supplied by single or multiple feeders with overcurrent protection, provided that the overcurrent protection that is common to an emergency system and any non-emergency system(s) is selectively coordinated with the next downstream overcurrent protective device in the nonemergency system(s)

Informational Note: For further information, see Informational Note Figure 700.10(B)(5)(b)(1) and Informational Note Figure 700.10(B)(5)(b)(2).

(See NEC for actual text)

Change Summary

- 700.5(B)(5) is modified to provide clarity where a switchboard or switchgear may supply emergency and other non-emergency loads.

- The previous exception is deleted and addressed in positive text, with two new figures added.

FR: 3613
SR: None

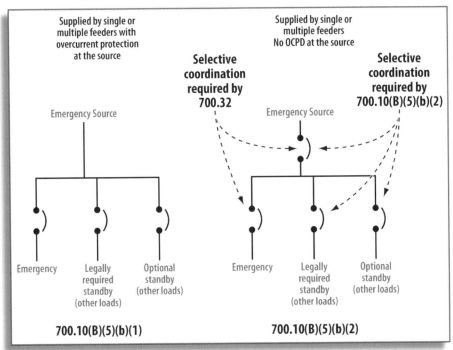

700.10(B)(5)(b)(1)

700.10(B)(5)(b)(2)

Significance of the Change

First level subdivision 700.5(B) permits two or more emergency circuits to occupy the same enclosure, raceway, etc. but requires emergency circuits to be kept entirely independent from all other wiring unless permitted in 700.10(B) (1) through (5). List item (5) addresses wiring from an emergency source to supply both emergency and non-emergency loads. This list item is revised for clarity to recognize that the wiring from the emergency source may also supply other "non-emergency loads," such as legally required and/or optional standby loads. List item 700.10(B)(5)(b) is revised to clarify that the common bus of separate sections of the switchgear, separate sections of the switchboard, or the individual enclosures permitted may be supplied in two ways. First, by single or multiple feeders without overcurrent protection at the source. This is clarified with new informational note figure 700.10(B)(5)(b)(1). Second, by single or multiple feeders with overcurrent protection, provided that the overcurrent protection that is common to an emergency system and any non-emergency system(s) is selectively coordinated with the next downstream overcurrent protective device in the nonemergency system(s). This requires that overcurrent protection supplying other systems, such as legally required standby or optional standby systems to be selectively coordinated with the upstream device supplying the common bus.

Fire Protection of Emergency System Wiring

Code Language

700.10 Wiring, Emergency System.

(D) Fire Protection. Emergency systems shall meet the additional requirements in (D)(1) through (D)(3) in the following occupancies:

(1) Assembly occupancies for not less than 1000 persons

(2) Buildings above 23 m (75 ft) in height

(3) Health care occupancies where persons are not capable of self preservation

(4) Educational occupancies with more than 300 occupants... (See *NEC* text)

(See NEC for actual text)

Significance of the Change

700.10(D) provides requirements for fire protection of emergency feeder circuit wiring, feeder circuit equipment and generator control wiring. The previous requirement mandated this fire protection for only assembly occupancies for not less than 1000 persons or buildings above 75 feet in height. This revision significantly expands those requirements to health care occupancies where persons are "not capable of self-preservation" which means persons who would need assistance exiting the facility in case of emergency and educational occupancies with more than 300 occupants. The previous requirement as literally applied did not apply to extremely large health care facilities that were not over 75 feet high and did not have an area rated for 1000 or more persons. The same exception existed for schools that were not over 75 feet high and did not have an area rated for 1000 or more persons. This revision now recognizes that schools and large hospitals that are not high-rise buildings or classed as assembly occupancies still require emergency systems that are protected from fire for a minimum of 2 hours.

Similar revisions are made in 700.12 for fire protection of equipment for sources of emergency power.

Change Summary

- The parent text of 700.10(D) for fire protection is separated into list items and significantly expanded.
- The fire protection requirements in 700.10(D) now apply to health care occupancies where persons are not capable of self-preservation and educational occupancies with more than 300 occupants.

FR: None
SRs: 3612, 3613

Branch Circuit Emergency Lighting Transfer Switch

Code Language

700.25 Branch Circuit Emergency Lighting Transfer Switch. Emergency lighting loads supplied by branch circuits rated at not greater than 20 amperes shall be permitted to be transferred from the normal branch circuit to an emergency branch circuit using a listed branch circuit emergency lighting transfer switch. The mechanically held requirement of 700.5(C) shall not apply to listed branch circuit emergency lighting transfer switches.

(See NEC for actual text)

Change Summary

• 700.2 now defines "Branch Circuit Emergency Lighting Transfer Switch" (BCELTS).

• New section 700.25 recognizes the use of a listed BCELTS for circuits not greater than 20-amps.

• The mechanically held requirement of 700.5(C) does not apply to listed BCELTS's.

FRs: 3620, 3607

SR: None

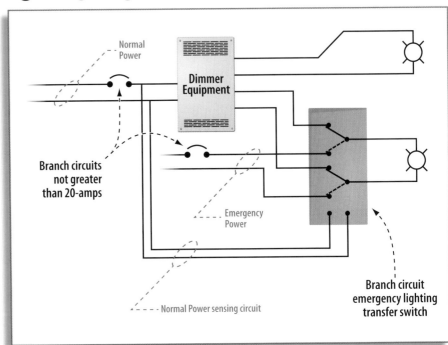

Significance of the Change

A new definition in 700.2 defies a *Branch Circuit Emergency Lighting Transfer Switch* (BCELTS) as a device connected on the load side of a branch circuit overcurrent protective device that transfers only emergency lighting loads from the normal supply to an emergency supply.

New section 700.25 now permits a listed BCELTS to transfer power from the normal branch circuit to an emergency branch circuit. These branch circuits are not permitted to be rated greater than 20 amps. The BCELTS contains terminations for both normal (could be fed through a dimmer) and emergency circuits. Transfer operation in a listed BCELTS switches both the ungrounded and grounded conductors. A BCELTS is essentially an automatic load control relay (ALCR), as permitted in 700.26, that is listed to UL 1008 and is additionally evaluated as a transfer switch. The difference between the ALCR and BCELTS is (1) the BCELTS is limited to emergency lighting loads on branch circuits rated not over 20 amperes, (2) certain construction requirements of UL 1008 are modified for the BCELTS, notably the modification of the mechanical hold requirement of a general purpose emergency transfer switch, and (3) the BCELTS is subject to additional testing requirements to provide safety equivalence between a general purpose transfer switch and the BCELTS.

Power Inlets Rated at 100 Amperes or Greater

Code Language

702.12 Outdoor Generator Sets.

(C) Power Inlets Rated at 100 Amperes or Greater, for Portable Generators. Equipment containing power inlets for the connection of a generator source shall be listed for the intended use. Systems with power inlets shall be equipped with an interlocked disconnecting means.

Exception No. 1: If the inlet device is rated as a disconnecting means

Exception No. 2: Supervised industrial installations where permanent space is identified for the portable generator located within line of sight of the power inlets shall not be required to have interlocked disconnecting means nor inlets rated as disconnects.

(See NEC for actual text)

Significance of the Change

New first level subdivision 702.12(C) is a safety driven revision recognizing that where a portable generator is out of the line of site from the point at which it electrically connects through a permanently installed inlet additional installation requirements are necessary. If an individual is inserting or removing a connector at a power inlet and cannot visibly see the generator to which it is connected, disconnecting under load can present a very serious safety hazard if the inlet is not rated for load break.

This new requirement addresses only power inlets rated at 100-amps or greater for portable generators. Equipment that contains power inlets rated at 100-amps or greater for the connection of a portable generator in an optional standby system is now required to be listed for the intended use. These power inlets must be equipped with an interlocked disconnecting means, which would prevent connection or opening under load. Two exceptions are added to recognize inlet devices that are rated as a disconnecting means and an exception for supervised industrial installations that include a permanent space for the portable generator that is located in the line of sight of the power inlets.

Change Summary

- New 702.12(C) requires power inlets rated at 100-amps or greater for portable generators in optional standby systems to be listed for the intended use.
- Power inlets must be equipped with an interlocked disconnecting means.
- Exceptions are added for inlet devices that are rated as a disconnecting means and for supervised industrial installations.

FR: 3632
SR: None

Part IV Microgrid Systems

Code Language

IV. Microgrid Systems.

705.150 System Operation. Microgrid systems shall be permitted to disconnect from the primary source of power or other interconnected electric power production sources and operate as a separate microgrid system.

705.160 Primary Power Source Connection. Connections to primary power sources that are external to the microgrid system shall comply with the requirements of 705.12.

705.165 Reconnection to Primary Power Source. Microgrid systems that reconnect to primary power sources shall be provided with the necessary equipment to establish a synchronous transition.

705.170 Microgrid Interconnect Devices (MID). Microgrid interconnect devices shall comply with the following: ...

(See NEC for actual text)

Change Summary

- New Part IV Microgrid Systems provides operation, interconnect and reconnection requirements.
- The key is the ability to disconnect and reconnect and operate as an island or microgrid.
- MID must be listed or field labeled for the application.

FR: 1045

SR: 1005

SCR: 116

Courtesy of the National Renewable Energy Laboratory

Significance of the Change

This new Part IV provides structure for several key requirements related to the installation of microgrid systems. The four sections in this new Part covers the devices that interconnect the microgrid systems, how these systems operate, connect, and reconnect after the microgrid separates from the primary power source.

Part IV of Article 705 is still fairly basic and general. It does not include a lot of detail on the installation of these types of systems. It refers to Article 705.12 that relates to how this equipment is physically interconnected with other power systems. It also requires that Microgrid Interconnect Devices (MIDs) be listed and labeled, or field labeled for the application. Currently, there are several multimodal inverters used with PV systems and energy storage systems that are listed and labeled for this application and meet the requirements of Part IV. In the past, these systems were referred to as intentionally islanded systems and stand-alone systems. These intentionally islanded systems are sometimes called microgrids. The term *microgrids* is the new term that is getting recognition as a way to add resiliency against loss of power in premises wiring systems.

Microgrid System, Microgrid Interconnect Device

Code Language

Microgrid Interconnect Device (MID). A device that allows a microgrid system to separate from and reconnect to a primary power source.

Microgrid System. A premises wiring system that has generation, energy storage, and load(s), or any combination thereof that includes the ability to disconnect from and parallel with the primary source.

Informational Note: The application of Article 705 to microgrid systems is limited by the exclusions in 90.2(B)(5) related to electric utilities.

(See NEC for actual text)

Significance of the Change

A new Part IV, Microgrid Systems, is added in Article 705 this *NEC* revision cycle to consolidate all types of interconnected sources within the same article. Two new definitions are added in 705.2 to explain in the *NEC* what those terms mean as they apply to new requirements in Part IV and for correlation throughout all of Article 705.

A *microgrid system* is defined as a premises wiring system that has generation, energy storage, and load(s), or any combination thereof, that includes the ability to disconnect from and parallel with the primary source. The key point here is the ability to "disconnect from and parallel with the primary source." Without that ability, a microgrid system exists wherever we have an electric power source (service supplied) and a generator, energy storage (battery for example), PV, wind generator or other source. This new term was titled *intentionally islanded system* during the first draft stage. A microgrid system can intentionally island itself. An informational note is included to inform the *Code* user that the application of Article 705 to these "microgrid systems" is limited by the exclusions in 90.2(B)(5) related to electric utilities. Such a system installed by a utility as part of generation and transmission is not covered by the *NEC*.

A *microgrid interconnect device* (MID allows a microgrid system to separate from and reconnect to a primary power source.

Change Summary

- Two new definitions are added to 705.2 to facilitate the use of these terms in new Part IV Microgrid Systems.

- An MID allows a microgrid system to separate from and reconnect to a primary power source.

- A microgrid system is a premises wiring system with generation, energy storage and load(s), or any combination thereof, that includes the ability to disconnect from and parallel with the primary source.

FR: 1046
SRs: 988, 989

Interactive System Disconnecting Means

Code Language

705.23 Interactive System Disconnecting Means. A readily accessible means shall be provided to disconnect the interactive system from all wiring systems including power systems, energy storage systems, and utilization equipment and its associated premises wiring.

(See NEC for actual text)

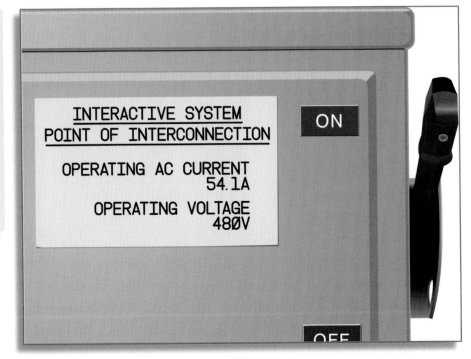

INTERACTIVE SYSTEM
POINT OF INTERCONNECTION

OPERATING AC CURRENT
54.1A

OPERATING VOLTAGE
480V

ON

OFF

Change Summary

- New section 705.23 requires a readily accessible interactive system disconnecting means.
- This disconnect separates the interactive system from all wiring systems including power systems, energy storage systems, and utilization equipment and its associated premises wiring.
- There may be more than one interactive system disconnecting means.

Significance of the Change

This new section is intended to differentiate the equipment disconnects from the interactive system disconnect(s). This new language is to provide consistency and clarity in the same way that Article 690 now clearly differentiates between the PV system disconnect and an equipment disconnect.

This change correlates with revisions in Article 690 that differentiate between the PV system disconnect and equipment disconnects. This distinction is key because electrical inspectors and installers have been confused about different types of disconnects in these systems for many years. A power source may be made up of numerous pieces of equipment that require isolation for service, but these switches may have nothing to do with shutting down the equipment to isolate the conductors from conductors of other systems. Establishing the difference between these types of systems is critical so that the requirements are properly applied. Many interactive systems will only have a single ac disconnect to separate the conductors from all other conductors in the building.

FR: 1047
SR: 999

Article 706 Energy Storage Systems

Code Language

706.1 Scope. This article applies to all permanently installed energy storage systems (ESS) operating at over 50 volts ac or 60 volts dc that may be stand-alone or interactive with other electric power production sources.

706.2 Energy Storage System. One or more components assembled together capable of storing energy for use at a future time. ESS(s) can include but is not limited to batteries, capacitors, and kinetic energy devices (e.g., flywheels and compressed air). These systems can have ac or dc output for utilization and can include inverters and converters to change stored energy into electrical energy.

(See NEC for actual text)

Significance of the Change

The need for energy storage systems to supplement alternative energy sources and to help with an aging transmission and distribution network has driven a new Article 706 for Energy Storage Systems (ESSs). These energy storage systems may consist of batteries, capacitors, and kinetic energy devices (e.g., flywheels and compressed air). New technologies are currently being evaluated including superconducting magnetic energy storage systems (SMES) which are designed to store energy in the magnetic field of a superconducting coil that is supercooled to a temperature below its superconducting critical temperature and compressed air energy storage systems (CAESs) that compress and store air in an underground cavern.

The definition of ESS is broad in nature and recognizes batteries, the most common energy storage as well as other technologies. An ESS can have ac or dc output for utilization and can include inverters and converters to change stored energy into electrical energy.

There are three additional defined terms under the general definition of ESS. They include *self-contained* ESS, which is typically manufactured by a single entity, pre-engineered of matched components ESS, which are not self-contained but are engineered by a single entity and other ESS, which are different components combined onsite.

Change Summary

- Associated technology and the need for energy storage systems is growing rapidly, and new Article 706 now provides requirements for energy storage systems (ESSs) in the *NEC*.

- The scope of Article 706 specifically limits application to permanently installed ESS over 50 volts AC or 60 volts DC to correlate with existing *NEC* requirements.

- This Article also correlates multiple other energy storage requirements in the *NEC*.

FR: 3662
SRs: 3643, 3638, 3658, 3635

Article 706 Energy Storage Systems, Part I General

Code Language

706.4 System Classification. ... self-contained, pre-engineered of matched components, or other ESS

706.5 Equipment. ...(See *NEC* text) shall be listed...(See *NEC* text)

706.7 Disconnecting Means.

(D) Notification. ...(See *NEC* text) legibly marked in the field...(See *NEC* text)

Exception: The labeling in 706.7(D) (1) through (4) shall not be required if an arc flash label is applied in accordance with acceptable industry practice.

Informational Note No. 1: Industry practices for equipment labeling are described in NFPA 70E-2015...(See *NEC* text)

(See NEC for actual text)

Change Summary

- ESS systems are classified as self-contained, pre-engineered of matched components, or other ESS.
- ESS electrical equipment including but not limited to monitors, controls, switches, fuses, circuit breakers, power conversion systems, inverters, transformers, etc. must be listed...
- ESS disconnecting means must be legibly marked with voltage, ASCC, clearing time or arc duration and the date the calculation was made unless labeled as seen in NFPA 70E.

FR: 3662
SRs: 3640, 3641, 3642
SCR: 87

⚠ WARNING

ARC FLASH HAZARD

Nominal System Voltage:	460 Volts DC
Arc Flash Boundary:	48 Inches
Available Incident Energy at 18 inches:	5.1 calories

Significance of the Change

Section 706.4 requires all ESS to be classified in one of three ways. All ESS are intended to have energy inputs and outputs to the system covered by the *NEC* as would be the case for any other technology using or providing electric power. Self-contained systems (prepackaged) or pre-engineered systems of matched components will be tested and listed to applicable standards and installed in accordance with the terms of the listing, manufacturer's installation instructions and the applicable provisions of Article 706. All electrical components of an ESS must be listed as required in section 706.5

Section 706.7 includes notification requirements in first level subdivision 706.7(D). This requires information to be legibly marked on the disconnecting means in the field. An exception exempts the required marking where the equipment is labeled in accordandance with NFPA 70E.

COPS Receptacle Identification

Significance of the Change

Critical Operations Power Systems (COPS) supply power for facilities or parts of facilities that require continuous operation for the reasons of public safety, emergency management, national security, or business continuity. The previous requirement in 708.10(A)(2) required that where COPS supplied receptacles occupied the same space as receptacles from other systems, the COPS supplied receptacles must have a distinctive color or marking on the cover plates or receptacles themselves so as to be readily identifiable.

This revision now requires nonlocking-type, 125-volt, 15- and 20-ampere receptacles in buildings with COPS and other power systems to have an illuminated face or an indicator light to indicate that there is power to the receptacle. This allows the end user in a COPS supplied facility to have real-time knowledge that the COPS supplied receptacles are energized and ready for use if needed.

This new requirement for an illuminated face or an indicator light to indicate that there is power to the receptacle for nonlocking-type, 125-volt, 15- and 20-amp receptacles does not relieve the marking requirement for the cover plate or receptacle itself. This marking is not limited to nonlocking-type, 125-volt, 15- and 20-ampere receptacles; it applies to all receptacles.

Code Language

708.10 Feeder and Branch Circuit Wiring.

(A) Identification.

(2) Receptacle Identification. In a building in which COPS are present with other types of power systems... (See *NEC* text) cover plates for the receptacles or the receptacles themselves...(See *NEC* text) shall have a distinctive color or marking so as to be readily identifiable. Nonlocking-type, 125-volt, 15- and 20-ampere receptacles supplied from the COPS shall have an illuminated face or an indicator light to indicate that there is power to the receptacle.

Exception: If the COPS supplies power to a DCOA that is a stand-alone building, receptacle cover plates or the receptacles themselves shall not be required to have distinctive marking.

(See NEC for actual text)

Change Summary

- Nonlocking-type, 125-volt, 15- and 20-ampere receptacles in buildings with COPS and other power systems are required to have an illuminated face or an indicator light to indicate that there is power to the receptacle.

- All COPS supplied receptacles installed where other power systems are present must have a distinctive color or marking on the cover plates or receptacles themselves so as to be readily identifiable.

FR: 3634
SR: None

712.2

NEW

Direct Current Microgrids

Code Language

712.2 Direct Current Microgrid (DC Microgrid). A direct current microgrid is a power distribution system consisting of more than one interconnected dc power source, supplying dc-dc converter(s), dc loads(s), and/or ac loads(s) powered by dc-ac inverters(s). A dc microgrid is typically not directly connected to an ac primary source of electricity, but some dc microgrids interconnect via one or more dc-ac bidirectional converters or dc–ac inverters.

Informational Note: Direct current power sources include ac-dc converters (rectifiers), bidirectional dc-ac inverters/converters, photovoltaic systems, wind generators, energy storage systems (including batteries), and fuel cells.

(See NEC for actual text)

Change Summary

• New Article 712 provides installation requirements for dc microgrids.

• DC microgrids eliminate power conversion resulting in more efficient use of renewable energy sources.

• DC power sources include ac-dc converters (rectifiers), bidirectional dc-ac inverters/converters, photovoltaic systems, wind generators, energy storage systems (including batteries), and fuel cells.

FR: 3627
SR: 3663

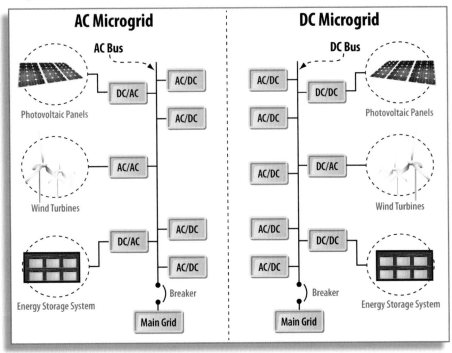

Significance of the Change

New Article 712 Direct Current Microgrids, is added to the *NEC* to provide installation requirements for power distribution systems that consist of more than one interconnected dc power source, supplying dc-dc converter(s), dc loads(s), and/or ac loads(s) powered by dc-ac inverters(s). A dc microgrid is typically not directly connected to an ac primary source of electricity, but some dc microgrids interconnect via one or more dc-ac bidirectional converters or dc–ac inverters. An informational note following the defined term *DC Microgrid*, explains that dc power sources include ac-dc converters (rectifiers), bidirectional dc-ac inverters/converters, photovoltaic systems, wind generators, energy storage systems (including batteries), and fuel cells.

These systems by design, are intended to utilize renewable energy in the most cost-effective manner by eliminating conversion losses from ac-to-direct current (dc) conversion when powering many common devices, as well as dc-to-ac losses when using locally produced dc power. Conventional ac systems also require grid-tie inverters, which prevents the use of solar photovoltaic (PV) power when grid power is lost.

These systems may directly supply dc utilization equipment including but not limited to LED lighting, dc high bay lighting, dc powered fans and many other dc loads with conversion losses.

Cable Routing Assemblies and Communications Raceways

Code Language

725.3/760.3 Other Articles

760.3(L), 725(M) Cable Routing Assemblies. (725-Class 2, Class 3 and Type PLTC) (760 power limited fire alarm) cables shall be permitted to be installed in plenum cable routing assemblies, riser cable routing assemblies, and general-purpose cable routing assemblies selected in accordance with the provisions of Table 800.154(c), listed in accordance with the provisions of 800.182, and installed in accordance with the provisions of 800.110(C) and 800.113.

760.3(M), 725.3(N) Communications Raceways. ...(See *NEC* text)

(See NEC for actual text)

Significance of the Change

Two new first level subdivisions are added to 725.3 and 760.3 *Other Articles* to specifically recognize permitted methods of installing Class 2 and 3 cables that are located in Articles of the *NEC*. Sections 725.3 and 760.3 specify that only the Articles or sections listed therein apply to Article 725 or Article 760 installations. Therefore, it is necessary to add these new first level subdivisions.

725.3(M) and 760.3(L) now permit (725-Class 2, Class 3 and Type PLTC) (760 power-limited fire alarm) cables to be installed in plenum cable routing assemblies, riser cable routing assemblies, and general-purpose cable routing assemblies. Specific sections in Article 800 are referenced for application.

725.3(N) and 760.3(M) now permit (725-Class 2, Class 3 and Type PLTC) (760 power-limited fire alarm) cables to be installed in plenum communications raceways, riser communications raceways, and general-purpose communications raceways. Specific sections in Articles 362, and 800 are referenced for application.

Section 725.135(C) now recognizes cable routing assemblies in 300.22(C) spaces.

Change Summary

- New 725.3(M) and 760.3(L) permits Class 2, Class 3 and Type PLTC cables in plenum cable routing assemblies, riser cable routing assemblies, and general-purpose cable routing assemblies.

- New 725.3(N) and 760.3(M) permits Class 2, Class 3 and Type PLTC cables in plenum communications raceways, riser communications raceways, and general-purpose communications raceways.

FRs: 622, 623, 626, 634, 640

SR: None

725.121(A), (C) and 725.170

Article 725

Part III Class 2 and Class 3 Circuits and IV Listing Requirements

NEW / **REVISION**

Power Sources for Class 2 and Class 3 Circuits

Code Language

725.121 Power Sources for Class 2 and Class 3 Circuits.

(A) Power Source. ...(See *NEC* text)

(4) Listed audio/video information technology (computer), communications and industrial equipment limited-power circuits.

Informational Note...(See *NEC* text)

(C) Marking. The power sources for limited power circuits in 725.121(A) (3) and limited power circuits for listed audio/video information technology (equipment) and listed industrial equipment in 725.121(A)(4) shall have a label indicating the maximum voltage and current output for each connection point. The effective date shall be January 1, 2018.

(See NEC for actual text)

Change Summary

- 725.121(A)(5) is modified to add listed audio/video, communications and industrial equipment limited-power circuits.
- The informational note to 725.121(A)(4) is modified to recognize another applicable product standard.
- New 725.121(C) requires marking of limited power circuits in 725.121(A)(3) and those for listed audio/video information technology (equipment) and listed industrial equipment in 725.121(A)(4).

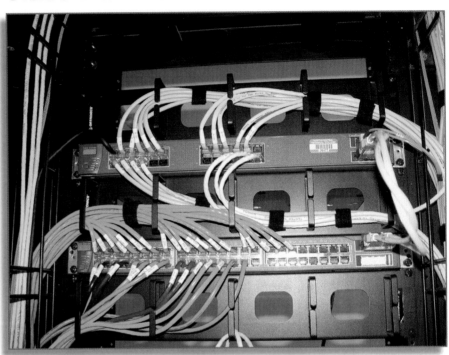

Significance of the Change

Recognized power sources in 725.121(A)(4) are expanded to include listed audio/video technology, communications and industrial equipment limited-power circuits. Article 725 permits limited-power circuits derived from UL 60950-1 listed equipment to be used as a source for a Class 2 Circuit. This revision provides clarity by including audio/video technology and communications equipment and also includes listed industrial equipment which complies with similar technical requirements. One of the potential applications may be sensors supplied by industrial equipment which may be located in the field.

New 725.121(C) now provides marking requirements for limited power circuit output connection points on listed IT equipment and listed industrial control panels and equipment. Where Class 2/3 conductors are supplied from listed audio/video information technology (computer), communications and industrial equipment limited-power circuits, the output ports identified must be identified with the current and voltage rating so the installer can connect the proper cable types. An effective date of January 1, 2018, was accepted to permit manufacturers to comply with this requirement.

New section 725.170 repeats the listing and marking requirements again in Part IV Listing Requirements.

FR: 620
SRs: 610, 614

Transmission of Power and Data

Code Language

725.144 Transmission of Power and Data. The requirements of 725.144(A) and (B) shall apply to Class 2 and Class 3 circuits that transmit power and data to a powered device. The requirements of Parts I and III of Article 725 and 300.11 shall apply to Class 2 and Class 3 circuits that transmit power and data. The conductors that carry power for the data circuits shall be copper. The current in the power circuit shall not exceed the current limitation of the connectors.

Table 725.144 Ampacities of Each Conductor in Amperes...(See *NEC* text)

(See NEC for actual text)

Significance of the Change

Power over the Ethernet (PoE) is commonly used to supply both power and data to equipment such as wireless access points and IP cameras. There are newer technologies including USB and Power over HDBase T for transmission of high performance videos, such as providing data and power to TVs in homes or commercial establishments. PoE is directed primarily at commercial installations of equipment such as CCTV cameras, nurses call systems and LED lighting. Both of these technologies supply power and data over category type cable.

Supplying data only on these category cables does not create a heat rise issue. However, supplying both power and data can create heat build up where these cables are bundled.

This new section contains parent text that mandates 725.144(A) and (B) will apply to Class 2 and Class 3 circuits that transmit power and data to a powered device. Conductors that supply power must be copper and Table 725.144 provides ampacities for conductors based on conductor types, sizes, number of cables bundled and ambient temperatures.

Change Summary

- A new section 725.144 is added to address requirements for Class 2 and Class 3 circuits that transmit power and data to a powered device.
- Table 725.144 lists permitted ampacities based on conductor types, sizes, number of cables bundled and ambient temperatures.
- Conductors that supply power for data circuits must be copper.

FR: None
SR: 611

Listing and Marking of Limited Power Cables

Code Language

725.179 Listing and Marking of Class 2, Class 3 and Type PLTC Cables.

(I) Limited Power (LP) Cables. Limited power (LP) cables shall be listed as suitable for carrying power and data circuits up to a specified current limit... (See *NEC* text) The cables shall be marked with the suffix "-LP" with the ampere limit located immediately following the suffix LP, where the current limit is in amperes per conductor.

Informational Note: The ampere limit located immediately following the suffix LP is the ampacity of each conductor in a cable. For example, 1 ampere Class 2 limited-power cables shall be marked CL2-LP (1.0A), CL2R-LP (1.0A), or CL2-LP (1.0A).

(See NEC for actual text)

Change Summary

- New 725.179(I) requires limited power cables to be listed as suitable for carrying power and data circuits up to a specified current limit for each conductor without exceeding the temperature rating of the cable.
- The LP cables shall be marked with the suffix "-LP(xxA), where the xx is the current limit in amperes per conductor.

FR: 630
SR: 615

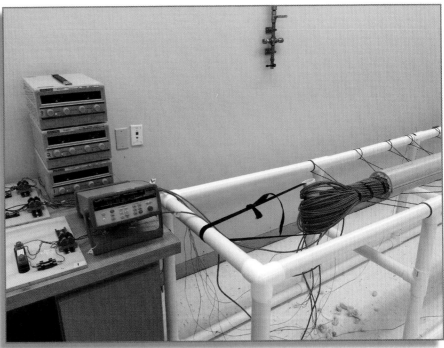

Courtesy of UL LLC

Significance of the Change

Cable heating due to the transmission of power and data in cables that are typically installed in bundles, raceways, cable trays, or cable routing assemblies is now addressed in new section 725.144. An accumulation of cables used for the transmission of power and data when bundled generate heat and may cause degradation of the cable insulation. This new requirement to list and mark type LP cable is based on an extensive fact-finding investigation by Underwriter's Laboratories. The UL fact-finding investigation shows that the ampacities listed in Table 725.144 are accurate for 4-pair cables without the "-LP" suffix. However, in actual installations, the quantity of cables routed together are often greater than 192 cables. The "LP" suffix provides a safety margin for installation in any quantity. In addition, it is important that the current rating of the cable is equal to or less than the nameplate rating of the power source. Further, 20 AWG was not tested as, presently, 22 AWG is the largest conductor that will fit into an RJ 45 connector. Extensive testing at UL LLC has shown that large bundles of 4-pair cables with 22 AWG or smaller conductors may exceed their temperature rating with all conductors carrying 1 ampere, which is well below the 1.67 ampere maximum current permitted in a 60 volt, 100 VA circuit.

Fire-Resistive Cable Installation

Code Language

728.4 General. Fire-resistive cables... (See *NEC* text) conductors... (See *NEC* text) components shall be tested and listed as a complete system... (See *NEC* text) designated for use in a specific fire-rated system... (See *NEC* text) not be interchangeable between systems.

728.5(C) Raceways and Couplings. Where the fire-resistive system is listed to be installed in a raceway... (See *NEC* text) The raceway fill for each system shall comply with the listing requirements for the system and shall not be greater than the fill permitted in Table 1, Chapter 9.

> Informational Note: Raceway fill may not be the same for all listed fire-resistive systems.

(See NEC for actual text)

Significance of the Change

728.4 requires fire resistive cables, conductors, and components to be tested and listed as a complete system. The last sentence in this section is deleted because it mandated that the "Fire-resistive cables, conductors, and components shall be approved." This led many to believe that the AHJ was capable of approving a given fire-resistive cable system which is incorrect and misleading.

These fire-resistive cable systems are tested and listed as a system, and the installation must be in strict compliance with instructions provided in the listing and labeling. 725.5(C) is modified to mandate that raceway fill for each system comply with the listing requirements (instructions) for the system and not be greater than the fill permitted in Table 1, Chapter 9. The permitted conduit fill for these systems may be less than what is permitted in Table 1 in Chapter 9. This new text is necessary to ensure proper installation of these critical circuits.

Change Summary

- 725.4 is revised by deleting the last sentence, "Fire-resistive cables, conductors, and components shall be approved."

- Fire-resistive cables, fire-resistive conductors, and components are tested and listed as a complete system, not approved by an AHJ.

- 725.5(C) is modified to mandate that raceway fill for each system comply with the listing requirements for the system and not be greater than the fill permitted in Table 1, Chapter 9.

FRs: 632, 623

SR: None

Overhead Optical Fiber Cables

Code Language

770.44 Overhead Optical Fiber Cables. Overhead optical fiber cables containing a non–current-carrying metallic member entering buildings shall comply with 840.44(A) and (B).

(A) On Poles and In-Span.

(1) Relative Location

(2) Attachment to Cross-Arms

(3) Climbing Space

(4) Clearance

(B) Above Roofs

Three Exceptions

(See NEC for actual text)

Change Summary

- New section 770.44 provides requirements for overhead optical fiber cables containing a non–current-carrying metallic member entering buildings.
- This requirement is similar to 840.44 for overhead optical fiber cable in premises-powered broadband communications systems.

Significance of the Change

New section 770.44 is added to provide requirements for overhead optical fiber cables containing a non–current-carrying metallic member entering buildings. This mirrors the requirement in 840.44 for overhead optical fiber cables in a premises-powered broadband communications system.

This new section provides requirements for optical fiber cable installed on the same pole or structure as light or power conductors. Optical fiber cable must be installed below power conductors and may not be supported on a cross arm that supports power conductors. A minimum distance of eight feet above roofs to the lowest point of the optical fiber cable is the general rule with three exceptions.

FR: 4519

SR: None

NECA 416-20xx Stored Energy Systems

Energy storage is an essential part of a smarter and more sustainable power infrastructure in both small and large scale applications. Energy storage can be in multiple forms such as battery technologies, compressed air, and thermal energy. With more expanded use of reliable renewable energy systems, such as wind power and solar photovoltaic power, the need for storing produced energy is increasing exponentially as the value of stored energy is understood. Stored energy and energy storage systems offer the benefits of backup power, uninterrupted power, load leveling, demand response, and economical electricity for consumers. While the *National Electrical Code* has long provided minimum safety rules for equipment used in energy storage systems, it fell short in addressing energy storage systems as a whole, until the 2017 edition. Through two *NEC* development cycles of work by many subject matter experts, the development of practical safety requirements timely emerged in the *NEC*.

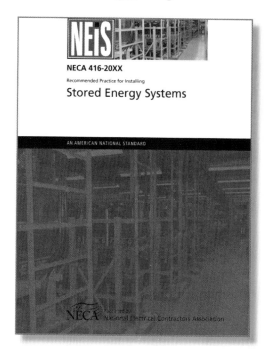

Energy storage is also an essential component of many micro-grids of all sizes and applications. A micro-grid is a discrete energy system consisting of distributed energy sources (including demand management, storage, and generation) and loads capable of operating in parallel with, or independently from, the main power grid. A micro-grid generally operates while connected to the grid, but importantly, it can break off and operate on its own using local energy generation in times of crisis like storms or power outages, or for other reasons. Because the micro-grid is not totally dependent on utility power, it offers increased reliability, which is an attractive feature to many.

New articles in the 2017 *National Electrical Code* related to the expanded use of energy storage systems are Articles 706 Energy Storage Systems, Article 710 Stand Alone Systems, and Article 712 Direct Current Micro-Grids. A more detailed look at these new articles is included within this textbook.

NECA has also developed a new National Electrical Installation Standard (NEIS) that provides essential information about quality workmanship, performance, and maintenance of energy storage systems. This standard is designated as NECA 416 and titled Recommended Practice for Installing Energy Storage Systems (ESS). NECA 416 is currently in the ANSI development process. This Recommended Practice describes installation practices for Energy Storage Systems (ESS) such as battery systems, flywheels, ultra-capacitors, and smart chargers used for electric vehicle (EV) vehicle-to-grid (V2G) applications. While Compressed Air Energy Storage (CAES), Pumped Hydro Storage (PHS), and Thermal Energy Storage (TES) are not covered by this Recommended Practice, electrical equipment and components for use in CAES, PHS, and TES should be installed in accordance with this Recommended Practice. For more information about NECA's National Electrical Installation Standards (NEIS) development program, visit www.neca-neis.org.

The National Electrical Contractors Association (NECA), International Brotherhood of Electrical Workers (IBEW), and the Electrical Training ALLIANCE have teamed with Penn State University to develop an enhanced training curriculum for energy storage system and micro-grid installations. The concept is to equip the industry with electrical contractors and a workforce that are well trained and experienced experts in all aspects of energy storage system applications that are experiencing more and more rapid deployment.

Chapter 8

Article 840
Communications Systems

Powering of Communications Equipment over Communications Cables

Code Language

840.160 Powering Circuits. Communications cables, in addition to carrying the communications circuit, shall also be permitted to carry circuits for powering communications equipment. Where the power supplied over a communications cable to communications equipment is greater than 60 watts, communication cables and the power circuit shall comply with 725.144 where communications cables are used in place of Class 2 and Class 3 cables.

840.170 Equipment and Cables.

(G) Power Source... (See *NEC* text)

(See NEC for actual text)

Change Summary

- A new Part VI is added in Article 840 to address Power Over the Ethernet (POE).
- 840.160 requires compliance with section 725.144 for POE.
- New 840.170 provides listing requirements for POE power sources.

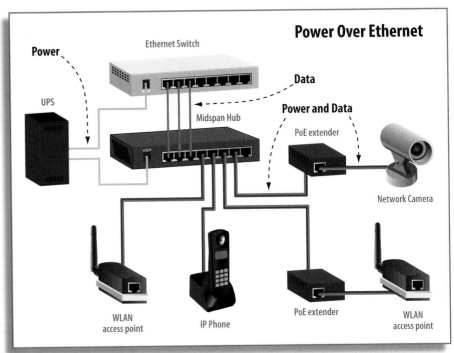

Power Over Ethernet

Ethernet Switch · Power · Data · UPS · Midspan Hub · Power and Data · PoE extender · Network Camera · WLAN access point · IP Phone · PoE extender · WLAN access point

Significance of the Change

A new Part VI Premises Powering of Communications Equipment over Communications Cables is added in Article 840 to address Power Over the Ethernet (POE) over communications cables. Section 840.160 now permits communications cables, in addition to carrying the communications circuit, to carry circuits for powering communications equipment. This permissive requirement has a limit of 60 watts before the communications cables used are required to comply with section 725.144.

POE is widely used with communications circuits, and each successive revision of the POE standards delivers more power to the powered devices raising concern about overheating of the cables. Bundling and bunching of cables carrying power to communications equipment can result in heating.

New first level subdivision 840.170(G) contains listing requirements for power sources that supply POE. The power source for circuits intended to provide power over communications cables to remote equipment must be limited in accordance with Table 11(B) in Chapter 9 for voltage sources up to 60 V dc. The power source must be listed as specified in 725.121(A)(1), (A)(2), (A)(3), or (A)(4) or be listed as communications equipment for limited-power circuits.

FRs: 4642, 4643, 4644
SRs: 4564, 4565